LINEAR SEQUENTIAL CIRCUITS

Analysis, Synthesis, and Applications

LINEAR SEQUENTIAL CIRCUITS
Analysis, Synthesis, and Applications

ARTHUR GILL
Associate Professor
University of California (Berkeley)

McGRAW-HILL BOOK COMPANY
New York
St. Louis
San Francisco
Toronto
London
Sydney

Linear Sequential Circuits—Analysis, Synthesis, and Applications

Library of Congress Catalog Card Number
66-29752

PREFACE

Linear sequential circuits (to be abbreviated LSCs) are of interest to engineers and applied mathematicians for two important reasons. First, LSCs constitute the intersection of the class of linear circuits and the class of sequential circuits, and thus form the natural common denominator of these two classes. Concepts and techniques developed for linear circuits and for sequential circuits separately, can be exploited simultaneously in the study of LSCs. Conversely, results obtained in the study of LSCs may offer useful clues as to how one should tackle problems concerning general linear systems on one hand, and general discrete systems on the other. Secondly, LSCs have found application in numerous digital tasks associated with computation, communication and automatic control, which provides ample justification for studying them from the practical viewpoint. Among the most noteworthy applications are computations in rings of polynomials, computations in finite fields, counting and timing, generation of linear codes, error correction and detection, memory addressing, generation of minimum-time test sequences, and generation of pseudorandom sequences (for use in the implementation of Monte Carlo programs, range measurements in radar, proabilistic experiments, etc.).

The objective of this book is to present a thorough mathematical treatment of the characterization, analysis and synthesis of LSCs, and to demonstrate the applicability of LSCs to various digital operations. It is not the intention of this book to delve into problems of circuit hardware or to embark upon wide discussion of areas of application, inasmuch as these subjects are already covered in other books. The author addresses himself primarily to "engineering scientists" and applied mathematicians interested in the theories of systems, automata, and control. The material should also be of interest to engineering students and practicing engineers working in the areas of information processing and digital computation.

The study of LSCs requires familiarity with a number of topics in abstract algebra—in particular the theories of finite fields and linear vector spaces. Chapter 1 contains a summary of definitions, theorems and algorithms concerned with the required mathematical topics. This chapter is included to establish notation and to serve as a ready reference, and is by no means a substitute for a basic course in modern algebra—the only prerequisite for the material in this book. Chapter 2 defines LSCs in terms of their elementary components as well as in mathematical terms. It develops the concepts of equivalence, similarity, minimality, canonicity, controllability, and predictability, as applied to LSCs. It demonstrates that the study of LSCs can be separated into the study of "autonomous LSCs" on one hand, and "quiescent LSCs" on the other. Accordingly, Chapter 3 is devoted to the analysis and synthesis of autonomous LSCs (with a detailed discussion of cyclic spaces), while Chapter 4 is devoted to the analysis and synthesis of quiescent LSCs (making full use of *d*-transform theory). Chapter 5 studies the internal state behavior of LSCs, developing the theory of cycle sets and tree sets. Chapter 6 describes various applications of LSCs, in particular those concerned with polynomial computations, Galois field computations, counting, encoding and decoding. Chapter 7, as an aside, introduces systems which, after a series of transformations, may be treated as LSCs. The Appendix contains a number of tables (most of which are not available in any other textbook) which facilitate many of the analysis and synthesis algorithms developed in preceding chapters. A bibliography appears at the end of the volume.

The author should like to express his gratitude to the Air Force Office of Scientific Research (Office of Aerospace Research, U.S. Air Force) and to the Information Systems Branch of the Office of Naval Research for supporting much of the research that went into the preparation of this book. Thanks are also due to Professors M. A. Harrison, E. Polak and L. A. Zadeh of the University of California (Berkeley), and to Dr. S. Even of the Israel Institute of Technology for many helpful discussions and suggestions.

ARTHUR GILL

Note to the Reader

This book is divided into chapters, and each chapter into sections. Section 7 in Chapter 2, for example, will be referred to as "Sec. **7**" when the reference is made within Chapter 2, and as "Sec. **2.7**" when the reference is made outside Chapter 2.

Most sections have a number of key "items" (equations, assertions, examples, etc.) which are numbered serially within each section. Item 5 in Section 7 of Chapter 2, for example, will be referred to as "**7-5**" when the reference is made within Chapter 2, but as "**2.7-5**" when the reference is made outside Chapter 2.

Figures and tables are numbered by chapter but not by section. For example, the third figure (or table) in Chapter 4 is referred to as "Fig. 4.3" (or "Table 4.3").

Numbers in superiors following an author's name refer to the number of the reference listed in the Bibliography.

CONTENTS

LINEAR SEQUENTIAL CIRCUITS
Analysis, Synthesis, and Applications

Chapter 1
Mathematical Prerequisites

1. Introduction

The study of linear sequential circuits requires familiarity with a number of areas in abstract algebra. This chapter presents definitions and results in these areas, to the extent that they bear upon material developed in subsequent chapters. The purpose of the chapter is to serve as an easy reference and to establish notation. It contains no proofs, and by no means constitutes a self-contained survey of algebra. For missing proofs and for more comprehensive coverage, the reader is referred to any of many good textbooks on modern algebra; among these, we suggest:

G. Birkhoff and S. MacLane, *A Survey of Modern Algebra,* Macmillan Co., New York (1953).

B. L. van der Waerden, *Modern Algebra,* Frederick Ungar Publishing Co., New York (1953).

G. D. Mostow, J. H. Sampson and J. -P. Meyer, *Fundamental Structures of Algebra,* McGraw-Hill Book Co., New York (1963)

A. A. Albert, *Fundamental Concepts of Higher Algebra,* University of Chicago Press, Chicago (1956).

2. Some Comments on Notatation

If S is a finite set consisting of the elements $\alpha_1, \alpha_2, \ldots, \alpha_n$, it will be written $\{\alpha_1, \alpha_2, \ldots, \alpha_n\}$. The order n of S will be denoted by $|S|$.

Vectors and matrices will be printed **boldface**. The element appearing in the ith row and jth column of a matrix is referred to as the (i,j) *element* of the matrix. An r-row, s-column (or $r \times s$) matrix $\mathbf{M}$, whose (i,j) element is m_{ij}, will sometimes be identified as $[m_{ij}]_{r\times s}$. The determinant of $\mathbf{M}$ is written as $|\mathbf{M}|$, the transpose as $\mathbf{M}^{\mathrm{TR}}$, and the adjoint as $\mathbf{M}^{\mathrm{AD}}$. $\mathbf{I}$ denotes the identity matrix, and, in particular, $\mathbf{I}_r$ denotes the $r \times r$ identity matrix. $\mathbf{0}$ denotes the all-zero (or *null*) vector or matrix. Blank positions in a matrix will mean 0 entries.

The greatest common divisor and the least common multiple of the integers or polynomials $a_1, a_2, \ldots, a_k$, are written, respectively, as

$$\gcd(a_1, a_2, \ldots, a_k)$$
$$\operatorname{lcm}(a_1, a_2, \ldots, a_k)$$

Additional notation and terminology will be introduced as needed.

3. Groups and Subgroups

The set G is a *group* if a single operation $*$ is defined for every pair of elements in G, and if it satisfies the following four postulates:

3–1 *Closure.* For all α and β in G, $\alpha * \beta$ is in G.

3–2 *Associativity.* For all α, β and γ in G, $\alpha * (\beta * \gamma) = (\alpha * \beta) * \gamma$.

3–3 G contains a (unique) element e, called the *identity* of G, such that, for every α in G, $e * \alpha = \alpha * e = \alpha$.

3–4 For every α in G there is a (unique) element α^{-1} in G, called the *inverse* of G, such that $\alpha * \alpha^{-1} = \alpha^{-1} * \alpha = e$.

G is an *Abelian group* if, in addition to **3–1, 3–2, 3–3**, and **3–4**, the following is satisfied:

3–5 *Commutativity:* For all α and β in G, $\alpha * \beta = \beta * \alpha$.

When the operation $*$ is $+$, G is an *additive group*, e is commonly written as 0, α^{-1} as $-\alpha$, and $\alpha + (-\beta)$ as $\alpha - \beta$. When the operation $*$ is $\cdot$, G is a *multiplicative group* ($\alpha \cdot \beta$ may be written as $\alpha\beta$) and e is commonly written as 1.

3–6 The *order* of an element α in a multiplicative group is the least integer i such that $\alpha^i = \alpha\alpha \ldots \alpha$ (i times) $= 1$.

3–7 A subset C_0 of G is called a *subgroup* if it satisfies all group postulates under $*$. For C_0 to be a subgroup it is necessary and sufficient that C_0 satisfy **3–1** and **3–4**.

3–8 *Example:* The set $\mathcal{I}$ of all positive and negative integers and 0 form an additive Abelian group under ordinary addition. The subset $\mathcal{I}_m$ of all multiples of a fixed integer m constitutes a subgroup of $\mathcal{I}$ (under $+$). The set of all $n \times n$ nonsingular matrices with real numbers (or complex numbers, or rational numbers) as elements, is a multiplicative (non-Abelian) group under matrix multiplication.

4. Cosets

Let G be an Abelian group with a subgroup C_0. Consider the following sets:

4–1

$$\begin{aligned}
C_0 &= \{\alpha_1, \quad \alpha_2, \quad \alpha_3, \quad \ldots, \alpha_k, \quad \ldots\} \\
C_1 &= \{\alpha_1 * \beta_1, \quad \alpha_2 * \beta_1, \quad \alpha_3 * \beta_1, \quad \ldots, \alpha_k * \beta_1, \quad \ldots\} \\
C_2 &= \{\alpha_1 * \beta_2, \quad \alpha_2 * \beta_2, \quad \alpha_3 * \beta_2, \quad \ldots, \alpha_k * \beta_2, \quad \ldots\} \\
&\;\;\vdots \\
C_{s-1} &= \{\alpha_1 * \beta_{s-1}, \alpha_2 * \beta_{s-1}, \alpha_3 * \beta_{s-1}, \ldots, \alpha_k * \beta_{s-1}, \ldots\}
\end{aligned}$$

where β_i is any element not contained in $C_0, C_1, \ldots, C_{i-1}$. These sets are called the *cosets* of G *induced by* C_0. s is the *index of* G *over* C_0.

4–2 Except for ordering, the cosets of G induced by C_0 are unique and form a partition of G. When G is finite,

4–3 $$|G| = s|C_0|$$

4–4 The elements α and β of G are in the same coset C_i if and only if $\alpha * \beta^{-1}$ is in C_0.

4–5 *Example:* Let G be $\mathscr{I}$ and C_0 be $\mathscr{I}_m$, as defined in **3–8**. Then the cosets are given by

$$
\begin{array}{rlllll}
C_0 = \{0, & m, & -m, & 2m, & -2m, & \ldots\} \\
C_1 = \{1, & m+1, & -m+1, & 2m+1, & -2m+1, & \ldots\} \\
C_2 = \{2, & m+2, & -m+2, & 2m+2, & -2m+2, & \ldots\} \\
\cdot & & & & & \\
\cdot & & & & & \\
\cdot & & & & & \\
C_{m-1} = \{m-1, & 2m-1, & -1, & 3m-1, & -m-1, & \ldots\}
\end{array}
\tag{4–6}
$$

Two integers α and β are in the same coset if and only if $\alpha - \beta$ is in C_0, i.e., if and only if $\alpha - \beta$ is a multiple of m.

5. Rings and Ideals

The set R is a *ring* if addition and multiplication are defined for every pair of elements in R, and if it satisfies the following four postulates:

5–1 R is an additive Abelian group.

5–2 *Closure:* For all α and β in R, $\alpha\beta$ is in R.

5–3 *Associativity:* For all α, β and γ in R, $\alpha(\beta\gamma) = (\alpha\beta)\gamma$.

5–4 *Distributivity:* For all α, β and γ in R, $\alpha(\beta + \gamma) = \alpha\beta + \alpha\gamma$ and $(\beta + \gamma)\alpha = \beta\alpha + \gamma\alpha$.

R is a *commutative ring* if, in addition to **5–1**, **5–2**, **5–3** and **5–4**, the following is satisfied:

5–5 *Commutativity:* For all α and β in R, $\alpha\beta = \beta\alpha$.

5–6 A subgroup I of the additive group R is called an *ideal* if, for every α in R and β in I, $\alpha\beta$ is also in I. An ideal consisting of all multiples of one ring element α, is called a *principal ideal* and denoted by (α); α is called a *generator* of this ideal. A ring in which every ideal is a principal ideal, is called a *principal ideal ring.*

5–7 *Example:* Let R_m be the set of integers $\{0, 1, \ldots, m-1\}$ where addition and multiplication are defined modulo m (i.e., $\alpha = \beta$ if and only if $\alpha - \beta$ is a multiple of m). R_m is a commutative ring. It is also a principal ideal ring (a subset of R_m is an ideal if and only if it consists of all multiples of some integer i, $0 \leq i < m$). R_m is called the *ring of integers modulo m.*

5–8 *Fermat's theorem:* If p is a prime integer which does not divide k, then, in R_p as defined in **5–7**, $k^{p-1} = 1$.

6. Fields

The commutative ring F is called a *field* if it satisfies the following two postulates:

6–1 F contains an element 1 such that, for every α in F, $1\alpha = \alpha 1 = \alpha$.

6–2 For every nonzero α in F, there is an element α^{-1} in F such that $\alpha\alpha^{-1} = \alpha^{-1}\alpha = 1$.

Thus, F is an additive Abelian group; F without the 0 element is a multiplicative Abelian group.

6–3 If α and β are elements of F, then $\alpha\beta = 0$ if and only if $\alpha = 0$ or $\beta = 0$.

6–4 *Example:* If p is a prime integer, then the ring of integers modulo p (see **5–7**) is a field. This field is denoted by $GF(p)$.

7. Polynominals over a Field

7–1 A *polynomial (in x) over a field F* is an expression of the form $f(x) = \alpha_0 + \alpha_1 x + \ldots + \alpha_n x^n$, where the coefficients α_i are from F. The *degree of* $f(x)$, denoted by $\partial(f(x))$, is the greatest i such that $\alpha_i \neq 0$ [the degree of $f(x) = 0$ is 0]. A polynomial of degree 0 is called a *constant.* If $\partial(f(x)) = n$, α_n is called the *leading coefficient* of $f(x)$. A polynomial whose leading coefficient is 1 is called a *monic polynomial.*

7–2 The set of all polynomials over F, with addition and multiplication of polynomials defined as in high-school algebra, forms a ring. This ring will be denoted by $F[x]$.

7–3 *Division algorithm:* For any $a(x)$ and $b(x)$ in $F[x]$, one can write (uniquely):

7–4
$$a(x) = q(x)b(x) + r(x) \qquad (0 \leq \partial(r(x)) < \partial(b(x)))$$

When $r(x) = 0$, $b(x)$ *divides* (or is a *divisor,* or a *factor,* of) $a(x)$, and $a(x)$ is a *multiple* of $b(x)$. If the only divisors of $a(x)$ are α or $\alpha a(x)$ (where α is any element from F), $a(x)$ is said to be *irreducible.*

7–5 *Euclidean algorithm:* Given the polynomials $a_0(x)$ and $a_1(x)$, where $\partial(a_0(x)) \geq \partial(a_1(x))$, consider the following equations:

7–6
$$\begin{aligned}
a_0(x) &= q_1(x)a_1(x) + a_2(x) && (\partial(a_2(x)) < \partial(a_1(x)))\\
a_1(x) &= q_2(x)a_2(x) + a_3(x) && (\partial(a_3(x)) < \partial(a_2(x)))\\
a_2(x) &= q_3(x)a_3(x) + a_4(x) && (\partial(a_4(x)) < \partial(a_3(x)))\\
&\ \ \vdots\\
a_{r-2}(x) &= q_{r-1}(x)a_{r-1}(x) + a_r(x) && (\partial(a_r(x)) < \partial(a_{r-1}(x)))\\
a_{r-1}(x) &= q_r(x)a_r(x)
\end{aligned}$$

Then:

7–7
$$a_r(x) = \gcd\,(a_0(x), a_1(x))$$

By successive substitution, one can always write [with some $b_0(x)$ and $b_1(x)$]:

7–8
$$\gcd\,(a_0(x), a_1(x)) = b_0(x)a_0(x) + b_1(x)a_1(x)$$

7–9 *Example:* Let $a_0(x) = 1 + x^2 + x^3 + x^4$ and $a_1(x) = 1 + x^4$ be polynomials over $GF(2)$. The Euclidean algorithm can be performed as shown in **7–12** below, from which we have:

7–10
$$\gcd\,(1 + x^2 + x^3 + x^4, 1 + x^4) = 1 + x$$

The form **7–8** can be obtained as follows:

7–11
$$\begin{aligned}
1 + x = a_4(x) &= a_2(x) - q_3(x)a_3(x)\\
&= a_0(x) - q_1(x)a_1(x) - q_3(x)a_1(x) + q_3(x)q_2(x)a_2(x)\\
&= a_0(x) - q_1(x)a_1(x) - q_3(x)a_1(x) + q_3(x)q_2(x)a_0(x)\\
&\qquad - q_3(x)q_2(x)q_1(x)a_1(x)\\
&= [1 + q_2(x)q_3(x)]a_0(x)\\
&\qquad + [- q_1(x) - q_3(x) - q_1(x)q_2(x)q_3(x)]a_1(x)\\
&= x^2(1 + x^2 + x^3 + x^4) + (1 + x + x^2)(1 + x^4)
\end{aligned}$$

7–12

$$
\begin{array}{rr}
 & 1 \quad \leftarrow q_1 \\
a_1 \rightarrow x^4 + 1 & \overline{)\, x^4 + x^3 + x^2 + 1} \quad \leftarrow a_0 \\
 & x^4 + 1 \\ \hline
a_2 \longrightarrow & x^3 + x^2
\end{array}
\qquad
\begin{array}{rr}
 & x + 1 \quad \leftarrow q_2 \\
a_2 \rightarrow x^3 + x^2 & \overline{)\, x^4 + 1} \quad \leftarrow a_1 \\
 & x^4 + x^3 \\ \hline
 & x^3 + 1 \\
 & x^3 + x^2 \\ \hline
a_3 \rightarrow & x^2 + 1
\end{array}
$$

$$
\begin{array}{rr}
 & x + 1 \quad \leftarrow q_3 \\
a_3 \rightarrow x^2 + 1 & \overline{)\, x^3 + x^2} \quad \leftarrow a_2 \\
 & x^3 + x \\ \hline
 & x^2 + x \\
 & x^2 + 1 \\ \hline
a_4 \rightarrow & x + 1
\end{array}
\qquad
\begin{array}{rr}
 & x + 1 \leftarrow q_4 \\
a_4 \rightarrow x + 1 & \overline{)\, x^2 + 1} \leftarrow a_3 \\
 & x^2 + x \\ \hline
 & x + 1 \\
 & x + 1 \\ \hline
 & 0
\end{array}
$$

7–13 *Unique factorization theorem:* Every nonconstant polynomial $f(x)$ can be written in the form

7–14 $$f(x) = \alpha[p_1(x)]^{e_1}[p_2(x)]^{e_2} \; . \; . \; . \; [p_r(x)]^{e_r} \qquad (e_i > 0)$$

where α is an element from F and the $p_i(x)$ are distinct, irreducible, monic, nonconstant polynomials over F. Except for ordering, the $p_i(x)$ are unique. The $[p_i(x)]^{e_i}$ are called the *prime factors* of $f(x)$.

7–15 The *reciprocal* $[f(x)]^*$ of a polynomial $f(x)$ of degree n, is defined as $x^n f(1/x)$. The prime factors of $[f(x)]^*$ are the reciprocals of the prime factors of $f(x)$.

8. Polynominals over $GF\ (p)$

In this section the polynomials referred to are over the field $GF(p)$ (see **6–4**), and all operations are in $GF(p)[x]$.

8–1 Every polynomial $f(x)$ indivisible by x is a factor of $1 - x^i$ for some integer i. The least such positive i is called the *exponent* of $f(x)$ (the exponent of a constant is 1). If $f(x)$ is of degree n and exponent T, then T is a divisor of $p^n - 1$ [when $f(x)$ is irreducible, n is the least integer ν such that T divides $p^\nu - 1$]. For every n and (prime) p there is at least one irreducible polynomial of degree n and exponent $p^n - 1$; it is called a *maximum-exponent polynomial.* The exponent of $f(x)$ is the same as that of its reciprocal $[f(x)]^*$. (The Appendix lists factors of $p^n - 1$; least integers n such that T divides $p^n - 1$; irreducible polynomials and their exponents; maximum-exponent polynomials.)

8–2 If $p(x)$ is an irreducible polynomial (other than x) of exponent T, then the exponent of $[p(x)]^j$ is $p^r T$, where $p^{r-1} < j \leq p^r$. Let $[p_1(x)]^{e_1}, [p_2(x)]^{e_2}, \; . \; . \; . \; ,$ $[p_r(x)]^{e_r}$ be the prime factors of $f(x)$ (indivisible by x), and let T_i be the exponent of $[p_i(x)]^{e_i}$. Then the exponent of $f(x)$ is lcm $(T_1, T_2, \; . \; . \; . \; , T_r)$.

8–3 The prime factors of $x - x^{p^k}$ are all irreducible polynomials over $GF(p)$ whose degrees divide k.

8–4 $1 - x^h$ divides $1 - x^k$ if and only if h divides k.

8–5 For any polynomial $f(x)$ over $GF(p)$,

$$[f(x)]^{p^k} = f(x^{p^k})$$

9. Modular Rings of Polynominals

9–1 $R_{m(\xi)}$ (over F) will denote the set of all polynomials in ξ (over F) where addition and multiplication are defined modulo $m(\xi)$ [i.e., $a(\xi) = b(\xi)$ if and only if $a(\xi) - b(\xi)$ is a multiple of $m(\xi)$]. $R_{m(\xi)}$ is a commutative ring, referred to as the *ring of polynomials over F modulo* $m(\xi)$; $m(x)$ is its *modulus polynominal.* If $m(x)$ is of degree n, $R_{m(\xi)}$ can be represented by the set of all p^n polynomials $\alpha_0 + \alpha_1\xi + \ldots + \alpha_{n-1}\xi^{n-1}$, where the α_i are from F.

9–2 $R_{m(\xi)}$ is a principal ideal ring (see **5–6**). Every ideal in $R_{m(\xi)}$ has a generator $g(\xi)$ such that $g(x)$ divides $m(x)$ (in $F[x]$). Conversely, for every polynomial $g(x)$ dividing $m(x)$, there is an ideal $(g(\xi))$ in $R_{m(\xi)}$. The generator $g(\xi)$ of any ideal I in $R_{m(\xi)}$ is unique up to a constant multiplier, and is a least-degree nonzero polynomial in I.

9–3 *Example:* Let $m(x) = (1 + x)(1 + x + x^2) = 1 + x^3$ be a polynomial over $GF(2)$. Then:

9–4 $$R_{1+\xi^3}, = \{0, 1, \xi, 1 + \xi, \xi^2, 1 + \xi^2, \xi + \xi^2, 1 + \xi + \xi^2\}$$

9–5 $$(1 + \xi) = \{0, 1 + \xi, 1 + \xi^2, \xi + \xi^2\}$$

9–6 $$(1 + \xi + \xi^2) = \{0, 1 + \xi + \xi^2\}$$

10. Galois Fields

10–1 If $p(x)$ is an irreducible polynomial over $GF(p)$, the ring of polynomials over GF(p) modulo $p(x)$ is a field. If the degree of $p(x)$ is n, this field can be represented by all p^n polynomials in ξ of degree $n - 1$ or less. It is called a *Galois field* (of order p^n) and denoted by $GF(p^n)$.

10–2 Every finite field F is isomorphic to some Galois field $GF(p^n)$ [i.e., every element in F can be placed in one-to-one correspondence with an element in $GF(p^n)$ in the following manner: if α and β in F correspond to $\overline{\alpha}$ and $\overline{\beta}$, respectively, in $GF(p^n)$, then $\alpha + \beta$ and $\alpha\beta$ in F correspond to $\overline{\alpha} + \overline{\beta}$ and $\overline{\alpha}\overline{\beta}$, respectively, in $GF(p^n)$].

10–3 Every nonzero element in $GF(p^n)$ can be expressed as a power of some element γ, called a *primitive element* of $GF(p^n)$:

10–4 $$GF(p^n) = \{0, 1, \gamma, \gamma^2, \ldots, \gamma^{p^n-2}\}$$

10–5 If $\zeta_1, \zeta_2, \ldots, \zeta_{p^n}$ are the elements of $GF(p^n)$, then

10–6 $$(x - \zeta_1)(x - \zeta_2) \ldots (x - \zeta_{p^n}) = x^{p^n} - x$$

i.e., every element of $GF(p^n)$ satisfies the equation

10–7 $$x - x^{p^n} = 0$$

10–8 If $p(x)$ is the modulus polynomial of $GF(p^n)$, and if ρ is any root of $p(x)$ in $GF(p^n)$ [i.e., $p(\rho) = 0$], then the set $\{\rho, \rho^p, \rho^{p^2}, \ldots, \rho^{p^{n-1}}\}$ constitutes the set of all roots of $p(x)$ in $GF(p^n)$. All these roots are of the same order, which equals the exponent of $p(x)$. $p(x)$ is a maximum-exponent polynomial if and only if all its roots are primitive elements of $GF(p^n)$ (and hence of order $p^n - 1$).

10–9 If ζ is any element in $GF(p^n)$, then the *minimum function* of ζ is the (unique) least-degree monic polynomial $m_\zeta(x)$ such that $m_\zeta(\zeta) = 0$. $m_\zeta(x)$ is irreducible and of degree at most n. It divides every polynomial $f(x)$ such that $f(\zeta) = 0$. The degree of $m_\zeta(x)$ is the least integer i such that the order of ζ divides $p^i - 1$.

10–10 *Example:* $F_1 = GF(3^2)$, constructed with $p(x) = 1 + x + 2x^2$, has the nonzero elements

10–11
$$\begin{aligned} \xi^0 &= 1 \\ \xi^1 &= \xi \\ \xi^2 &= 1 + \xi \\ \xi^3 &= 1 + 2\xi \\ \xi^4 &= 2 \\ \xi^5 &= 2\xi \\ \xi^6 &= 2 + 2\xi \\ \xi^7 &= 2 + \xi \end{aligned}$$

(and $\xi^8 = 1$). Hence, ξ is a primitive element of F_1. For $F_2 = GF(3^2)$ constructed with $p(x) = 1 + x^2$, we have $\xi^0 = 1$, $\xi^1 = \xi$, $\xi^2 = 2$, $\xi^3 = 2\xi$, $\xi^4 = 1$. Hence, ξ is not a primitive element of F_2. However, $1 + \xi$ is a primitive element:

10–12
$$\begin{aligned} (1+\xi)^0 &= 1 \\ (1+\xi)^1 &= 1 + \xi \\ (1+\xi)^2 &= 2\xi \\ (1+\xi)^3 &= 1 + 2\xi \\ (1+\xi)^4 &= 2 \\ (1+\xi)^5 &= 2 + 2\xi \\ (1+\xi)^6 &= \xi \\ (1+\xi)^7 &= 2 + \xi \end{aligned}$$

F_1 and F_2 are isomorphic, with the following correspondences:

10–13

F_1		F_2
0	$\longleftrightarrow$	0
1	$\longleftrightarrow$	1
2	$\longleftrightarrow$	2
ξ	$\longleftrightarrow$	$2 + 2\xi$
$1 + \xi$	$\longleftrightarrow$	2ξ
$2 + \xi$	$\longleftrightarrow$	$1 + 2\xi$
2ξ	$\longleftrightarrow$	$1 + \xi$
$1 + 2\xi$	$\longleftrightarrow$	$2 + \xi$
$2 + 2\xi$	$\longleftrightarrow$	ξ

The roots of $1 + x + 2x^2$ in F_1 and of $1 + x^2$ in F_2 are ξ and ξ^3. The order of the roots in F_1 is 8, and in F_2 is 4 (these are the exponents of $1 + x + 2x^2$ and $1 + x^2$, respectively).

10–14 To find the minimum function of ξ^7 in F_1, first determine its degree which, by **10–9**, is 2 (the least integer i such that the order 8 of ξ^7 divides $3^i - 1$), and then assume $m_{\xi^7}(x) = \alpha_0 + \alpha_1 x + x^2$. This implies:

10–15 $$\alpha_0 + \alpha_1\xi^7 + \xi^{14} = \alpha_0 + \alpha_1(2 + \xi) + (2 + 2\xi) = 0$$

Equating coefficients of powers of ξ to 0, we have:

10–16 $$\begin{aligned} \alpha_0 + 2\alpha_1 &= 1 \\ \alpha_1 &= 1 \end{aligned}$$

Hence $\alpha_0 = 2$, $\alpha_1 = 1$ and $m_{\xi^7}(x) = 2 + x + x^2$.

11. Vector Spaces and Subspaces

Let V be an additive Abelian group and let F be a field. V is called a *vector space over F* if the following four postulates are satisfied:

11–1 *Closure:* For all α in F and $\mathbf{v}$ in V, $\alpha\mathbf{v}$ is defined and is in V.

11–2 *Associativity:* For all α and β in F and $\mathbf{v}$ in V, $(\alpha\beta)\mathbf{v} = \alpha(\beta\mathbf{v})$.

11–3 *Distributivity:* For all α and β in F and $\mathbf{u}$ and $\mathbf{v}$ in V, $\alpha(\mathbf{u} + \mathbf{v}) = \alpha\mathbf{u} + \alpha\mathbf{v}$ and $(\alpha + \beta)\mathbf{v} = \alpha\mathbf{v} + \beta\mathbf{v}$.

11–4 For all $\mathbf{v}$ in V, $1\mathbf{v} = \mathbf{v}$.

Elements of V are called *vectors* and those of F *scalars*. $\mathbf{0}$ denotes the zero of V and is called the *null vector*.

11–5 A *linear combination* of the vectors $\mathbf{v}_1, \mathbf{v}_2, \ldots, \mathbf{v}_n$ is a vector of the form $\alpha_1\mathbf{v}_1 + \alpha_2\mathbf{v}_2 + \cdots + \alpha_n\mathbf{v}_n$ where the α_i are scalars. $\mathbf{v}_1, \mathbf{v}_2, \ldots, \mathbf{v}_n$ are *linearly independent* if $\alpha_1\mathbf{v}_1 + \alpha_2\mathbf{v}_2 + \cdots + \alpha_n\mathbf{v}_n = \mathbf{0}$ implies $\alpha_1 = \alpha_2 = \cdots = \alpha_n = 0$. $\mathbf{v}_1, \mathbf{v}_2, \ldots, \mathbf{v}_n$ are said to *span* V if every vector in V can be expressed as their linear combination. When $\mathbf{v}_1, \mathbf{v}_2, \ldots, \mathbf{v}_n$ are linearly independent and span V, they form a *basis* for V. All bases of a given vector space have the same order, which is called the *dimension* of the space.

11–6 A subset U of a vector space V is called a *subspace* of V if it satisfies all postulates of V. For U to be a subspace it is necessary and sufficient that, for all α_1 and α_2 in F and $\mathbf{u}_1$ and $\mathbf{u}_2$ in U, $\alpha_1\mathbf{u}_1 + \alpha_2\mathbf{u}_2$ be in U.

11–7 *Example:* $R_{m(\xi)}$ over F (see **9–1**) is a vector space over F. If $m(x)$ is of degree n, $R_{m(\xi)}$ is n-dimensional with a basis $\{1, \xi, \xi^2, \ldots, \xi^{n-1}\}$. If $g(x)$ is any divisor of $m(x)$, the ideal $(g(\xi))$ in $R_{m(\xi)}$ is a subspace whose dimension is the degree of $m(x)/g(x)$, say, k; the set $\{g(\xi), \xi g(\xi), \xi^2 g(\xi), \ldots, \xi^{k-1} g(\xi)\}$ forms a basis for $(g(\xi))$.

12. Matrices

A matrix with elements from a field F is referred to as a *matrix over F*. All matrices discussed in this section will be of this kind.

12–1 The rows (columns) of a matrix $\mathbf{M}$ may be regarded as vectors, referred to as *row* (*column*) *vectors* (addition of two vectors is performed by adding their corresponding components; multiplication of a vector by a scalar is performed by multiplying every component by the scalar). If the number of elements in every row (column) of $\mathbf{M}$ is n, its row (column) vectors span a subspace U in an n-dimensional space V. This subspace is called the *row* (*column*) *space* of $\mathbf{M}$. If $\mathbf{M}$ has k linearly independent rows (columns), the dimension of U is k. This dimension is called the *row* (*column*) *rank* of **M**. The row and column ranks of a matrix are equal, and may be referred to simply as the *rank* of the matrix.

12–2 Matrices can be processed by a sequence of row (column) operations of the following types: (a) Interchange of any two rows (columns). (b) Multiplication of every row (column) by a nonzero scalar. (c) Addition of any scalar-multiple of one row (column) to another row (column). If $\mathbf{M}_2$ is obtained from $\mathbf{M}_1$ by a sequence of row (column) operations, they are said to be *row-* (*column-*) *equivalent*. If $\mathbf{M}_1$ and $\mathbf{M}_2$ are row- (column-) equivalent, they have the same row (column) space.

12–3 If U and V are as defined in **12–1**, a basis for U may be identified with the k nonzero rows (columns) of a matrix called the *row-* (*column-*) *reduced echelon canonical form* of **M**, which is row- (column-) equivalent to **M**. In this matrix the first nonzero element in every nonzero row (column) is 1; every column (row) containing such a 1 has 0 for all other elements; the first 1 in every nonzero row (column) is to the right of (below) the first 1 in the preceding row (column); zero rows (columns) appear below (to the right of) all nonzero rows (columns).

12–4 *Example:* Let

12–5
$$\mathbf{M} = \begin{pmatrix} 1 & 1 & 1 & 1 & 0 & 1 \\ 1 & 1 & 0 & 0 & 1 & 1 \\ 0 & 0 & 1 & 1 & 1 & 1 \\ 1 & 1 & 1 & 1 & 0 & 0 \\ 0 & 0 & 0 & 0 & 0 & 1 \end{pmatrix}$$

be a matrix over $GF(2)$. The following shows the row operations leading to the row-reduced echelon canonical form of **M** ($\rho_i + \rho_j \rightarrow \rho_j$ stands for "row i plus row j replaces row j")

12–6
$$\begin{pmatrix} 1 & 1 & 1 & 1 & 0 & 1 \\ 1 & 1 & 0 & 0 & 1 & 1 \\ 0 & 0 & 1 & 1 & 1 & 1 \\ 1 & 1 & 1 & 1 & 0 & 0 \\ 0 & 0 & 0 & 0 & 0 & 1 \end{pmatrix} \rightarrow \begin{pmatrix} 1 & 1 & 1 & 1 & 0 & 1 \\ 0 & 0 & 1 & 1 & 1 & 0 \\ 0 & 0 & 1 & 1 & 1 & 1 \\ 0 & 0 & 0 & 0 & 0 & 1 \\ 0 & 0 & 0 & 0 & 0 & 1 \end{pmatrix} \rightarrow$$

$$\begin{matrix} \rho_1 + \rho_2 \rightarrow \rho_2 \\ \rho_1 + \rho_4 \rightarrow \rho_4 \end{matrix} \qquad \begin{matrix} \rho_2 + \rho_1 \rightarrow \rho_1 \\ \rho_2 + \rho_3 \rightarrow \rho_3 \end{matrix}$$

$$\begin{pmatrix} 1 & 1 & 0 & 0 & 1 & 1 \\ 0 & 0 & 1 & 1 & 1 & 0 \\ 0 & 0 & 0 & 0 & 0 & 1 \\ 0 & 0 & 0 & 0 & 0 & 1 \\ 0 & 0 & 0 & 0 & 0 & 1 \end{pmatrix} \rightarrow \begin{pmatrix} 1 & 1 & 0 & 0 & 1 & 0 \\ 0 & 0 & 1 & 1 & 1 & 0 \\ 0 & 0 & 0 & 0 & 0 & 1 \\ 0 & 0 & 0 & 0 & 0 & 0 \\ 0 & 0 & 0 & 0 & 0 & 0 \end{pmatrix}$$

$$\begin{matrix} \rho_3 + \rho_1 \rightarrow \rho_1 \\ \rho_3 + \rho_4 \rightarrow \rho_4 \\ \rho_3 + \rho_5 \rightarrow \rho_5 \end{matrix}$$

Thus, the row space of **M** is 3-dimensional; its basis may be taken as the first three row vectors in the last matrix in **12–6**.

13. Null Space of a Matrix

13–1 Let $\mathbf{M}$ be a $k \times n$ matrix over F, of rank k. The set of all column vectors $\mathbf{v}$ such that $\mathbf{Mv} = \mathbf{0}$ is an $(n - k)$-dimensional subspace of the row space of $\mathbf{M}$ and is called the *null space* of $\mathbf{M}$. The dimension of the null space of $\mathbf{M}$ is called the *nullity* of $\mathbf{M}$.

13–2 If $\mathbf{M} = (\mathbf{I}_k, \mathbf{Q})$, where $\mathbf{Q}$ is a $k \times (n - k)$ submatrix, the null space of $\mathbf{M}$ is given by the column space of the matrix

13–3
$$\mathbf{N} = \begin{pmatrix} -\mathbf{Q} \\ \mathbf{I}_{n-k} \end{pmatrix}$$

If the columns of $\mathbf{M}$ are permuted (as may be the case in the row-reduced echelon canonical form without the zero rows), the rows of the corresponding $\mathbf{N}$ should be subjected to the same permutation.

13–4 *Example:* To find the null space of $\mathbf{M}$ of **12–5**, first determine the row-reduced echelon canonical form of $\mathbf{M}$ as in **12–6** (zero rows may be omitted):

13–5
$$\mathbf{M}' = \begin{pmatrix} 1 & 1 & 0 & 0 & 1 & 0 \\ 0 & 0 & 1 & 1 & 1 & 0 \\ 0 & 0 & 0 & 0 & 0 & 1 \end{pmatrix}$$
$$\underbrace{\qquad\uparrow\qquad\qquad\uparrow\quad\uparrow}_{\mathbf{Q}}$$

Hence:

13–6
$$\mathbf{N} = \begin{pmatrix} 1 & 0 & 1 \\ 1 & 0 & 0 \\ 0 & 1 & 1 \\ 0 & 1 & 0 \\ 0 & 0 & 1 \\ 0 & 0 & 0 \end{pmatrix} \begin{matrix} \leftarrow \\ \\ \leftarrow \\ \\ \\ \leftarrow \end{matrix} \; -\mathbf{Q}$$

14. The Inverse of a Matrix

14–1 A $k \times k$ matrix over F of rank k is called a *nonsingular* matrix. The *inverse* of a $k \times k$ nonsingular matrix $\mathbf{M}$ is the (unique) matrix $\mathbf{M}^{-1}$ such that $\mathbf{MM}^{-1} = \mathbf{M}^{-1}\mathbf{M} = \mathbf{I}_k$. $\mathbf{M}^{-1}$ can be constructed as follows: Perform on $\mathbf{I}_k$ all the row operations performed on $\mathbf{M}$ in obtaining the row-reduced echelon canonical form of $\mathbf{M}$; the final form of $\mathbf{I}_k$ is $\mathbf{M}^{-1}$.

14–2 If $\mathbf{M}$ is a $k \times n$ matrix of rank k, one can define a *right inverse* of $\mathbf{M}$ as any matrix $\mathbf{R}$ such that $\mathbf{MR} = \mathbf{I}_k$. $\mathbf{R}$ can be constructed as follows: Pick any k linearly independent columns in $\mathbf{M}$, say columns $j_1, j_2, \ldots, j_k$. If these columns form a matrix $\mathbf{Q}$, construct $\mathbf{Q}^{-1}$. $\mathbf{R}$ is then the $n \times k$ matrix where rows $j_1, j_2, \ldots, j_k$ are occupied by rows $1, 2, \ldots, k$, respectively, of $\mathbf{Q}^{-1}$, and where all other rows are zero.

14–3 *Example:* Let

14–4
$$\mathbf{M} = \begin{pmatrix} 1 & 1 & 1 & 1 & 0 & 1 \\ 1 & 1 & 0 & 0 & 1 & 1 \\ 0 & 0 & 1 & 1 & 1 & 1 \end{pmatrix}$$

be a matrix (of rank 3) over $GF(2)$. To find a right inverse of $\mathbf{M}$, we choose

14–5
$$\mathbf{Q} = \begin{pmatrix} 1 & 1 & 1 \\ 1 & 0 & 1 \\ 0 & 1 & 1 \end{pmatrix}$$

(columns 1, 3 and 6 of **M**). The following illustrates the construction of $\mathbf{Q}^{-1}$:

14–6
$$\underbrace{\begin{pmatrix} 1 & 1 & 1 \\ 1 & 0 & 1 \\ 0 & 1 & 1 \end{pmatrix}}_{\mathbf{Q}} \;\vdots\; \underbrace{\begin{pmatrix} 1 & 0 & 0 \\ 0 & 1 & 0 \\ 0 & 0 & 1 \end{pmatrix}}_{\mathbf{I}} \rightarrow \begin{pmatrix} 1 & 1 & 1 & \vdots & 1 & 0 & 0 \\ 0 & 1 & 0 & \vdots & 1 & 1 & 0 \\ 0 & 1 & 1 & \vdots & 0 & 0 & 1 \end{pmatrix} \rightarrow$$

$$\rho_1 + \rho_2 \rightarrow \rho_2 \qquad\qquad \rho_2 + \rho_1 \rightarrow \rho_1$$
$$\rho_2 + \rho_3 \rightarrow \rho_3$$

$$\begin{pmatrix} 1 & 0 & 1 & \vdots & 0 & 1 & 0 \\ 0 & 1 & 0 & \vdots & 1 & 1 & 0 \\ 0 & 0 & 1 & \vdots & 1 & 1 & 1 \end{pmatrix} \rightarrow \begin{pmatrix} 1 & 0 & 0 & \vdots & 1 & 0 & 1 \\ 0 & 1 & 0 & \vdots & 1 & 1 & 0 \\ 0 & 0 & 1 & \vdots & 1 & 1 & 1 \end{pmatrix}$$

$$\underbrace{}_{\mathbf{I}}\;\;\underbrace{}_{\mathbf{Q}^{-1}}$$

$$\rho_3 + \rho_1 \rightarrow \rho_1$$

Hence:

14–7
$$\mathbf{R} = \begin{pmatrix} 1 & 0 & 1 \\ 0 & 0 & 0 \\ 1 & 1 & 0 \\ 0 & 0 & 0 \\ 0 & 0 & 0 \\ 1 & 1 & 1 \end{pmatrix} \begin{matrix} \leftarrow \\ \\ \leftarrow \\ \\ \\ \leftarrow \end{matrix} \; \mathbf{Q}^{-1}$$

15. Elementary Divisors

15–1   In this section we shall deal with matrices whose elements are polynomials over a field. For such matrices, the following row (column) operations will be defined: (a) The interchange of two rows (columns) i and j [denoted by $\rho_i \leftrightarrow \rho_j$ $(\kappa_i \leftrightarrow \kappa_j)$]. (b) The addition of $f(x)$-multiplied row (column) i to row (column) j [denoted by $f(x)\rho_i + \rho_j \rightarrow \rho_j$ $(f(x)\kappa_i + \kappa_j \rightarrow \kappa_j)$]. (c) The multiplication of row (column) i by a nonzero field element α [denoted by $\alpha\rho_i \rightarrow \rho_i$ $(\alpha\kappa_i \rightarrow \kappa_i)$].

15–2   If **M** is an $n \times n$ matrix over F, and $\mathbf{M}_1 = \mathbf{M} - x\mathbf{I}$, the *similarity invariants* of **M** are l unique (nonzero) monic polynomials $(l \leq n)$ given by

15–3
$$\begin{aligned} g_1(x) &= f_1(x) \\ g_2(x) &= f_1(x)f_2(x) \\ &\;\;\vdots \\ g_l(x) &= f_1(x)f_2(x) \ldots f_l(x) \end{aligned}$$

The following is an algorithm for determining $f_1(x)$, $f_2(x)$, $\ldots$, $f_l(x)$ by a sequence of operations performed on $\mathbf{M}_1$. At each stage of the algorithm, $\mathbf{M}_k = [m_{ij}]_{(n-k+1) \times (n-k+1)}$ refers to the matrix *as it appears at that stage of the algorithm.*

15–4   (i) Set index k to 1.

(ii) $\mathbf{M}_k = \mathbf{0}$? *Yes:* go to (xvii). *No:* go to (iii).

(iii) Let m_{ab} be a nonzero element of least degree in $\mathbf{M}_k$.

(iv) $\rho_1 \leftrightarrow \rho_a$ [puts m_{ab} in $(1, b)$].

(v) $\kappa_1 \leftrightarrow \kappa_b$ [puts m_{1b} in $(1,1)$].

(vi) Are the $(1,j)$ elements 0 for all $j \neq 1$? *Yes:* go to (x). *No:* go to (vii).

(vii) Let m_{1c} be any nonzero elements in row 1 of $\mathbf{M}_k$ $(c \neq 1)$. Let $m_{1c} = q_1 m_{11} + r_1$, where $r_1 = 0$ or $\partial(r_1) < \partial(m_{11})$. $(-q_1)\kappa_1 + \kappa_c \rightarrow \kappa_c$ [puts r_1 in $(1,c)$].

(viii) $r_1=0$? *Yes:* return to (vi). *No:* go to (ix).

(ix) Let $b=c$. Return to (v).

(x) Are the $(i,1)$ elements 0 for all $i\neq 1$? *Yes:* go to (xiii). *No:* go to (xi).

(xi) Let m_{d1} be any nonzero element in column 1 of $\mathbf{M}_k$ $(d\neq 1)$. Let $m_{d1}=q_2m_{11}+r_2$, where $r_2=0$ or $\partial(r_2)<\partial(m_{11})$. $(-q_2)\rho_1+\rho_d\rightarrow\rho_d$ [puts r_2 in $(d,1)$]. $r_2=0$? *Yes:* return to (x). *No:* go to (xii).

(xii) $\rho_1\leftrightarrow\rho_d$ [puts m_{d1} in (1,1)]. Go to (xi).

(xiii) Does m_{11} divide every element in $\mathbf{M}_k$? *Yes:* go to (xv). *No:* go to (xiv).

(xiv) Let m_{ef} be any element in $\mathbf{M}_k$ not divisible by m_{11} $(e\neq 1,\ f\neq 1)$. Let $m_{ef}=q_3m_{11}+r_3$ where $\partial(r_3)<\partial(m_{11})$. $(q_3)\kappa_1+\kappa_f\rightarrow\kappa_f$ [puts q_3m_{11} in $(1,f)$]. $(-1)\rho_1+\rho_e\rightarrow\rho_e$ [puts r_3 in (e,f)]. Let $a=e$, $b=f$. Return to (iv).

(xv) Let leading coefficient of m_{11} be α. $(\alpha^{-1})\rho_1\rightarrow\rho_1$ [makes m_{11} monic]. $m_{11}=f_k(x)$. $k=n$? *Yes:* go to (xvii). *No:* go to (xvi).

(xvi) Let $f_k(x)$ $\mathbf{M}_{k+1}$ be the matrix obtained from $\mathbf{M}_k$ by deleting row 1 and column 1. Increment k by 1. Return to (ii).

(xvii) Halt.

15–5 The similarity invariants of **M** can be written in a prime-factored form as follows:

15–6
$$\begin{aligned}
g_l(x)&=[p_1(x)]^{h_{l1}}[p_2(x)]^{h_{l2}}\cdots[p_r(x)]^{h_{lr}}\\
g_{l-1}(x)&=[p_1(x)]^{h_{(l-1)1}}[p_2(x)]^{h_{(l-1)2}}\cdots[p_r(x)]^{h_{(l-1)r}}\\
&\ \vdots\\
g_1(x)&=[p_1(x)]^{h_{11}}[p_2(x)]^{h_{12}}\cdots[p_r(x)]^{h_{1r}}
\end{aligned}$$

where $h_{lj}\geq h_{(l-1)j}\geq\cdots\geq h_{1j}\geq 0$. The *elementary divisors* of **M** are all the factors $[p_i(x)]^{h_{ij}}$ which are nonconstant (i.e., where $h_{ij}>0$).

15–7 *Example:* Let

15–8
$$\mathbf{M}=\begin{pmatrix}
0&0&1&1&1&1&1&1\\
0&1&0&0&0&0&0&0\\
0&1&1&1&1&1&1&1\\
0&0&0&0&1&1&1&1\\
0&0&0&0&1&0&0&0\\
0&0&0&0&0&1&0&1\\
0&0&0&0&0&0&1&1\\
0&0&0&0&0&0&1&0
\end{pmatrix}$$

be a matrix over $GF(2)$. The following illustrates algorithm **15–4**:

15–9
$$\mathbf{M}_1=\begin{pmatrix}
x&0&1&1&1&1&1&1\\
0&1+x&0&0&0&0&0&0\\
0&1&1+x&1&1&1&1&1\\
0&0&0&x&1&1&1&1\\
0&0&0&0&1+x&0&0&0\\
0&0&0&0&0&1+x&0&1\\
0&0&0&0&0&0&1+x&1\\
0&0&0&0&0&0&1&x
\end{pmatrix}\rightarrow\begin{pmatrix}
1&0&x&1&1&1&1&1\\
0&1+x&0&0&0&0&0&0\\
1+x&1&0&1&1&1&1&1\\
0&0&0&x&1&1&1&1\\
0&0&0&0&1+x&0&0&0\\
0&0&0&0&0&1+x&0&1\\
0&0&0&0&0&0&1+x&1\\
0&0&0&0&0&0&1&x
\end{pmatrix}$$

$\kappa_1\leftrightarrow\kappa_3$

$$\to\begin{pmatrix} 1 & 0 & 0 & 0 & 0 & 0 & 0 & 0 \\ 0 & 1+x & 0 & 0 & 0 & 0 & 0 & 0 \\ 1+x & 1 & x+x^2 & x & x & x & x & x \\ 0 & 0 & 0 & x & 1 & 1 & 1 & 1 \\ 0 & 0 & 0 & 0 & 1+x & 0 & 0 & 0 \\ 0 & 0 & 0 & 0 & 0 & 1+x & 0 & 1 \\ 0 & 0 & 0 & 0 & 0 & 0 & 1+x & 1 \\ 0 & 0 & 0 & 0 & 0 & 0 & 1 & x \end{pmatrix} \to \begin{pmatrix} \textcircled{1} & 0 & 0 & 0 & 0 & 0 & 0 & 0 \\ 0 & 1+x & 0 & 0 & 0 & 0 & 0 & 0 \\ 0 & 1 & x+x^2 & x & x & x & x & x \\ 0 & 0 & 0 & x & 1 & 1 & 1 & 1 \\ 0 & 0 & 0 & 0 & 1+x & 0 & 0 & 0 \\ 0 & 0 & 0 & 0 & 0 & 1+x & 0 & 1 \\ 0 & 0 & 0 & 0 & 0 & 0 & 1+x & 1 \\ 0 & 0 & 0 & 0 & 0 & 0 & 1 & x \end{pmatrix}$$

$x\kappa_1+\kappa_3\to\kappa_3$ $\qquad (1+x)\rho_1+\rho_3\to\rho_3$

$\kappa_1+\kappa_4\to\kappa_4$

$\kappa_1+\kappa_5\to\kappa_5$

$\kappa_1+\kappa_6\to\kappa_6$

$\kappa_1+\kappa_7\to\kappa_7$

$\kappa_1+\kappa_8\to\kappa_8$

15–10 $$\mathbf{M}_2 = \begin{pmatrix} 1+x & 0 & 0 & 0 & 0 & 0 & 0 \\ 1 & x+x^2 & x & x & x & x & x \\ 0 & 0 & x & 1 & 1 & 1 & 1 \\ 0 & 0 & 0 & 1+x & 0 & 0 & 0 \\ 0 & 0 & 0 & 0 & 1+x & 0 & 1 \\ 0 & 0 & 0 & 0 & 0 & 1+x & 1 \\ 0 & 0 & 0 & 0 & 0 & 1 & x \end{pmatrix} \to \begin{pmatrix} 1 & x+x^2 & x & x & x & x & x \\ 1+x & 0 & 0 & 0 & 0 & 0 & 0 \\ 0 & 0 & x & 1 & 1 & 1 & 1 \\ 0 & 0 & 0 & 1+x & 0 & 0 & 0 \\ 0 & 0 & 0 & 0 & 1+x & 0 & 1 \\ 0 & 0 & 0 & 0 & 0 & 1+x & 1 \\ 0 & 0 & 0 & 0 & 0 & 1 & x \end{pmatrix}$$

$\rho_1\leftrightarrow\rho_2$

$$\to\begin{pmatrix} 1 & 0 & 0 & 0 & 0 & 0 & 0 \\ 1+x & x+x^3 & x+x^2 & x+x^2 & x+x^2 & x+x^2 & x+x^2 \\ 0 & 0 & x & 1 & 1 & 1 & 1 \\ 0 & 0 & 0 & 1+x & 0 & 0 & 0 \\ 0 & 0 & 0 & 0 & 1+x & 0 & 1 \\ 0 & 0 & 0 & 0 & 0 & 1+x & 1 \\ 0 & 0 & 0 & 0 & 0 & 1 & x \end{pmatrix} \to \begin{pmatrix} \textcircled{1} & 0 & 0 & 0 & 0 & 0 & 0 \\ 0 & x+x^3 & x+x^2 & x+x^2 & x+x^2 & x+x^2 & x+x^2 \\ 0 & 0 & x & 1 & 1 & 1 & 1 \\ 0 & 0 & 0 & 1+x & 0 & 0 & 0 \\ 0 & 0 & 0 & 0 & 1+x & 0 & 1 \\ 0 & 0 & 0 & 0 & 0 & 1+x & 1 \\ 0 & 0 & 0 & 0 & 0 & 1 & x \end{pmatrix}$$

$(x+x^2)\kappa_1+\kappa_2\to\kappa_2$ $\qquad (1+x)\rho_1+\rho_2\to\rho_2$

$x\kappa_1+\kappa_3\to\kappa_3$

$x\kappa_1+\kappa_4\to\kappa_4$

$x\kappa_1+\kappa_5\to\kappa_5$

$x\kappa_1+\kappa_6\to\kappa_6$

$x\kappa_1+\kappa_7\to\kappa_7$

15–11 $$\mathbf{M}_3 = \begin{pmatrix} x+x^3 & x+x^2 & x+x^2 & x+x^2 & x+x^2 & x+x^2 \\ 0 & x & 1 & 1 & 1 & 1 \\ 0 & 0 & 1+x & 0 & 0 & 0 \\ 0 & 0 & 0 & 1+x & 0 & 1 \\ 0 & 0 & 0 & 0 & 1+x & 1 \\ 0 & 0 & 0 & 0 & 1 & x \end{pmatrix} \to \begin{pmatrix} 0 & x & 1 & 1 & 1 & 1 \\ x+x^3 & x+x^2 & x+x^2 & x+x^2 & x+x^2 & x+x^2 \\ 0 & 0 & 1+x & 0 & 0 & 0 \\ 0 & 0 & 0 & 1+x & 0 & 1 \\ 0 & 0 & 0 & 0 & 1+x & 1 \\ 0 & 0 & 0 & 0 & 1 & x \end{pmatrix}$$

$\rho_1\leftrightarrow\rho_2$

$$\to\begin{pmatrix} 1 & x & 0 & 1 & 1 & 1 \\ x+x^2 & x+x^2 & x+x^3 & x+x^2 & x+x^2 & x+x^2 \\ 1+x & 0 & 0 & 0 & 0 & 0 \\ 0 & 0 & 0 & 1+x & 0 & 1 \\ 0 & 0 & 0 & 0 & 1+x & 1 \\ 0 & 0 & 0 & 0 & 1 & x \end{pmatrix}$$

$\kappa_1\leftrightarrow\kappa_3$

$$\rightarrow\begin{pmatrix} 1 & 0 & 0 & 0 & 0 & 0 \\ x+x^2 & x+x^3 & x+x^3 & 0 & 0 & 0 \\ 1+x & x+x^2 & 0 & 1+x & 1+x & 1+x \\ 0 & 0 & 0 & 1+x & 0 & 1 \\ 0 & 0 & 0 & 0 & 1+x & 1 \\ 0 & 0 & 0 & 0 & 1 & x \end{pmatrix}\rightarrow\begin{pmatrix} \textcircled{1} & 0 & 0 & 0 & 0 & 0 \\ 0 & x+x^3 & x+x^3 & 0 & 0 & 0 \\ 0 & x+x^2 & 0 & 1+x & 1+x & 1+x \\ 0 & 0 & 0 & 1+x & 0 & 1 \\ 0 & 0 & 0 & 0 & 1+x & 1 \\ 0 & 0 & 0 & 0 & 1 & x \end{pmatrix}$$

$x\kappa_1 + \kappa_2 \rightarrow \kappa_2$ $\quad(x + x^2)\rho_1 + \rho_2 \rightarrow \rho_2$

$\kappa_1 + \kappa_4 \rightarrow \kappa_4$ $\quad(1 + x)\rho_1 + \rho_3 \rightarrow \rho_3$

$\kappa_1 + \kappa_5 \rightarrow \kappa_5$

$\kappa_1 + \kappa_6 \rightarrow \kappa_6$

15–12 $\mathbf{M}_4 = \begin{pmatrix} x+x^3 & x+x^3 & 0 & 0 & 0 \\ x+x^2 & 0 & 1+x & 1+x & 1+x \\ 0 & 0 & 1+x & 0 & 1 \\ 0 & 0 & 0 & 1+x & 1 \\ 0 & 0 & 0 & 1 & x \end{pmatrix}\rightarrow\begin{pmatrix} 0 & 0 & 1+x & 0 & 1 \\ x+x^2 & 0 & 1+x & 1+x & 1+x \\ x+x^3 & x+x^3 & 0 & 0 & 0 \\ 0 & 0 & 0 & 1+x & 1 \\ 0 & 0 & 0 & 1 & x \end{pmatrix}$

$\rho_1 \leftrightarrow \rho_3$

$$\rightarrow\begin{pmatrix} 1 & 0 & 1+x & 0 & 0 \\ 1+x & 0 & 1+x & 1+x & x+x^2 \\ 0 & x+x^3 & 0 & 0 & x+x^3 \\ 1 & 0 & 0 & 1+x & 0 \\ x & 0 & 0 & 1 & 0 \end{pmatrix}\rightarrow\begin{pmatrix} 1 & 0 & 0 & 0 & 0 \\ 1+x & 0 & x+x^2 & 1+x & x+x^2 \\ 0 & x+x^3 & 0 & 0 & x+x^3 \\ 1 & 0 & 1+x & 1+x & 0 \\ x & 0 & x+x^2 & 1 & 0 \end{pmatrix}$$

$\kappa_1 \leftrightarrow \kappa_5$ $\quad(1 + x)\kappa_1 + \kappa_3 \rightarrow \kappa_3$

$$\rightarrow\begin{pmatrix} \textcircled{1} & 0 & 0 & 0 & 0 \\ 0 & 0 & x+x^2 & 1+x & x+x^2 \\ 0 & x+x^3 & 0 & 0 & x+x^3 \\ 0 & 0 & 1+x & 1+x & 0 \\ 0 & 0 & x+x^2 & 1 & 0 \end{pmatrix}$$

$(1 + x)\rho_1 + \rho_2 \rightarrow \rho_2$

$\rho_1 + \rho_4 \rightarrow \rho_4$

$x\rho_1 + \rho_5 \rightarrow \rho_5$

15–13 $\mathbf{M}_5 = \begin{pmatrix} 0 & x+x^2 & 1+x & x+x^2 \\ x+x^3 & 0 & 0 & x+x^3 \\ 0 & 1+x & 1+x & 0 \\ 0 & x+x^2 & 1 & 0 \end{pmatrix}\rightarrow\begin{pmatrix} 0 & x+x^2 & 1 & 0 \\ x+x^3 & 0 & 0 & x+x^3 \\ 0 & 1+x & 1+x & 0 \\ 0 & x+x^2 & 1+x & x+x^2 \end{pmatrix}$

$\rho_1 \leftrightarrow \rho_4$

$$\rightarrow\begin{pmatrix} 1 & x+x^2 & 0 & 0 \\ 0 & 0 & x+x^3 & x+x^3 \\ 1+x & 1+x & 0 & 0 \\ 1+x & x+x^2 & 0 & x+x^2 \end{pmatrix}\rightarrow\begin{pmatrix} 1 & 0 & 0 & 0 \\ 0 & 0 & x+x^3 & x+x^3 \\ 1+x & 1+x^3 & 0 & 0 \\ 1+x & x^2+x^3 & 0 & x+x^2 \end{pmatrix}$$

$\kappa_1 \leftrightarrow \kappa_3$ $\quad(x + x^2)\,\kappa_1 + \kappa_2 \rightarrow \kappa_2$

$$\rightarrow\begin{pmatrix} \textcircled{1} & 0 & 0 & 0 \\ 0 & 0 & x+x^3 & x+x^3 \\ 0 & 1+x^3 & 0 & 0 \\ 0 & x^2+x^3 & 0 & x+x^2 \end{pmatrix}$$

$(1 + x)\rho_1 + \rho_3 \rightarrow \rho_3$

$(1 + x)\rho_1 + \rho_4 \rightarrow \rho_4$

15–14

$$\mathbf{M}_6 = \begin{pmatrix} 0 & x+x^3 & x+x^3 \\ 1+x^3 & 0 & 0 \\ x^2+x^3 & 0 & x+x^2 \end{pmatrix} \to \underset{\rho_1 \leftrightarrow \rho_3}{\begin{pmatrix} x^2+x^3 & 0 & x+x^2 \\ 1+x^3 & 0 & 0 \\ 0 & x+x^3 & x+x^3 \end{pmatrix}} \to \underset{\kappa_1 \leftrightarrow \kappa_3}{\begin{pmatrix} x+x^2 & 0 & x^2+x^3 \\ 0 & 0 & 1+x^3 \\ x+x^3 & x+x^3 & 0 \end{pmatrix}}$$

$$\to \underset{x\kappa_1 + \kappa_3 \to \kappa_3}{\begin{pmatrix} x+x^2 & 0 & 0 \\ 0 & 0 & 1+x^3 \\ x+x^3 & x+x^3 & x^2+x^4 \end{pmatrix}} \to \underset{(1+x)\rho_1 + \rho_3 \to \rho_3}{\begin{pmatrix} x+x^2 & 0 & 0 \\ 0 & 0 & 1+x^3 \\ 0 & x+x^3 & x^2+x^4 \end{pmatrix}} \to \underset{(1+x)\kappa_1 + \kappa_3 \to \kappa_3}{\begin{pmatrix} x+x^2 & 0 & x+x^3 \\ 0 & 0 & 1+x^3 \\ 0 & x+x^3 & x^2+x^4 \end{pmatrix}}$$

$$\to \underset{\rho_1 + \rho_2 \to \rho_2}{\begin{pmatrix} x+x^2 & 0 & x+x^3 \\ x+x^2 & 0 & 1+x \\ 0 & x+x^3 & x^2+x^4 \end{pmatrix}} \to \underset{\rho_1 \leftrightarrow \rho_2}{\begin{pmatrix} x+x^2 & 0 & 1+x \\ x+x^2 & 0 & x+x^3 \\ 0 & x+x^3 & x^2+x^4 \end{pmatrix}} \to \underset{\kappa_1 \leftrightarrow \kappa_3}{\begin{pmatrix} 1+x & 0 & x+x^2 \\ x+x^3 & 0 & x+x^2 \\ x^2+x^4 & x+x^3 & 0 \end{pmatrix}}$$

$$\to \underset{x\kappa_1 + \kappa_3 \to \kappa_3}{\begin{pmatrix} 1+x & 0 & 0 \\ x+x^3 & 0 & x+x^4 \\ x^2+x^4 & x+x^3 & x^3+x^4 \end{pmatrix}} \to \underset{\substack{(x+x^2)\rho_1 + \rho_2 \to \rho_2 \\ (x^2+x^3)\rho_1 + \rho_3 \to \rho_3}}{\begin{pmatrix} \textcircled{1+x} & 0 & 0 \\ 0 & 0 & x+x^4 \\ 0 & x+x^3 & x^3+x^4 \end{pmatrix}}$$

15–15

$$\mathbf{M}_7 = \begin{pmatrix} 0 & x+x^2+x^3 \\ x+x^2 & x^3+x^4 \end{pmatrix} \to \underset{\rho_1 \leftrightarrow \rho_2}{\begin{pmatrix} x+x^2 & x^3+x^4 \\ 0 & x+x^2+x^3 \end{pmatrix}} \to \underset{x^2\kappa_1 + \kappa_2 \to \kappa_2}{\begin{pmatrix} x+x^2 & 0 \\ 0 & x+x^2+x^3 \end{pmatrix}}$$

$$\to \underset{x\kappa_1 + \kappa_2 \to \kappa_2}{\begin{pmatrix} x+x^2 & x^2+x^3 \\ 0 & x+x^2+x^3 \end{pmatrix}} \to \underset{\rho_1 + \rho_2 \to \rho_2}{\begin{pmatrix} x+x^2 & x^2+x^3 \\ x+x^2 & x \end{pmatrix}} \to \underset{\rho_1 \leftrightarrow \rho_2}{\begin{pmatrix} x+x^2 & x \\ x+x^2 & x^2+x^3 \end{pmatrix}}$$

$$\to \underset{\kappa_1 \leftrightarrow \kappa_2}{\begin{pmatrix} x & x+x^2 \\ x^2+x^3 & x+x^2 \end{pmatrix}} \to \underset{(1+x)\kappa_1 + \kappa_2 \to \kappa_2}{\begin{pmatrix} x & 0 \\ x^2+x^3 & x+x^4 \end{pmatrix}} \to \underset{(x+x^2)\rho_1 + \rho_2 \to \rho_2}{\begin{pmatrix} \textcircled{x} & 0 \\ 0 & x+x^4 \end{pmatrix}}$$

15–16 $\mathbf{M}_8 = (1 + x^3)$

Thus, we have:

15–17 $f_1(x) = \ldots = f_5(x) = 1,\ f_6(x) = 1 + x,\ f_7(x) = x,$

$$f_8(x) = 1 + x^3 = (1 + x)(1 + x + x^2)$$

15–18 $g_1(x) = \ldots = g_5(x) = 1,\ g_6(x) = 1 + x,\ g_7(x) = (1 + x)x,$

$$g_8(x) = (1 + x)^2\, x(1 + x + x^2)$$

The elementary divisors of **M**, therefore, are

15–19

$$\begin{array}{ccc} 1+x, & 1+x, & (1+x)^2 \\ & x, & x \\ & & 1+x+x^2 \end{array}$$

16. Characteristic and Minimum Polynominals of a Matrix

16–1 The elementary divisors of a matrix **M** over F can be arranged in an array of the form:

16-2

$$\begin{matrix} [p_1(x)]^{e_{11}}, [p_1(x)]^{e_{12}}, \ldots, [p_1(x)]^{e_{1l_1}} \\ [p_2(x)]^{e_{21}}, [p_2(x)]^{e_{22}}, \ldots, [p_2(x)]^{e_{2l_2}} \\ \cdot \\ \cdot \\ \cdot \\ [p_r(x)]^{e_{r1}}, [p_r(x)]^{e_{r2}}, \ldots, [p_r(x)]^{e_{rl_r}} \end{matrix}$$

where $0 \leq e_{\nu 1} \leq e_{\nu 2} \leq \ldots \leq e_{\nu l_\nu}$ $(\nu = 1, 2, \ldots, r)$, and where the $p_i(x)$ are distinct, nonconstant, monic, irreducible polynomials over F. The r elementary divisors $[p_i(x)]^{e_{il_i}}$ (rightmost in each row) are called the *leading elementary divisors* of **M**.

16-3 The *characteristic polynomial* of **M**, denoted by $\phi_{\mathbf{M}}(x)$, is defined as $|\mathbf{M} - x\mathbf{I}|$. It equals, within a constant multiplier, to the product of all elementary divisors of **M**. **M** satisfies the equation $\phi_{\mathbf{M}}(x) = 0$ (i.e., $\phi_{\mathbf{M}}(\mathbf{M}) = \mathbf{0}$). **M** is nonsingular if and only if $\phi_{\mathbf{M}}(x)$ is indivisible by x.

16-4 The *minimum polynomial* of **M**, denoted by $m_{\mathbf{M}}(x)$, is the (unique) least-degree monic polynomial such that $m_{\mathbf{M}}(\mathbf{M}) = \mathbf{0}$. It equals the product of all leading elementary divisors of **M**. It divides every polynomial $f(x)$ such that $f(\mathbf{M}) = \mathbf{0}$ [and, in particular, it divides $\phi_{\mathbf{M}}(x)$].

16-5 *Example:* For **M** of Example **15-7**,

16-6 $$\phi_{\mathbf{M}}(x) = (1 + x)^4x^2(1 + x + x^2)$$

16-7 $$m_{\mathbf{M}}(x) = (1 + x)^2x(1 + x + x^2)$$

17. The Rational Canonical Form

17-1 Two square matrices **M** and $\overline{\mathbf{M}}$ over F are said to be *similar* (to each other) if a nonsingular matrix **P** exists such that $\overline{\mathbf{M}} = \mathbf{PMP}^{-1}$. **P** is called the *similarity transformation matrix from* **M** *to* $\overline{\mathbf{M}}$. Two matrices are similar if and only if they have the same set of elementary divisors.

17-2 Let

$$d(x) = \alpha_0 + \alpha_1 x + \ldots + \alpha_{n-1}x^{n-1} + x^n$$

17-3 $$= [p_1(x)]^{e_1}[p_2(x)]^{e_2} \ldots [p_r(x)]^{e_r} \qquad (n \geq 1)$$

(where the $[p_i(x)]^{e_i}$ are distinct, nonconstant, monic and irreducible) be a monic polynomial over F. The *companion matrix* of $d(x)$, denoted by $\mathbf{M}_{d(x)}$, is an $n \times n$ matrix given by

17-4 $$\mathbf{M}_{d(x)} = \begin{pmatrix} & 1 & & & & \\ & & 1 & & & \\ & & & \cdot & & \\ & & & & \cdot & \\ & & & & & \cdot \\ & & & & & 1 \\ -\alpha_0 & -\alpha_1 & -\alpha_2 & \cdot & \cdot & \cdot & -\alpha_{n-1} \end{pmatrix}$$

$d(x)$ is the minimum polynomial and—within a constant multiplier—the characteristic polynomial of $\mathbf{M}_{d(x)}$. The $[p_i(x)]^{e_i}$ are the elementary divisors of $\mathbf{M}_{d(x)}$.

17-5 $\mathbf{M}_{d(x)}$ is similar to its transpose

17–6

$$\mathbf{M}_{d(x)}^{\mathrm{TR}} = \begin{pmatrix} & & & & -\alpha_0 \\ 1 & & & & -\alpha_1 \\ & 1 & & & -\alpha_2 \\ & & \cdot & & \cdot \\ & & & \cdot & \cdot \\ & & & \cdot & \cdot \\ & & & 1 & -\alpha_{n-1} \end{pmatrix}$$

If $d(x) = [p(x)]^e$, $\mathbf{M}_{d(x)}$ is also similar to the *hypercompanion matrix* of $d(x)$, given by

17–7

$$\mathbf{H}_{d(x)} = \begin{pmatrix} \mathbf{M}_{p(x)} & \mathbf{J} & & & \\ & \mathbf{M}_{p(x)} & \mathbf{J} & & \\ & & \cdot & & \\ & & & \cdot & \\ & & & \cdot & \\ & & & \mathbf{M}_{p(x)} & \mathbf{J} \\ & & & & \mathbf{M}_{p(x)} \end{pmatrix}$$

where $\mathbf{M}_{p(x)}$ appears e times, and where $\mathbf{J}$ is a matrix with 1 in the lower left-hand corner and 0 elsewhere.

17–8 The matrix $\mathbf{M}$ with the elementary divisors $d_1(x), d_2(x), \ldots, d_w(x)$ (and every matrix similar to $\mathbf{M}$) is similar to

17–9

$$\mathbf{M}^* = \begin{pmatrix} \mathbf{M}_{d_1(x)} & & & & \\ & \mathbf{M}_{d_2(x)} & & & \\ & & \cdot & & \\ & & & \cdot & \\ & & & \cdot & \\ & & & & \mathbf{M}_{d_w(x)} \end{pmatrix}$$

$\mathbf{M}^*$ is called the *rational canonical form* of $\mathbf{M}$. The submatrices $\mathbf{M}_{d_i(x)}$ are called the *elementary blocks* of $\mathbf{M}^*$. Similarity of $\mathbf{M}^*$ to $\mathbf{M}$ is not impaired when the order of the elementary blocks is changed, or when any elementary block is replaced by its transpose, or when an $\mathbf{M}_{d_i(x)}$ is replaced by $\mathbf{H}_{d_i(x)}$.

17–10 *Example:* For $\mathbf{M}$ of Example **15–7**, we have

17–11

$$\mathbf{M}^* = \begin{pmatrix} \mathbf{M}_{1+x} & & & & & \\ & \mathbf{M}_{1+x} & & & & \\ & & \mathbf{M}_{(1+x)^2} & & & \\ & & & \mathbf{M}_{1+x+x^2} & & \\ & & & & \mathbf{M}_x & \\ & & & & & \mathbf{M}_x \end{pmatrix} = \begin{pmatrix} 1 & & & & & & & \\ & 1 & & & & & & \\ & & 0 & 1 & & & & \\ & & 1 & 0 & & & & \\ & & & & 0 & 1 & & \\ & & & & 1 & 1 & & \\ & & & & & & 0 & \\ & & & & & & & 0 \end{pmatrix}$$

18. Similarity Transformation Matrices

18–1 Let $\mathbf{M}_1$ and $\mathbf{M}_2 = \mathbf{P}\mathbf{M}_1\mathbf{P}^{-1}$ be two similar $n \times n$ matrices over F. If $\mathbf{M}_1$ and $\mathbf{M}_2$ are given but $\mathbf{P} = [p_{ij}]_{n \times n}$ is not, we can write

18–2

$$\mathbf{Q} = [q_{ij}]_{n \times n} = \mathbf{P}\mathbf{M}_1 - \mathbf{M}_2\mathbf{P} = \mathbf{0}$$

which yields a system of n^2 homogeneous equations in the p_{ij}. These can be put in the form

18–3
$$\begin{pmatrix} q_{11} \\ \cdot \\ \cdot \\ \cdot \\ q_{1n} \\ q_{21} \\ \cdot \\ \cdot \\ \cdot \\ q_{2n} \\ \cdot \\ \cdot \\ \cdot \\ q_{n1} \\ \cdot \\ \cdot \\ \cdot \\ q_{nn} \end{pmatrix} = \mathbf{K} \begin{pmatrix} p_{11} \\ \cdot \\ \cdot \\ \cdot \\ p_{1n} \\ p_{21} \\ \cdot \\ \cdot \\ \cdot \\ p_{2n} \\ \cdot \\ \cdot \\ \cdot \\ p_{n1} \\ \cdot \\ \cdot \\ \cdot \\ p_{nn} \end{pmatrix} = \mathbf{0}$$

When the vectors are arranged as in **18–3**, **K** assumes the form

18–4
$$\mathbf{K} = \begin{pmatrix} \mathbf{M}_1^{\mathrm{TR}} & & & \\ & \mathbf{M}_1^{\mathrm{TR}} & & \\ & & \ddots & \\ & & & \mathbf{M}_1^{\mathrm{TR}} \end{pmatrix} + \begin{pmatrix} m'_{11}\mathbf{I}_n & m'_{12}\mathbf{I}_n & \cdots & m'_{1n}\mathbf{I}_n \\ m'_{21}\mathbf{I}_n & m'_{22}\mathbf{I}_n & & m'_{2n}\mathbf{I}_n \\ \cdot & & & \\ \cdot & & & \\ \cdot & & & \\ m'_{n1}\mathbf{I}_n & m'_{n2}\mathbf{I}_n & & m'_{nn}\mathbf{I}_n \end{pmatrix}$$

where m'_{ij} is the (i,j) element of $\mathbf{M}_2$. The p_{ij} can be determined (in general, not uniquely) from any vector in the null space of **K**

18–5 *Example:* Let

18–6
$$\mathbf{M}_1 = \begin{pmatrix} 0 & 1 & 1 \\ 0 & 0 & 1 \\ 1 & 0 & 0 \end{pmatrix} \qquad \mathbf{M}_2 = \begin{pmatrix} 0 & 1 & 0 \\ 0 & 0 & 1 \\ 1 & 1 & 0 \end{pmatrix}$$

be (similar) matrices over $GF(2)$. In this case:

18–7
$$\mathbf{K} = \begin{pmatrix} 0 & 0 & 1 & & & & & & \\ 1 & 0 & 0 & & & & & & \\ 1 & 1 & 0 & & & & & & \\ & & & 0 & 0 & 1 & & & \\ & & & 1 & 0 & 0 & & & \\ & & & 1 & 1 & 0 & & & \\ & & & & & & 0 & 0 & 1 \\ & & & & & & 1 & 0 & 0 \\ & & & & & & 1 & 1 & 0 \end{pmatrix} + \begin{pmatrix} & & & 1 & 0 & 0 & & & \\ & & & 0 & 1 & 0 & & & \\ & & & 0 & 0 & 1 & & & \\ & & & & & & 1 & 0 & 0 \\ & & & & & & 0 & 1 & 0 \\ & & & & & & 0 & 0 & 1 \\ 1 & 0 & 0 & 1 & 0 & 0 & & & \\ 0 & 1 & 0 & 0 & 1 & 0 & & & \\ 0 & 0 & 1 & 0 & 0 & 1 & & & \end{pmatrix}$$

The row-reduced echelon canonical form of **K** (with zero rows omitted) is given by

18–8
$$\mathbf{K}' = \begin{pmatrix} 1 & & & & & & 0 & 1 & 1 \\ & 1 & & & & & 1 & 1 & 1 \\ & & 1 & & & & 0 & 1 & 0 \\ & & & 1 & & & 0 & 1 & 0 \\ & & & & 1 & & 0 & 1 & 1 \\ & & & & & 1 & 1 & 0 & 0 \end{pmatrix}$$

By **13–2**, the null space of $\mathbf{K}'$ is spanned by

18–9
$$\mathbf{N} = \begin{pmatrix} 0 & 1 & 1 \\ 1 & 1 & 1 \\ 0 & 1 & 0 \\ 0 & 1 & 0 \\ 0 & 1 & 1 \\ 1 & 0 & 0 \\ 1 & & \\ & 1 & \\ & & 1 \end{pmatrix}$$

Any linear combination of column vectors of $\mathbf{N}$ yields a possible set of p_{ij}. For example, from the first column vector:

18–10
$$\mathbf{P} = \begin{pmatrix} 0 & 1 & 0 \\ 0 & 0 & 1 \\ 1 & 0 & 0 \end{pmatrix} \qquad \mathbf{P}^{-1} = \begin{pmatrix} 0 & 0 & 1 \\ 1 & 0 & 0 \\ 0 & 1 & 0 \end{pmatrix}$$

18–11 A similarity transformation matrix of special interest is that from a companion matrix $\mathbf{M}_{d(x)}$ to its transpose. $\mathbf{P}$ such that $\mathbf{M}_{d(x)}^{\mathrm{TR}} = \mathbf{P}\mathbf{M}_{d(x)}\mathbf{P}^{-1}$, where $\mathbf{M}_{d(x)}$ is as defined in **17–4**, is given by

18–12
$$\mathbf{P} = \begin{pmatrix} & & & & & \alpha_0 \\ & & & & \alpha_0 & \alpha_1 \\ & & & \alpha_0 & \alpha_1 & \alpha_2 \\ & & & & & \cdot \\ & & & & & \cdot \\ & & & & & \cdot \\ & \alpha_0 & & \alpha_{n-4} & \alpha_{n-3} & \alpha_{n-2} \\ \alpha_0 & \alpha_1 & \cdots & \alpha_{n-3} & \alpha_{n-2} & \alpha_{n-1} \end{pmatrix} \qquad (\alpha_0 \neq 0)$$

18–13
$$\mathbf{P} = \begin{pmatrix} \alpha_1 & \alpha_2 & \cdots & \alpha_{n-2} & \alpha_{n-1} & 1 \\ \alpha_2 & \alpha_3 & & \alpha_{n-1} & 1 & \\ \alpha_3 & \alpha_4 & & 1 & & \\ \cdot & & & & & \\ \cdot & & & & & \\ \cdot & & & & & \\ \alpha_{n-1} & 1 & & & & \\ 1 & & & & & \end{pmatrix} \qquad (\alpha_0 = 0)$$

Chapter 2

Linear Sequential Circuits—General Properties

1. Introduction

In this chapter, a linear sequential circuit (abbreviated LSC) is defined in terms of the basic components from which it can be constructed. This leads to the mathematical characterization of LSCs and to a general formula which relates the output of an LSC to the input and to the structure of the LSC. Subsequently, the concepts of equivalence, similarity and minimality of LSCs are discussed in detail, and algorithms are given for determining the minimal form and the canonical form of an arbitrary LSC. The chapter ends with a discussion of controllability and predictability in LSCs.

The material in this chapter is based in part on the work of Cohn,[22,24] Cohn and Even,[25] Friedland,[35] Hotz,[57] and Hsiao and Sih.[58]

2. "Black Box" Representation of an LSC

A linear sequential circuit (LSC) is a network with a finite number of *input terminals* available for the application of external signals, and a finite number of *output terminals* available for the observation and utilization of response signals. The network itself consists of an interconnection of a finite number of *primitive components* to be introduced shortly.

External signals applied to the input terminals of an LSC are taken out of the finite field $GF(p) = \{0, 1, \ldots, p-1\}$ (for some fixed p). These signals are applied simultaneously to all input terminals at discrete instants of time which, for convenience, will be represented by integers. The time interval between two successive such instants will be called a *dit* (a *discrete interval of time*).

Each primitive component either adds its inputs (instantaneously) as per rules of $GF(p)$, multiplies its input (instantaneously) by a constant as per rules of $GF(p)$, or delays its input one dit. The operations are performed in unison at one dit intervals, with the result that the signals obtained at the output terminals are also from $GF(p)$ and spaced one dit apart.

Fig. 2.1 shows the "black box" representation of an LSC with l input terminals and m output terminals.

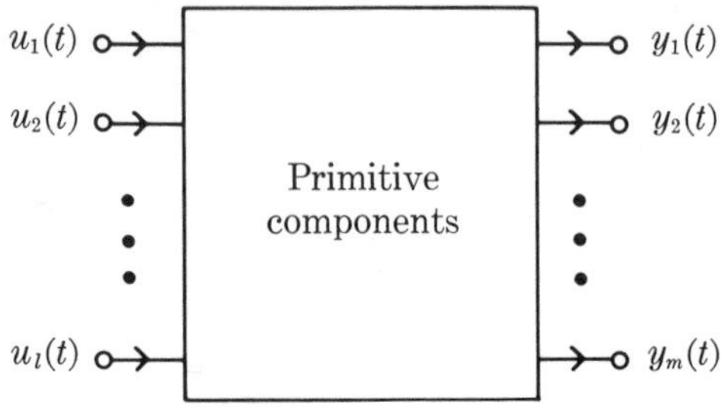

FIG. 2.1—"Black box" representation of an LSC

3. The Primitive Components

The following defines the three types of components, called *primitive components over GF(p):*

3–1 *Adders:* An adder has l input terminals and one output terminal. If the inputs are $u_1(t), u_2(t), \ldots, u_l(t)$, the output is $u_1(t) + u_2(t) + \ldots + u_l(t)$ (modulo p).

3–2 *Scalers:* A scaler with *constant* α [from $GF(p)$] has one input and one output terminal. If the input is $u(t)$, the output is $\alpha u(t)$ (modulo p).

3–3 *Delayers:* A delayer has one input and one output terminal. If the input is $u(t)$, the output is $u(t-1)$. [$u(t)$ is often referred to as the *contents* of the delayer between time t and time $t+1$].

Fig. 2.2 shows the symbols employed in this book for the three primitive components.

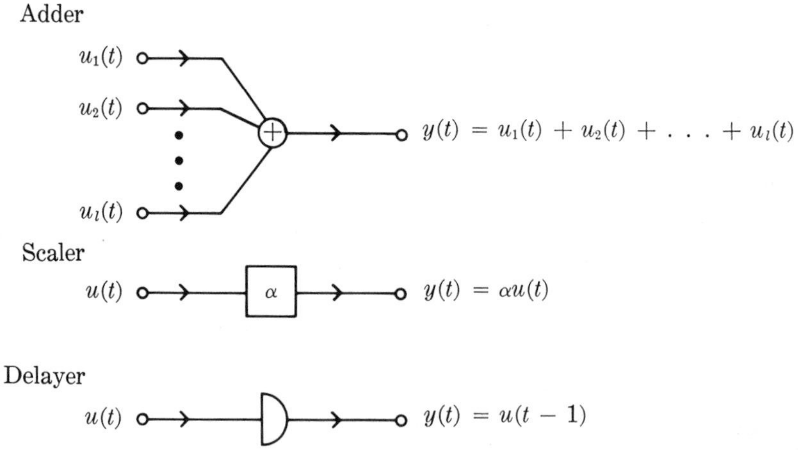

FIG. 2.2—Primitive components

To form an LSC, any interconnection is permitted of any finite number of primitive components, with one exception: No closed loop is allowed which does not contain at least one delayer. (The violation of this rule may result in a line which carries an indeterminate signal.)

An LSC with primitive components over $GF(p)$ is referred to as an *LSC over* $GF(p)$. Unless otherwise specified, an "LSC" will mean an "LSC over $GF(p)$." The number of delayers in an LSC is called the *dimension* of the LSC (the LSC is *n-dimensional* when it has n delayers). For purpose of identification, input terminals, output terminals, and delayers in an LSC will commonly be assigned serial numbers 1, 2, 3, etc.

Scalers with constants 0 and 1 signify an open connection and a closed connection, respectively. Thus, an LSC over $GF(2)$ (a *binary* LSC) consists only of adders modulo 2 (commonly known as "EXCLUSIVE-OR gates") and delayers (commonly implemented by means of "flip-flops"). Hence the practical attractiveness of binary LSCs.

Scalers with constant $p - 1 = -1$ act as "inverters"—they simply reverse the signs of the input signals.

3-4 *Example:* Fig. 2.3 shows a 4-dimensional LSC over $GF(3)$.

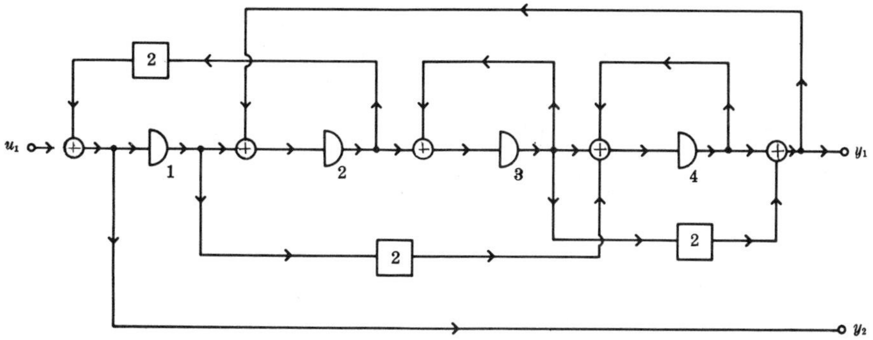

FIG. 2.3—An LSC over $GF(3)$

4. Basic Circuit Variables

Fig. 2.4 represents a general n-dimensional LSC, where the n delayers have been isolated from all other circuit components. This representation places in evidence the basic variables of the LSC.

4-1 *Inputs:* The *input variables* are $u_1(t), u_2(t), \ldots, u_l(t)$, where $u_i(t)$ is the signal applied to input terminal i at time t. The *input vector* (or simply *input*) $\mathbf{u}(t)$ is given by

$$\mathbf{u}(t) = \begin{pmatrix} u_1(t) \\ u_2(t) \\ \cdot \\ \cdot \\ \cdot \\ u_l(t) \end{pmatrix}$$

When t is understood, $u_i(t)$ and $\mathbf{u}(t)$ can be written as u_i and $\mathbf{u}$, respectively.

4–2 *Outputs:* The *output variables* are $y_1(t), y_2(t), \ldots, y_m(t)$, where $y_i(t)$ is the signal appearing at output terminal i at time t. The *output vector* (or simply *output*) $\mathbf{y}(t)$ is given by

$$\mathbf{y}(t) = \begin{pmatrix} y_1(t) \\ y_2(t) \\ \cdot \\ \cdot \\ \cdot \\ y_m(t) \end{pmatrix}$$

When t is understood, $y_i(t)$ and $\mathbf{y}(t)$ can be written as y_i and $\mathbf{y}$, respectively.

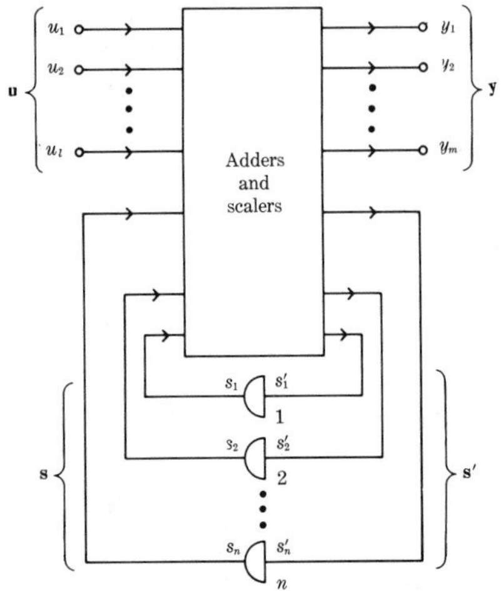

FIG. 2.4—Input, output, and state variables

4–3 *States:* The *state variables* are $s_1(t), s_2(t), \ldots, s_n(t)$, where $s_i(t)$ is the output of delayer i at time t. The *state vector* (or simply *state*) $\mathbf{s}(t)$ is given by

$$\mathbf{s}(t) = \begin{pmatrix} s_1(t) \\ s_2(t) \\ \cdot \\ \cdot \\ \cdot \\ s_n(t) \end{pmatrix}$$

When t is understood, $s_i(t)$ and $\mathbf{s}(t)$ can be written as s_i and $\mathbf{s}$, respectively. $s_i'(t)$ will denote the input of delayer i at time t. Thus:

4–4 $$s_i'(t) = s_i(t+1)$$

Correspondingly, we shall define the *next-state vector*

4–5 $$\mathbf{s}'(t) = \mathbf{s}(t+1)$$

When t is understood, $s_i'(t)$ and $\mathbf{s}'(t)$ can be written as s_i' and $\mathbf{s}'$, respectively.

The n-dimensional space of state vectors is called the *state space* of the LSC and denoted by S_n. An LSC and its state space have the same dimension. The order of S_n (i.e., p^n), is the number of distinct states which the LSC can assume.

5. The Characterizing Matrices

The paths originating at the input terminals and delayer outputs and terminating at the input of a given delayer i, form a "tree" as indicated in Fig. 2.5. This tree can be traced by proceeding from the input of delayer i "upstream" until an input terminal u_j or a delayer output s_j is encountered. If a_{ij} denotes the product of scaler constants encountered on the path s_j to s'_i (or the sum of such products if there are two or more such paths) and b_{ij} denotes the corresponding quantity for the path u_j to s'_i, then the variable s'_i can be written as

5–1 $$s'_i = \sum_{j=1}^{n} a_{ij}s_j + \sum_{j=1}^{l} b_{ij}u_j$$

The system of equations **5–1** (for $i = 1, 2, \ldots, n$) is called the *state equations* of the LSC.

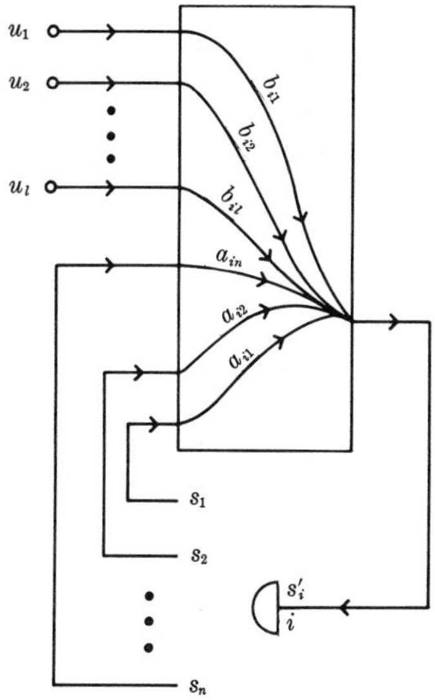

FIG. 2.5—
Construction of state equations

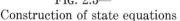

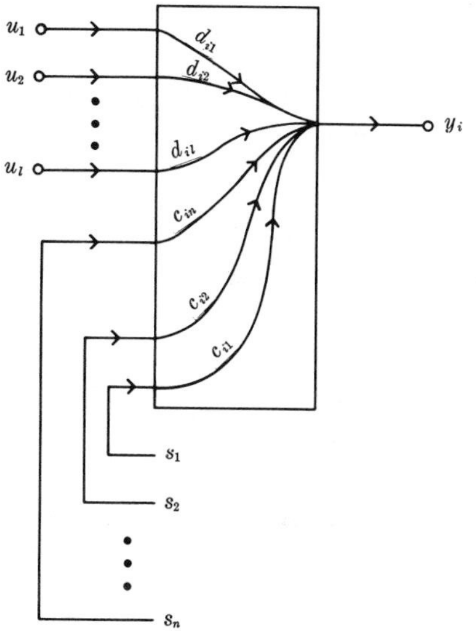

FIG. 2.6—
Construction of output equations

Similarly, the paths originating from the input terminals and delayer outputs and terminating at the output terminal y_i, form a tree as shown in Fig. 2.6. If c_{ij} denotes the product of scaler constants encountered on the path s_j to y_i (or the sum of such products if there are two or more such paths) and d_{ij} the corresponding quantity for the path u_j to y_i, then the variable y_i can be written as

5–2 $$y_i = \sum_{j=1}^{n} c_{ij}s_j + \sum_{j=1}^{l} d_{ij}u_j$$

The system of equations **5–2** (for $i = 1, 2, \ldots, m$) is called the *output equations* of the LSC.

Writing the state and output equations in a matrix form, we have:

5–3 $$\mathbf{s}(t+1) = \mathbf{As}(t) + \mathbf{Bu}(t) \qquad \text{or} \qquad \mathbf{s}' = \mathbf{As} + \mathbf{Bu}$$

5–4 $$\mathbf{y}(t) = \mathbf{Cs}(t) + \mathbf{Du}(t) \qquad \text{or} \qquad \mathbf{y} = \mathbf{Cs} = \mathbf{Du}$$

where

5–5 $$\mathbf{A} = [a_{ij}]_{n\times n} \qquad \mathbf{B} = [b_{ij}]_{n\times l}$$
$$\mathbf{C} = [c_{ij}]_{m\times n} \qquad \mathbf{D} = [d_{ij}]_{m\times l}$$

A, **B**, **C** and **D** are called the *characterizing matrices* of the LSC; **A** is called its *characteristic matrix.*

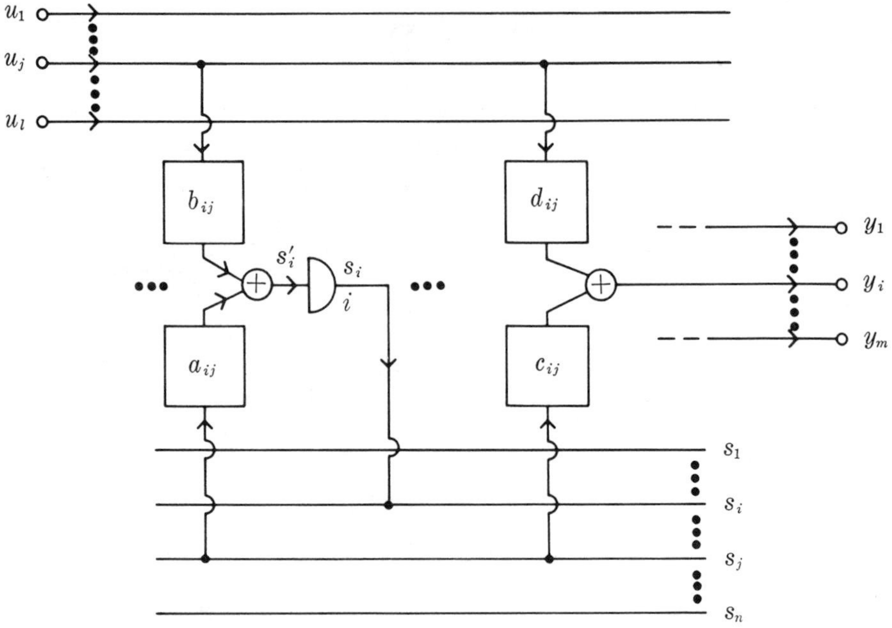

FIG. 2.7—LSC realization from characterizing matrices

To determine **A** and **C** of a "physically" given LSC, one can disconnect all delayer outputs from the circuit, apply 1 to s_j (and 0 to all u_i and all other s_i). Under these conditions:

5–6 $$a_{ij} = s'_i \qquad c_{ij} = y_i$$

To determine **B** and **D**, 1 is applied to u_j (and 0 to all s_i and all other u_i). Under these conditions:

5–7 $$b_{ij} = s'_i \qquad d_{ij} = y_i$$

5–8 *Example:* The characterizing matrices of the LSC of Fig. 2.3 are given by

5–9 $$\mathbf{A} = \begin{pmatrix} 0 & 2 & 0 & 0 \\ 1 & 0 & 2 & 1 \\ 0 & 1 & 1 & 0 \\ 2 & 0 & 1 & 1 \end{pmatrix} \qquad \mathbf{B} = \begin{pmatrix} 1 \\ 0 \\ 0 \\ 0 \end{pmatrix}$$

$$\mathbf{C} = \begin{pmatrix} 0 & 0 & 2 & 1 \\ 0 & 2 & 0 & 0 \end{pmatrix} \qquad \mathbf{D} = \begin{pmatrix} 0 \\ 1 \end{pmatrix}$$

6. LSC Synthesis from Characterizing Matrices

Given four matrices **A**, **B**, **C** and **D** over $GF(p)$, with dimensions as specified in **5–5**, an LSC with l input terminals, m output terminals and n delayers can always be constructed whose characterizing matrices are the given ones. Such a circuit is referred to as a *realization* of **A**, **B**, **C** and **D**. The construction of a realization can be carried out as follows (see Fig. 2.7): (i) Draw l input lines $u_1, u_2, \ldots, u_l$, m output lines $y_1, y_2, \ldots, y_m$, and n state lines $s_1, s_2, \ldots, s_n$ emanating from n delayers numbered $1, 2, \ldots, n$, respectively. (ii) Insert an adder in each output line y_i and at the input of each delayer. (iii) The inputs to the adder of delayer i ($i = 1, 2, \ldots, n$) are: s_j applied via a scaler with constant a_{ij} ($j = 1, 2, \ldots, n$) and u_j applied via a scaler with constant b_{ij} ($j = 1, 2, \ldots, l$). (iv) The inputs to the adder of output y_i ($i = 1, 2, \ldots, m$) are: s_j applied via a scaler with constant c_{ij} ($j = 1, 2, \ldots, n$) and u_j applied via a scaler with constant d_{ij} ($j = 1, 2, \ldots, l$).

A realization often can be simplified by eliminating or combining adders and scalers.

6–1 *Example:* The realization of the 4-dimensional LSC characterized in **5–9** is shown in Fig. 2.8.

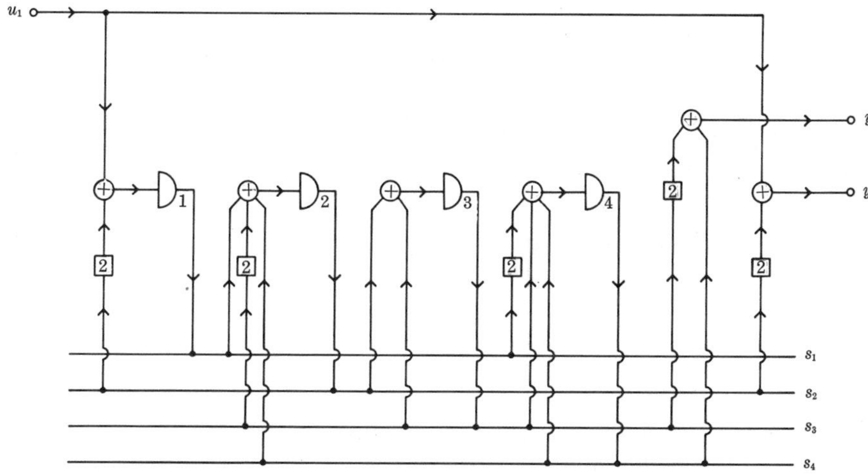

FIG. 2.8—Realization of LSC of Example **5–8**

7. Internal Circuits

The *internal circuit* of an LSC is that part of a realization of **A**, **B**, **C** and **D** which is specified by **A** alone (i.e., that part which consists of the delayer interconnections only). It can be obtained from the complete circuit by deleting all input and output lines and all scalers with constants b_{ij}, c_{ij} and d_{ij} (adders with a single input may be replaced with a direct connection). An internal circuit characterized by **A** is said to be a *realization* of **A**.

An internal circuit realizing a companion matrix such as

7–1 $$\mathbf{M}_{d(x)} = \begin{pmatrix} & 1 & & & \\ & & 1 & & \\ & & & \ddots & \\ & & & & 1 \\ -\alpha_0 & -\alpha_1 & -\alpha_2 & \cdots & -\alpha_{n-1} \end{pmatrix}$$

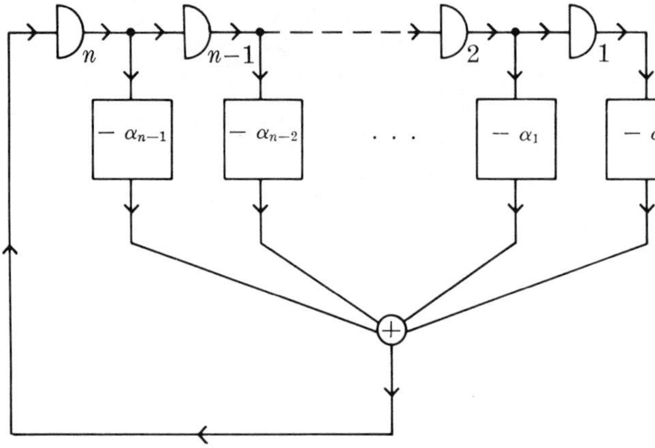

FIG. 2.9—Shift-register realization of $\mathbf{M}_{\alpha_0+\alpha_1 x+\ldots+\alpha_{n-1}x^{n-1}+x^n}$

(see Fig. 2.9) is called a *shift register*. An internal circuit realizing a transposed companion matrix such as

7–2 $$\mathbf{M}^{\mathrm{TR}}_{d(x)} = \begin{pmatrix} & & & & -\alpha_0 \\ 1 & & & & -\alpha_1 \\ & 1 & & & -\alpha_2 \\ & & \ddots & & \vdots \\ & & & 1 & -\alpha_{n-1} \end{pmatrix}$$

(see Fig. 2.10) is called a *multi-adder shift register*. From a practical standpoint, shift registers or multi-adder shift registers are easy to construct and control, and hence are considered highly desirable as internal circuits for LSCs.

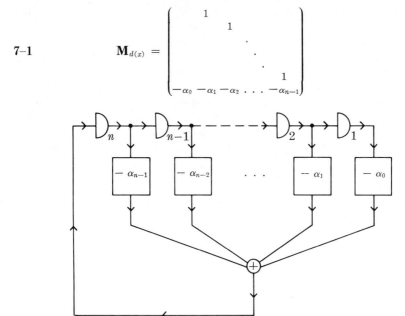

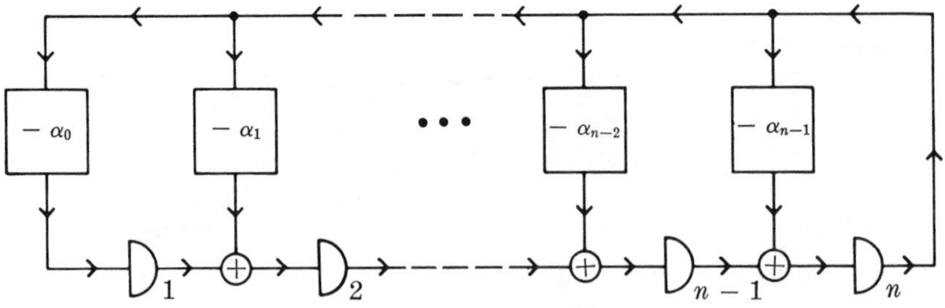

FIG. 2.10—Multi-adder shift register, realizing $\mathbf{M}^{\mathrm{TR}}_{\alpha_0+\alpha_1 x+\ldots+\alpha_{n-1}x^{n-1}+x^n}$

An internal circuit realizing a characteristic matrix of the form

7–3
$$\mathbf{A} = \begin{pmatrix} \mathbf{A}_1 & & & & \\ & \mathbf{A}_2 & & & \\ & & \cdot & & \\ & & & \cdot & \\ & & & & \cdot \\ & & & & & \mathbf{A}_w \end{pmatrix}$$

consists of the assemblage, or "union", of the individual realizations of the $\mathbf{A}_i$ ($i = 1, 2, \ldots, w$). If the $\mathbf{A}_i$ are companion matrices or transposed companion matrices (as is the case when $\mathbf{A}$ is a rational canonical matrix or a transposed rational canonical matrix, respectively), the realization of $\mathbf{A}$ consists of the union of w shift registers or w multi-adder shift registers, respectively.

8. State-Output Diagrams

The *state-output diagram* of an n-dimensional LSC over $GF(p)$ is a weighted directed graph, consisting of p^n vertices labeled as the p^n states of the circuit. If $\mathbf{As} + \mathbf{Bu} = \mathbf{s}'$ and $\mathbf{Cs} + \mathbf{Du} = \mathbf{y}$, then a branch is drawn between vertices $\mathbf{s}$ and $\mathbf{s}'$, labeled $\mathbf{u}/\mathbf{y}$, with an arrow sign pointing from $\mathbf{s}$ to $\mathbf{s}'$ (we say that $\mathbf{s}$ *leads to* $\mathbf{s}'$ *with* $\mathbf{u}/\mathbf{y}$). All branches leading from $\mathbf{s}$ to $\mathbf{s}'$ may be merged into one branch, bearing all the original branch labels. State-output diagrams are often advantageous in the search for symmetry or other structural features in the behavior of LSCs. They can also be used to trace readily the sequence of states or outputs resulting from any specified sequence of inputs and any specified initial state.

Let $\mathcal{A}$ be an LSC characterized by $\mathbf{A}, \mathbf{B}, \mathbf{C}$ and $\mathbf{D}$, and $\bar{\mathcal{A}}$ an LSC characterized by $\bar{\mathbf{A}}, \bar{\mathbf{B}}, \bar{\mathbf{C}}$ and $\bar{\mathbf{D}}$. $\mathcal{A}$ and $\bar{\mathcal{A}}$ are *isomorphic* if one-to-one relationship can be established between their state spaces in the following manner: If $\mathbf{s}$ of $\mathcal{A}$ corresponds to $\bar{\mathbf{s}}$ of $\bar{\mathcal{A}}$, then, for every input $\mathbf{u}$, $\mathbf{Cs} + \mathbf{Du} = \bar{\mathbf{C}}\bar{\mathbf{s}} + \bar{\mathbf{D}}\mathbf{u}$ and $\mathbf{s}' = \mathbf{As} + \mathbf{Bu}$ in $\mathcal{A}$ corresponds to $\bar{\mathbf{s}}' = \bar{\mathbf{A}}\bar{\mathbf{s}} + \bar{\mathbf{B}}\mathbf{u}$ in $\bar{\mathcal{A}}$. Thus, if $\mathcal{A}$ and $\bar{\mathcal{A}}$ are isomorphic, their state-output diagrams are identical except, possibly, for vertex labeling.

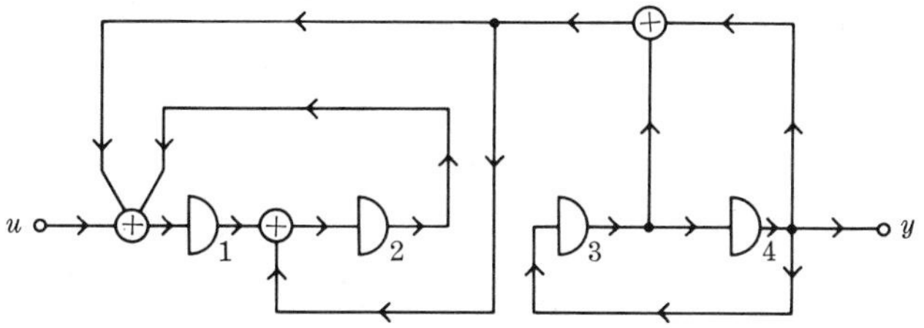

FIG. 2.11—An LSC over $GF(2)$

8–1 *Example:* Fig. 2.11 shows an LSC over $GF(2)$, characterized by

8–2
$$\mathbf{A} = \begin{pmatrix} 0 & 1 & 1 & 1 \\ 1 & 0 & 1 & 1 \\ 0 & 0 & 0 & 1 \\ 0 & 0 & 1 & 0 \end{pmatrix} \qquad \mathbf{B} = \begin{pmatrix} 1 \\ 0 \\ 0 \\ 0 \end{pmatrix}$$
$$\mathbf{C} = (0, 0, 0, 1) \qquad \mathbf{D} = (0)$$

The state-output diagram of this LSC is shown in Fig. 2.12.

9. The General Response Formula

Given an initial state and an input sequence, the corresponding output sequence of an LSC can be computed recursively from **5–3** and **5–4**, or derived by inspection of the state-output diagram. It can also be computed directly from the characterizing matrices, as will be shown here.

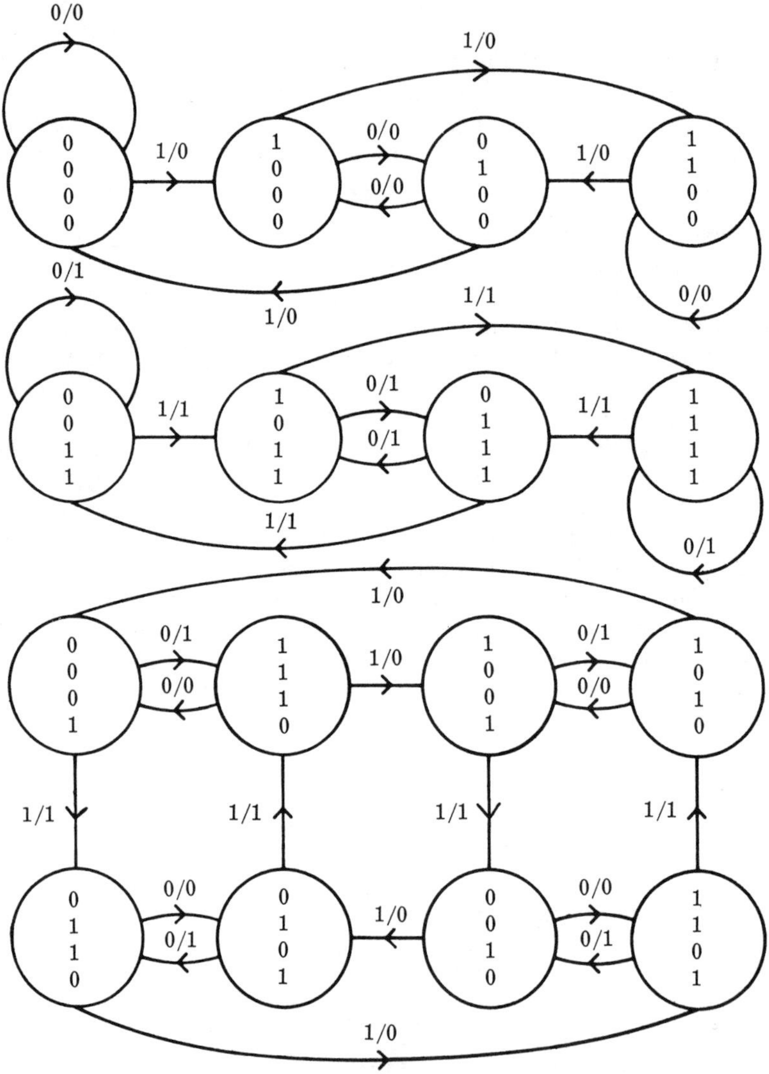

FIG. 2.12—State-output diagram of LSC of Fig. 2.11

9–1 *Assertion:* For any $t > 0$,

9–2
$$\mathbf{s}(t) = \mathbf{A}^t\mathbf{s}(0) + \sum_{\nu=0}^{t-1} \mathbf{A}^{t-\nu-1}\mathbf{B}\mathbf{u}(\nu)$$

Proof (by induction on t): Setting $t = 0$ in **5–3**, we have $\mathbf{s}(1) = \mathbf{As}(0) + \mathbf{Bu}(0)$, which proves **9–2** for $t = 1$. Hypothesizing that **9–1** is true, we have by **5–3**:

9–3
$$\mathbf{s}(t+1) = \mathbf{A}[\mathbf{A}^t\mathbf{s}(0) + \sum_{\nu=0}^{t-1}\mathbf{A}^{t-\nu-1}\mathbf{Bu}(\nu)] + \mathbf{Bu}(t)$$
$$= \mathbf{A}^{t+1}\mathbf{s}(0) + \sum_{\nu=0}^{t}\mathbf{A}^{t-\nu}\mathbf{Bu}(\nu)$$

which proves **9–2** for $t + 1$.

9–4 *Assertion:* For any $t \geq 0$,

9–5
$$\mathbf{y}(t) = \mathbf{CA}^t\mathbf{s}(0) + \sum_{\nu=0}^{t}\mathbf{H}(t-\nu)\mathbf{u}(\nu)$$

where

9–6
$$\mathbf{H}(t) = \begin{cases}\mathbf{D} & (t = 0)\\ \mathbf{CA}^{t-1}\mathbf{B} & (t > 0)\end{cases}$$

Proof: Setting $t = 0$ in **5–4**, we have $\mathbf{y}(0) = \mathbf{Cs}(0) + \mathbf{Du}(0)$, which proves **9–5** for $t = 0$. For $t > 0$, **9–2** can be substituted in **5–4** to yield

9–7
$$\mathbf{y}(t) = \mathbf{C}[\mathbf{A}^t\mathbf{s}(0) + \sum_{\nu=0}^{t-1}\mathbf{A}^{t-\nu-1}\mathbf{Bu}(\nu)] + \mathbf{Du}(t)$$
$$= \mathbf{CA}^t\mathbf{s}(0) + \sum_{\nu=0}^{t}\mathbf{H}(t-\nu)\mathbf{u}(\nu)$$

where $\mathbf{H}(t-\nu) = \mathbf{CA}^{t-\nu-1}\mathbf{B}$ when $t - \nu - 1 \geq 0$, and $\mathbf{H}(t-\nu) = \mathbf{D}$ when $t - \nu - 1 = -1$.

9–5 will be referred to as the *general response formula.* It reveals that the output of an LSC can be decomposed into two components: The *free response*

9–8
$$\mathbf{y}(t)|_{\text{free}} = \mathbf{CA}^t\mathbf{s}(0)$$

obtained by setting $\mathbf{u}(t) = 0$ for all $t \geq 0$, and the *forced response*

9–9
$$\mathbf{y}(t)|_{\text{forced}} = \sum_{\nu=0}^{t}\mathbf{H}(t-\nu)\mathbf{u}(\nu)$$

obtained by setting $\mathbf{s}(0) = \mathbf{0}$. Given any input sequence $\mathbf{u}(t)$ ($t = 0, 1, 2, \ldots$) and initial state $\mathbf{s}(0)$, these two components can be found separately and then added up. This is a fortunate circumstance, since the ideas and techniques found advantageous in the study of the free response (developed in Chap. 3) are quite different from those found advantageous in the study of the forced response (developed in Chap. 4).

10. Equivalent States and Equivalent LSCs

State $\mathbf{s}_1$ of LSC $\mathcal{A}_1$ and $\mathbf{s}_2$ of LSC $\mathcal{A}_2$ are said to be *equivalent* if $\mathcal{A}_1$ at state $\mathbf{s}_1$ and $\mathcal{A}_2$ at state $\mathbf{s}_2$, when presented with the same input sequence, yield the same output sequence. ($\mathcal{A}_1$ and $\mathcal{A}_2$ may refer to the same LSC). The *equivalence partition* of $\mathcal{A}_1$ and $\mathcal{A}_2$ divides the union of the state spaces of $\mathcal{A}_1$ and $\mathcal{A}_2$ into *equivalence classes* such that two states are in the same class if and only if they are equivalent.

The LSCs $\mathcal{A}_1$ and $\mathcal{A}_2$ are said to be *equivalent* if to each state $\mathbf{s}_1$ of $\mathcal{A}_1$ there corresponds at least one state of $\mathcal{A}_2$ which is equivalent to $\mathbf{s}_1$, and to each state $\mathbf{s}_2$ of $\mathcal{A}_2$ there corresponds at least one state of $\mathcal{A}_1$ which is equivalent to $\mathbf{s}_2$. Thus, equivalent LSCs are those whose difference cannot be detected by any input-output observation, and hence LSCs which—insofar as the "black box" behavior is concerned—are entirely interchangeable.

Directly from the definitions of isomorphism and equivalence of LSCs, we have:

10–1 *Assertion:* Isomorphic LSCs are equivalent.

10–2 That the converse of **10–1** is not always true can be demonstrated by the 1-dimensional LSCs $\mathcal{A}$ and $\bar{\mathcal{A}}$ over $GF(2)$ which are characterized, respectively, by

10–3 $$\mathbf{A} = (0) \qquad \mathbf{B} = (0) \qquad \mathbf{C} = (0) \qquad \mathbf{D} = (0)$$

10–4 $$\bar{\mathbf{A}} = (1) \qquad \bar{\mathbf{B}} = (0) \qquad \bar{\mathbf{C}} = (0) \qquad \bar{\mathbf{D}} = (0)$$

These LSCs are trivially equivalent (output is invariably 0) but nonisomorphic, as can be verified from the state-output diagram.

11. Similar LSCs

11–1 If $\mathcal{A}$ is an LSC characterized by **A**, **B**, **C** and **D**, and $\bar{\mathcal{A}}$ is an LSC characterized by

11–2 $$\bar{\mathbf{A}} = \mathbf{PAP}^{-1} \qquad \bar{\mathbf{B}} = \mathbf{PB} \qquad \bar{\mathbf{C}} = \mathbf{CP}^{-1} \qquad \bar{\mathbf{D}} = \mathbf{D}$$

(where **P** is some nonsingular matrix), then $\mathcal{A}$ and $\bar{\mathcal{A}}$ are said to be *similar*. (The characteristic matrices of similar LSCs are similar.)

11–3 *Assertion:* If $\mathcal{A}$ and $\bar{\mathcal{A}}$ (as defined in **11–1**) are similar, then states **s** of $\mathcal{A}$ and $\bar{\mathbf{s}} = \mathbf{Ps}$ of $\bar{\mathcal{A}}$ are equivalent.

Proof: For any input $\mathbf{u}(t)$, the output $\mathbf{y}(t)$ of $\mathcal{A}$ at state **s** is given by **9–5**. Also, by **9–5**, the output $\bar{\mathbf{y}}(t)$ of $\bar{\mathcal{A}}$ at state $\bar{\mathbf{s}}$, for the same input $\mathbf{u}(t)$, is given by

$$\bar{\mathbf{y}}(t) = \bar{\mathbf{C}}\bar{\mathbf{A}}^t\bar{\mathbf{s}} + \sum_{\nu=0}^{t}\bar{\mathbf{H}}(t-\nu)\mathbf{u}(\nu)$$

11–4 $$= (\mathbf{CP}^{-1})(\mathbf{PAP}^{-1})^t(\mathbf{Ps}) + \sum_{\nu=0}^{t}\bar{\mathbf{H}}(t-\nu)\mathbf{u}(\nu)$$

$$= \mathbf{CA}^t\mathbf{s} + \sum_{\nu=0}^{t}\bar{\mathbf{H}}(t-\nu)\mathbf{u}(\nu)$$

where

11–5 $$\bar{\mathbf{H}}(t) = \begin{cases} \bar{\mathbf{D}} = \mathbf{D} & (t = 0) \\ \bar{\mathbf{C}}\bar{\mathbf{A}}^{t-1}\bar{\mathbf{B}} = (\mathbf{CP}^{-1})(\mathbf{PAP}^{-1})^{t-1}(\mathbf{PB}) = \mathbf{CA}^{t-1}\mathbf{B} & (t > 0) \end{cases}$$
$$= \mathbf{H}(t)$$

Hence $\bar{\mathbf{y}}(t) = \mathbf{y}(t)$.

11–6 *Assertion:* Similar LSCs are isomorphic (and hence equivalent).

Proof: Consider the one-to-one correspondence $\mathbf{s} \longleftrightarrow \bar{\mathbf{s}} = \mathbf{Ps}$. By **11–3**, $\mathbf{Cs} + \mathbf{Du} = \bar{\mathbf{C}}\bar{\mathbf{s}} + \bar{\mathbf{D}}\mathbf{u}$ for any $\mathbf{u}$. Also, for any $\mathbf{u}$,

11–7 $\bar{\mathbf{s}}' = \bar{\mathbf{A}}\bar{\mathbf{s}} + \bar{\mathbf{B}}\mathbf{u} = (\mathbf{PAP}^{-1})(\mathbf{Ps}) + (\mathbf{PB})\mathbf{u} = \mathbf{P}(\mathbf{As} + \mathbf{Bu}) = \mathbf{Ps}'$

and hence $\mathbf{s}' \longleftrightarrow \bar{\mathbf{s}}' = \mathbf{Ps}'$.

11–8 That the converse of **11–6** is not always true can be demonstrated by the 1-dimensional LSCs $\mathcal{A}$ and $\bar{\mathcal{A}}$ over $GF(5)$ which are characterized, respectively, by

11–9 $\mathbf{A} = (2) \quad \mathbf{B} = (0) \quad \mathbf{C} = (0) \quad \mathbf{D} = (0)$

11–10 $\bar{\mathbf{A}} = (3) \quad \bar{\mathbf{B}} = (0) \quad \bar{\mathbf{C}} = (0) \quad \bar{\mathbf{D}} = (0)$

These LSCs are isomorphic (as can be verified from the state-output diagram) but nonsimilar (the elementary divisors of $\mathbf{A}$ and $\bar{\mathbf{A}}$ are $3 + x$ and $2 + x$, respectively).

By **11–6**, given any LSC $\mathcal{A}$ with the characteristic matrix $\mathbf{A}$, and given any matrix $\bar{\mathbf{A}} = \mathbf{PAP}^{-1}$ similar to $\mathbf{A}$, one can construct an LSC $\bar{\mathcal{A}}$ equivalent to $\mathcal{A}$ (and characterized as in **11–2**) such that $\bar{\mathcal{A}}$ has $\bar{\mathbf{A}}$ as the characteristic matrix. In particular, $\bar{\mathcal{A}}$ can be chosen to have the rational canonical form of $\mathbf{A}$ as a characteristic matrix. In this case

11–11
$$\bar{\mathbf{A}} = \begin{pmatrix} \mathbf{M}_{d_1(x)} & & & & \\ & \mathbf{M}_{d_2(x)} & & & \\ & & \cdot & & \\ & & & \cdot & \\ & & & & \cdot \\ & & & & & \mathbf{M}_{d_w(x)} \end{pmatrix}$$

where the $d_i(x)$ are the elementary divisors of $\mathbf{A}$, and the internal circuit of $\bar{\mathcal{A}}$ consists of a union of w shift registers. In conclusion, we have:

11–12 *Assertion:* Every LSC is equivalent to an LSC whose internal circuit is the union of shift registers.

12. Minimal LSCs

A *minimal* LSC is one in which no two states are equivalent.

12–1 *Assertion:* Let the LSC $\mathcal{A}$ be equivalent to a minimal LSC $\check{\mathcal{A}}$ of dimension r. Then no LSC equivalent to $\mathcal{A}$ has dimension less than r.

Proof: Suppose an LSC $\mathcal{A}'$ has the dimension $k < r$, and suppose $\mathcal{A}'$ is equivalent to $\mathcal{A}$. Hence, $\mathcal{A}'$ is also equivalent to $\check{\mathcal{A}}$ and every state in $\check{\mathcal{A}}$ is equivalent to at least one state in $\mathcal{A}'$. Thus, there are at least two states in $\check{\mathcal{A}}$ which are equivalent to the same state in $\mathcal{A}'$; hence $\check{\mathcal{A}}$ has two equivalent states and cannot be minimal. **12–1** follows by contradiction.

12–2 *Assertion:* If $\mathcal{A}$ and $\bar{\mathcal{A}}$ are equivalent and minimal LSCs, they are isomorphic.

Proof: Let $\mathcal{A}$ be characterized by $\mathbf{A}$, $\mathbf{B}$, $\mathbf{C}$ and $\mathbf{D}$, and $\bar{\mathcal{A}}$ by $\bar{\mathbf{A}}$, $\bar{\mathbf{B}}$, $\bar{\mathbf{C}}$ and $\bar{\mathbf{D}}$. If state $\mathbf{s}$ of $\mathcal{A}$ is equivalent to $\bar{\mathbf{s}}$ of $\bar{\mathcal{A}}$, $\mathbf{Cs} + \mathbf{Du} = \bar{\mathbf{C}}\bar{\mathbf{s}} + \bar{\mathbf{D}}\mathbf{u}$ for all $\mathbf{u}$. Moreover, for all $\mathbf{u}$, $\mathbf{As} + \mathbf{Bu}$ must be equivalent to $\bar{\mathbf{A}}\bar{\mathbf{s}} + \bar{\mathbf{B}}\mathbf{u}$, since otherwise there would exist an input sequence yielding distinct outputs in $\mathcal{A}$ at $\mathbf{s}$ and $\bar{\mathcal{A}}$ at $\bar{\mathbf{s}}$. Since $\mathcal{A}$ and $\bar{\mathcal{A}}$ are equivalent and minimal, the correspondence $\mathbf{s} \longleftrightarrow \bar{\mathbf{s}}$ is one to one; it is, therefore, the one-to-one correspondence required to establish the isomorphism of $\mathcal{A}$ and $\bar{\mathcal{A}}$.

Isomorphic LSCs must, of course, be equivalent, but they need not be minimal (as evidenced by $\mathcal{A}$ and $\bar{\mathcal{A}}$ of **11–8**, both of which are equivalent to the same 0-dimensional LSC).

In subsequent sections we shall show how a minimal LSC $\check{\mathcal{A}}$, equivalent to a given LSC $\mathcal{A}$, can be determined. In view of **12–1**, $\check{\mathcal{A}}$ constitutes an LSC with the least number of delayers which—insofar as the input-output behavior is concerned—can replace $\mathcal{A}$. In view of **12–2**, the state-output diagram of $\check{\mathcal{A}}$ is unique up to vertex labeling. $\check{\mathcal{A}}$ is called a *minimal form* of $\mathcal{A}$, and its construction is referred to as the *minimization* of $\mathcal{A}$.

13. Determination of Equivalence Classes

Let $\mathcal{A}$ be an n-dimensional LSC characterized by **A**, **B**, **C** and **D**. The *diagnostic matrix* of $\mathcal{A}$ is defined by

13–1
$$\mathbf{K} = \begin{bmatrix} \mathbf{C} \\ \mathbf{CA} \\ \mathbf{CA}^2 \\ \cdot \\ \cdot \\ \cdot \\ \mathbf{CA}^{n-1} \end{bmatrix}$$

13–2 *Assertion:* $\mathbf{CA}^t\mathbf{s} = \mathbf{0}$ for all $t \geq 0$, if and only if $\mathbf{Ks} = \mathbf{0}$.

Proof: If $\mathbf{Ks} = \mathbf{0}$, then $\mathbf{Cs} = \mathbf{CAs} = \mathbf{CA}^2\mathbf{s} = \ldots = \mathbf{CA}^{n-1}\mathbf{s} = \mathbf{0}$. Since the minimum polynomial of **A** is of degree at most n, $\mathbf{A}^t$ for any $t \geq n$ can be expressed as a polynomial in **A** of degree at most $n - 1$; hence $\mathbf{CA}^t\mathbf{s}$ for any $t \geq n$ can be expressed as a linear combination of $\mathbf{Cs}$, $\mathbf{CAs}$, $\mathbf{CA}^2\mathbf{s}$, $\ldots$, $\mathbf{CA}^{n-1}\mathbf{s}$, which must be **0**. Thus, if $\mathbf{Ks} = \mathbf{0}$, $\mathbf{CA}^t\mathbf{s} = \mathbf{0}$ for all $t \geq 0$. The converse is trivial.

13–3 *Assertion:* States $\mathbf{s}_1$ and $\mathbf{s}_2$ of $\mathcal{A}$ are equivalent if and only if

13–4
$$\mathbf{Ks}_1 = \mathbf{Ks}_2$$

Proof: By the general response formula, $\mathbf{s}_1$ and $\mathbf{s}_2$ are equivalent if and only if, for all $t \geq 0$ and $\mathbf{u}(t)$,

13–5
$$\mathbf{CA}^t\mathbf{s}_1 + \sum_{\nu=0}^{t} \mathbf{H}(t-\nu)\mathbf{u}(\nu) = \mathbf{CA}^t\mathbf{s}_2 + \sum_{\nu=0}^{t} \mathbf{H}(t-\nu)\mathbf{u}(\nu)$$

or if and only if, for all $t \geq 0$,

13–6
$$\mathbf{CA}^t\mathbf{s}_1 = \mathbf{CA}^t\mathbf{s}_2$$

Assertion **13–3** then follows from **13–2**.

The set of all states which are equivalent to the null state **0** will be denoted by E_0. By **13–3**, E_0 is the null space of **K**.

E_0, being a subspace of the state space S_n of $\mathcal{A}$, is also a subgroup of the additive Abelian group S_n. This subgroup induces a coset partition on S_n which can be found by inspection of E_0.

13–7 *Assertion:* The cosets of S_n induced by E_0 are the equivalence classes of S_n.

Proof: $\mathbf{s}_1$ and $\mathbf{s}_2$ are in the same coset if and only if $\mathbf{s}_1 - \mathbf{s}_2$ is in E_0; hence if and only if $\mathbf{K}(\mathbf{s}_1 - \mathbf{s}_2) = \mathbf{0}$; hence if and only if $\mathbf{Ks}_1 = \mathbf{Ks}_2$; hence—by **13–3**—if and only if $\mathbf{s}_1$ and $\mathbf{s}_2$ are equivalent.

13–8 *Example:* For the LSC of Example **8–1**,

13–9
$$\mathbf{K} = \begin{pmatrix} \mathbf{C} \\ \mathbf{CA} \\ \mathbf{CA}^2 \\ \mathbf{CA}^3 \end{pmatrix} = \begin{pmatrix} 0 & 0 & 0 & 1 \\ 0 & 0 & 1 & 0 \\ 0 & 0 & 0 & 1 \\ 0 & 0 & 1 & 0 \end{pmatrix}$$

E_0 is the null space of **K**, or the null space of the row-reduced echelon canonical form of **K**, given by

13–10
$$\mathbf{K}' = \begin{pmatrix} 0 & 0 & 1 & 0 \\ 0 & 0 & 0 & 1 \end{pmatrix}$$

Hence, the equivalence classes are given by:

$$E_0 = \left\{ \begin{pmatrix} 0 \\ 0 \\ 0 \\ 0 \end{pmatrix}, \begin{pmatrix} 0 \\ 1 \\ 0 \\ 0 \end{pmatrix}, \begin{pmatrix} 1 \\ 0 \\ 0 \\ 0 \end{pmatrix}, \begin{pmatrix} 1 \\ 1 \\ 0 \\ 0 \end{pmatrix} \right\}$$

$$E_1 = \left\{ \begin{pmatrix} 0 \\ 0 \\ 0 \\ 1 \end{pmatrix}, \begin{pmatrix} 0 \\ 1 \\ 0 \\ 1 \end{pmatrix}, \begin{pmatrix} 1 \\ 0 \\ 0 \\ 1 \end{pmatrix}, \begin{pmatrix} 1 \\ 1 \\ 0 \\ 1 \end{pmatrix} \right\}$$

13–11
$$E_2 = \left\{ \begin{pmatrix} 0 \\ 0 \\ 1 \\ 0 \end{pmatrix}, \begin{pmatrix} 0 \\ 1 \\ 1 \\ 0 \end{pmatrix}, \begin{pmatrix} 1 \\ 0 \\ 1 \\ 0 \end{pmatrix}, \begin{pmatrix} 1 \\ 1 \\ 1 \\ 0 \end{pmatrix} \right\}$$

$$E_3 = \left\{ \begin{pmatrix} 0 \\ 0 \\ 1 \\ 1 \end{pmatrix}, \begin{pmatrix} 0 \\ 1 \\ 1 \\ 1 \end{pmatrix}, \begin{pmatrix} 1 \\ 0 \\ 1 \\ 1 \end{pmatrix}, \begin{pmatrix} 1 \\ 1 \\ 1 \\ 1 \end{pmatrix} \right\}$$

14. Minimization of LSCs

Let $\mathcal{A}$ be an n-dimensional LSC characterized by **A**, **B**, **C** and **D**. If r is the rank of the diagnostic matrix **K** of $\mathcal{A}$ ($r \leq n$), let **T** denote the $r \times n$ matrix formed from the first r linearly independent rows of **K**, and let **R** denote an $n \times r$ right inverse matrix of **T** (see Sec. **1.14**). The r-dimensional LSC $\breve{\mathcal{A}}$ is defined by the characterizing matrices

14–1
$$\breve{\mathbf{A}} = \mathbf{TAR} \qquad \breve{\mathbf{B}} = \mathbf{TB}$$
$$\breve{\mathbf{C}} = \mathbf{CR} \qquad \breve{\mathbf{D}} = \mathbf{D}$$

14–2 *Assertion:* State **s** of $\mathcal{A}$ is equivalent to state $\breve{\mathbf{s}} = \mathbf{Ts}$ of $\breve{\mathcal{A}}$ (and $\breve{\mathbf{s}}$ of $\breve{\mathcal{A}}$ to $\mathbf{s} = \mathbf{R}\breve{\mathbf{s}}$ of $\mathcal{A}$).

Proof: Define:

14–3
$$\tilde{\mathbf{s}} = (\mathbf{I} - \mathbf{RT})\mathbf{s}$$

Since $\mathbf{TR} = \mathbf{I}$, we have:

14–4
$$\mathbf{T}\tilde{\mathbf{s}} = (\mathbf{T} - \mathbf{TRT})\mathbf{s} = (\mathbf{T} - \mathbf{T})\mathbf{s} = \mathbf{0}$$

Thus, $\tilde{\mathbf{s}}$ is in the null space of **T** and hence in the null space of **K**. By **13–3**, $\tilde{\mathbf{s}}$ is equivalent to **0** and hence $\mathbf{A}\tilde{\mathbf{s}}$ is equivalent to $\mathbf{A0} = \mathbf{0}$. Thus $\mathbf{A}\tilde{\mathbf{s}}$ is in the null space of **K**, and

14–5
$$\mathbf{TA}\tilde{\mathbf{s}} = \mathbf{0}$$

We thus have:

14–6 $$\mathbf{Cs} + \mathbf{Du} = \mathbf{C}(\check{\mathbf{s}} + \mathbf{RTs}) + \mathbf{Du} = \mathbf{C}\check{\mathbf{s}} + \mathbf{CRTs} + \mathbf{Du}$$
$$= \mathbf{0} + (\mathbf{CR})(\mathbf{Ts}) + \mathbf{Du} = \check{\mathbf{C}}\check{\mathbf{s}} + \check{\mathbf{D}}\mathbf{u}$$

14–7 $$\mathbf{T}(\mathbf{As} + \mathbf{Bu}) = \mathbf{T}[\mathbf{A}(\check{\mathbf{s}} + \mathbf{RTs}) + \mathbf{Bu}] = \mathbf{TA}\check{\mathbf{s}} + \mathbf{TARTs} + \mathbf{TBu}$$
$$= \mathbf{0} + (\mathbf{TAR})(\mathbf{Ts}) + (\mathbf{TB})\mathbf{u} = \check{\mathbf{A}}\check{\mathbf{s}} + \check{\mathbf{B}}\mathbf{u}$$

14–6 and **14–7** imply that if **s** in $\mathcal{A}$ and **Ts** in $\check{\mathcal{A}}$ are presented with any input **u**, their outputs are identical and their successors are **s**′ and **Ts**′, respectively. By induction, then, **s** and **Ts** yield identical output sequences when presented with the same input sequence of *any* length, which implies **14–2.** (State $\mathbf{R}\check{\mathbf{s}}$ of $\mathcal{A}$ is equivalent to state $\mathbf{T}(\mathbf{R}\check{\mathbf{s}}) = \check{\mathbf{s}}$ of $\check{\mathcal{A}}$).

14–8 *Assertion:* $\check{\mathcal{A}}$ is a minimal form of $\mathcal{A}$.

Proof: The number of equivalence classes of $\mathcal{A}$ equals the index of S_n over E_0, which equals $p^n/p^{n-r} = p^r$. By **14–2,** for every state **s** in $\mathcal{A}$ there is a state equivalent to **s** in $\check{\mathcal{A}}$. Since $\check{\mathcal{A}}$ has exactly p^r states, $\mathcal{A}$ and $\check{\mathcal{A}}$ are equivalent, and no two states in $\check{\mathcal{A}}$ are equivalent. **14–8**, then, follows from the definition of a minimal form.

The construction of **T** is facilitated by the following:

14–9 *Assertion:* If all rows of $\mathbf{CA}^i$ $(i \geq 1)$ are linearly dependent on rows of

14–10 $$\mathbf{K}_i = \begin{pmatrix} \mathbf{C} \\ \mathbf{CA} \\ \mathbf{CA}^2 \\ \cdot \\ \cdot \\ \cdot \\ \mathbf{CA}^{i-1} \end{pmatrix}$$

then, for all $t > i$, all rows of $\mathbf{CA}^t$ are linearly dependent on rows of $\mathbf{K}_i$.

Proof: If rows of $\mathbf{CA}^i$ are some linear combination of rows of $\mathbf{K}_i$, then rows of $\mathbf{CA}^{i+1}$ are the same linear combination of rows of $\mathbf{K}_i\mathbf{A}$, or of rows of $\mathbf{CA}, \mathbf{CA}^2, \ldots, \mathbf{CA}^i$. But rows of $\mathbf{CA}^i$ are linearly dependent on rows of $\mathbf{C}, \mathbf{CA}, \mathbf{CA}^2, \ldots, \mathbf{CA}^{i-1}$; hence $\mathbf{CA}^{i+1}$ is some linear combination of rows of $\mathbf{C}, \mathbf{CA}, \mathbf{CA}^2, \ldots, \mathbf{CA}^{i-1}$, or rows of $\mathbf{K}_i$. **14–9** then follows by induction.

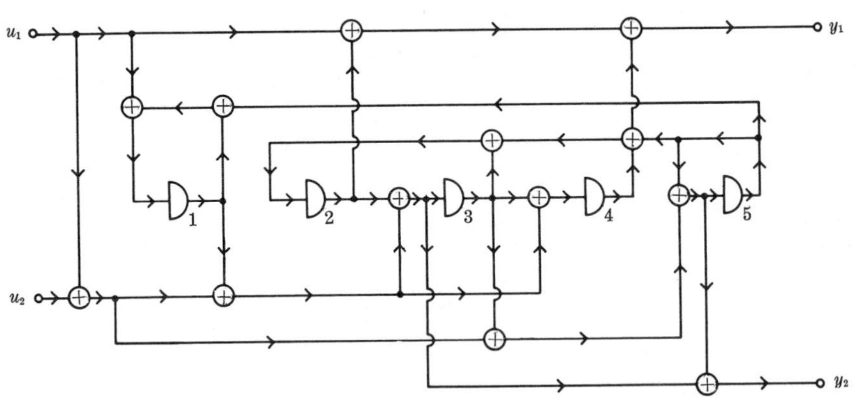

FIG. 2.13—LSC over $GF(2)$

Thus, if one compiles linearly independent rows of **K** to form **T**, the compilation may terminate as soon as a $\mathbf{CA}^i$ block is obtained where all rows are linearly dependent on previously compiled rows.

14–11 *Example:* Fig. 2.13 shows an LSC over $GF(2)$, characterized by

14–12
$$\mathbf{A} = \begin{pmatrix} 1 & 0 & 0 & 0 & 1 \\ 0 & 0 & 1 & 1 & 1 \\ 1 & 1 & 0 & 0 & 0 \\ 1 & 0 & 1 & 0 & 0 \\ 0 & 0 & 1 & 0 & 1 \end{pmatrix} \qquad \mathbf{B} = \begin{pmatrix} 1 & 0 \\ 0 & 0 \\ 1 & 1 \\ 1 & 1 \\ 1 & 1 \end{pmatrix}$$
$$\mathbf{C} = \begin{pmatrix} 0 & 1 & 0 & 1 & 1 \\ 1 & 1 & 1 & 0 & 1 \end{pmatrix} \qquad \mathbf{D} = \begin{pmatrix} 1 & 0 \\ 0 & 0 \end{pmatrix}$$

In this case:

14–13
$$\mathbf{K} = \begin{pmatrix} \mathbf{C} \\ \mathbf{CA} \\ \mathbf{CA}^2 \\ \mathbf{CA}^3 \\ \mathbf{CA}^4 \end{pmatrix} = \begin{pmatrix} 0 & 1 & 0 & 1 & 1 \\ 1 & 1 & 1 & 0 & 1 \\ \hdashline 1 & 0 & 1 & 1 & 0 \\ 0 & 1 & 0 & 1 & 1 \\ \hdashline 1 & 1 & 1 & 0 & 1 \\ 1 & 0 & 1 & 1 & 0 \\ \hdashline 0 & 1 & 0 & 1 & 1 \\ 1 & 1 & 1 & 0 & 1 \\ \hdashline 1 & 0 & 1 & 1 & 0 \\ 0 & 1 & 0 & 1 & 1 \end{pmatrix}$$

14–14
$$\mathbf{T} = \begin{pmatrix} 0 & 1 & 0 & 1 & 1 \\ 1 & 1 & 1 & 0 & 1 \end{pmatrix}$$

14–15
$$\mathbf{R} = \begin{pmatrix} 1 & 1 \\ 1 & 0 \\ 0 & 0 \\ 0 & 0 \\ 0 & 0 \end{pmatrix}$$

14–16
$$\breve{\mathbf{A}} = \mathbf{TAR} = \begin{pmatrix} 1 & 1 \\ 1 & 0 \end{pmatrix} \qquad \breve{\mathbf{B}} = \mathbf{TB} = \begin{pmatrix} 0 & 0 \\ 1 & 0 \end{pmatrix}$$
$$\breve{\mathbf{C}} = \mathbf{CR} = \begin{pmatrix} 1 & 0 \\ 0 & 1 \end{pmatrix} \qquad \breve{\mathbf{D}} = \mathbf{D} = \begin{pmatrix} 1 & 0 \\ 0 & 0 \end{pmatrix}$$

The minimal form of the LSC, characterized by the matrices **14–16**, is shown in Fig. 2.14. (This form reveals that the output of the circuit is actually independent of u_2.)

15. Diagnostic Matrix of a Minimal LSC

Let $\mathcal{A}$ be an LSC characterized by **A**, **B**, **C** and **D**, and $\breve{\mathcal{A}}$ its r-dimensional minimal form, obtained as described in Sec. **14** and characterized by $\breve{\mathbf{A}}$, $\breve{\mathbf{B}}$, $\breve{\mathbf{C}}$ and $\breve{\mathbf{D}}$ of **14–1**.

15–1 *Assertion:* For all $t \geq 0$,

15–2
$$\breve{\mathbf{A}}^t = \mathbf{TA}^t\mathbf{R}$$

Proof (by induction on t): For $t=0$, $\breve{\mathbf{A}}^t = \mathbf{I}$ and $\mathbf{TA}^t\mathbf{R} = \mathbf{TR} = \mathbf{I}$. Hypothesize that **15–2** is true for $t-1$. Then:

15–3
$$\breve{\mathbf{A}}^t = \breve{\mathbf{A}}\breve{\mathbf{A}}^{t-1} = \breve{\mathbf{A}}\mathbf{TA}^{t-1}\mathbf{R}$$

Now, by **14–2**, state $\mathbf{Ts}$ of $\breve{\mathcal{A}}$ is equivalent to $\mathbf{s}$ of $\mathcal{A}$, and hence, for all $\mathbf{s}$, $\breve{\mathbf{A}}(\mathbf{Ts}) = \mathbf{T}(\mathbf{As})$, or $\breve{\mathbf{A}}\mathbf{T} = \mathbf{TA}$. Substituting in **15–3** yields $\breve{\mathbf{A}}^t = \mathbf{TAA}^{t-1}\mathbf{R} = \mathbf{TA}^t\mathbf{R}$.

15–4 *Assertion:* The diagnostic matrix $\breve{\mathbf{K}}$ of $\breve{\mathcal{A}}$ is given by

15–5 $$\breve{\mathbf{K}} = \mathbf{KR}$$

Proof: By **15–2**, for all $t \geq 0$,

15–6 $$\breve{\mathbf{C}}\breve{\mathbf{A}}^t = \breve{\mathbf{C}}\mathbf{TA}^t\mathbf{R}$$

As in the proof for **15–1**, for all $\mathbf{s}$ we must have $\breve{\mathbf{C}}(\mathbf{Ts}) = \mathbf{Cs}$ and hence $\breve{\mathbf{C}}\mathbf{T} = \mathbf{C}$. Substituting in **15–6** yields $\breve{\mathbf{C}}\breve{\mathbf{A}}^t = (\mathbf{CA}^t)\mathbf{R}$ for all $t \geq 0$, which implies **15–4**.

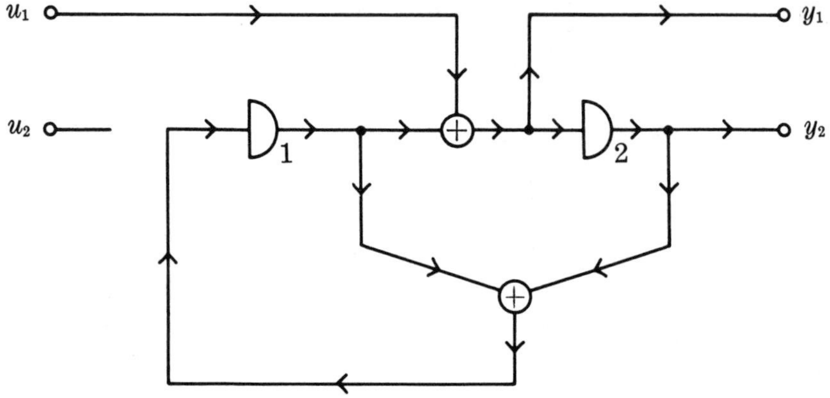

FIG. 2.14—Minimal form of LSC of Fig. 2.13

15–7 *Assertion:* If $\mathbf{T}$ is the $r \times r$ matrix formed from the first r linearly independent rows of $\breve{\mathbf{K}}$, then $\breve{\mathbf{T}} = \mathbf{I}_r$.

Proof: Let $\mathbf{v}$ be some linear combination of rows of $\mathbf{K}$. By **15–4**, the same linear combination of rows of $\breve{\mathbf{K}}$ yields $\mathbf{vR} = \breve{\mathbf{v}}$. Clearly, when $\mathbf{v} = \mathbf{0}$ also $\breve{\mathbf{v}} = \mathbf{0}$. Since $\mathbf{TR} = \mathbf{I}_r$ and since $\mathbf{v}$ can also be expressed as some linear combination of rows of $\mathbf{T}$, $\mathbf{vR} = \mathbf{0}$ only if $\mathbf{v} = \mathbf{0}$. Thus $\breve{\mathbf{v}} = \mathbf{0}$ if and only if $\mathbf{v} = \mathbf{0}$, and the first r linearly independent rows of $\mathbf{K}$ are also the first r linearly independent rows of $\breve{\mathbf{K}}$. By **15–4**, then, $\breve{\mathbf{T}} = \mathbf{TR} = \mathbf{I}_r$.

15–8 *Assertion:* Let $\breve{\mathbf{T}}$, as defined in **15–7**, consist of rows $i_1, i_2, \ldots, i_r$ of $\breve{\mathbf{K}}$. Let $\breve{\mathbf{s}}(0)$ be the initial state of $\breve{\mathcal{A}}$, and $\mathbf{y}_0(t)$ the output of $\breve{\mathcal{A}}$ at time $t \geq 0$, with $\mathbf{u}(t) = \mathbf{0}$ for all $t \geq 0$. Let $\mathbf{Y}_i$ denote the ith element in the column vector

15–9 $$\mathbf{Y} = \begin{pmatrix} \mathbf{y}_0(0) \\ \mathbf{y}_0(1) \\ \cdot \\ \cdot \\ \cdot \\ \mathbf{y}_0(r-1) \end{pmatrix}$$

Then

15–10 $$\breve{\mathbf{s}}(0) = (\mathbf{Y}_{i_1}, \mathbf{Y}_{i_2}, \ldots, \mathbf{Y}_{i_r})$$

Proof: Since $\mathbf{y}_0(t) = \breve{\mathbf{C}}\breve{\mathbf{A}}\breve{\mathbf{s}}^t(0)$, we have $\mathbf{Y} = \breve{\mathbf{K}}\breve{\mathbf{s}}(0)$. **15–8** then follows from **15–7**.

Thus, given the diagnostic matrix $\breve{\mathbf{K}}$ and the first r outputs, the LSC $\breve{\mathcal{A}}$ can be immediately "diagnosed"—i.e., its initial state can be uniquely identified.

15–11 *Assertion:* At any time t, the state of an r-dimensional minimal LSC is uniquely determined by the inputs and outputs at times $t-1$, $t-2$, $\ldots, t-r$:

15–12
$$\mathbf{s}(t) = f(\mathbf{u}(t-1), \mathbf{u}(t-2), \ldots, \mathbf{u}(t-r), \mathbf{y}(t-1), \mathbf{y}(t-2), \ldots, \mathbf{y}(t-r))$$

Proof: By **9–5** and the definition of $\mathbf{y}_0(t)$,

15–13
$$\mathbf{y}_0(t) = \mathbf{y}(t) - \sum_{\nu=0}^{t} \mathbf{H}(t-\nu)\mathbf{u}(\nu)$$

Hence, by **15–8**,

15–14
$$\begin{aligned}\mathbf{s}(0) &= f_1(\mathbf{y}_0(0), \mathbf{y}_0(1), \ldots, \mathbf{y}_0(r-1)) \\ &= f_2(\mathbf{y}(0), \mathbf{y}(1), \ldots, \mathbf{y}(r-1), \\ &\qquad \mathbf{u}(0), \mathbf{u}(1), \ldots, \mathbf{u}(r-1))\end{aligned}$$

Following **9–2**:

15–15
$$\begin{aligned}\mathbf{s}(r) &= \mathbf{A}^r\mathbf{s}(0) + \sum_{\nu=0}^{r-1} \mathbf{A}^{r-\nu-1}\mathbf{B}\mathbf{u}(\nu) \\ &= f(\mathbf{u}(r-1), \mathbf{u}(r-2), \ldots, \mathbf{u}(0), \\ &\qquad \mathbf{y}(r-1), \mathbf{y}(r-2), \ldots, \mathbf{y}(0))\end{aligned}$$

15–11 then follows by induction.

16. Minimal LSCs and Similarity

16–1 *Assertion.* Let $\mathcal{A}$ and $\bar{\mathcal{A}}$ be equivalent LSCs, and suppose every state $\mathbf{s}$ of $\mathcal{A}$ is equivalent to state $\mathbf{Ps}$ of $\bar{\mathcal{A}}$, where $\mathbf{P}$ is some nonsingular matrix. Then $\mathcal{A}$ and $\bar{\mathcal{A}}$ are similar LSCs.

Proof: Let $\mathcal{A}$ be characterized by $\mathbf{A}$, $\mathbf{B}$, $\mathbf{C}$, and $\mathbf{D}$, and $\bar{\mathcal{A}}$ by $\bar{\mathbf{A}}$, $\mathbf{B}$, $\bar{\mathbf{C}}$, and $\bar{\mathbf{D}}$. Then, for every $\mathbf{s}$ and for every $\mathbf{u}$, state $\mathbf{As} + \mathbf{Bu}$ of $\mathcal{A}$ is equivalent to state $\bar{\mathbf{A}}(\mathbf{Ps}) + \mathbf{Bu}$ of $\bar{\mathcal{A}}$, or

16–2
$$\mathbf{P}(\mathbf{As} + \mathbf{Bu}) = \bar{\mathbf{A}}\mathbf{Ps} + \mathbf{Bu}$$

Also, for every $\mathbf{s}$ and for every $\mathbf{u}$,

16–3
$$\mathbf{Cs} + \mathbf{Du} = \bar{\mathbf{C}}\mathbf{Ps} + \bar{\mathbf{D}}\mathbf{u}$$

Setting $\mathbf{u} = \mathbf{0}$ in **16–2**, we have $\mathbf{PAs} = \bar{\mathbf{A}}\mathbf{Ps}$ for every $\mathbf{s}$, or $\mathbf{PA} = \bar{\mathbf{A}}\mathbf{P}$; hence

16–4
$$\bar{\mathbf{A}} = \mathbf{PAP}^{-1}$$

Setting $\mathbf{s} = \mathbf{0}$ in **16–2**, we have $\mathbf{PBu} = \mathbf{Bu}$ for every $\mathbf{u}$; hence

16–5
$$\mathbf{B} = \mathbf{PB}$$

Setting $\mathbf{u} = \mathbf{0}$ in **16–3**, we have $\mathbf{Cs} = \bar{\mathbf{C}}\mathbf{Ps}$ for every $\mathbf{s}$; hence $\mathbf{C} = \bar{\mathbf{C}}\mathbf{P}$, or

16–6
$$\bar{\mathbf{C}} = \mathbf{CP}^{-1}$$

Setting $\mathbf{s} = \mathbf{0}$ in **16–3**, we have $\mathbf{Du} = \bar{\mathbf{D}}\mathbf{u}$ for every $\mathbf{u}$; hence

16–7
$$\bar{\mathbf{D}} = \mathbf{D}$$

16–4, 16–5, 16–6 and **16–7** imply that $\mathcal{A}$ and $\bar{\mathcal{A}}$ are similar.

16–8 *Assertion:* Let $\mathcal{A}$ and $\bar{\mathcal{A}}$ be equivalent minimal LSCs. Then every state $\mathbf{s}$ of $\mathcal{A}$ is equivalent to state $\mathbf{Ps}$ of $\bar{\mathcal{A}}$, where $\mathbf{P}$ is some nonsingular matrix.

Proof: Let $\mathcal{A}$ and $\bar{\mathcal{A}}$ be r-dimensional and characterized as in the proof to **16–1**. Since $\mathbf{CA}^t\mathbf{0} = \bar{\mathbf{C}}\bar{\mathbf{A}}^t\mathbf{0}$ for all $t \geq 0$, and since $\mathcal{A}$ is minimal, $\mathbf{0}$ is the only state in $\mathcal{A}$ which is equivalent to state $\mathbf{0}$ in $\bar{\mathcal{A}}$. Now, let the states

16–9 $$\mathbf{s}_1 = \begin{pmatrix} 1 \\ 0 \\ \cdot \\ \cdot \\ \cdot \\ 0 \end{pmatrix}, \quad \mathbf{s}_2 = \begin{pmatrix} 0 \\ 1 \\ \cdot \\ \cdot \\ \cdot \\ 0 \end{pmatrix}, \quad \ldots, \quad \mathbf{s}_r = \begin{pmatrix} 0 \\ 0 \\ \cdot \\ \cdot \\ \cdot \\ 1 \end{pmatrix}$$

of $\mathcal{A}$ be equivalent to states $\bar{\mathbf{s}}_1, \bar{\mathbf{s}}_2, \ldots, \bar{\mathbf{s}}_r$, respectively, of $\bar{\mathcal{A}}$. Then, for all $t \geq 0$, $\mathbf{CA}^t\mathbf{s}_i = \bar{\mathbf{C}}\bar{\mathbf{A}}^t\bar{\mathbf{s}}_i$ $(i = 1, 2, \ldots, r)$ and hence

16–10 $$\mathbf{CA}^t = \mathbf{CA}^t(\mathbf{s}_1, \mathbf{s}_2, \ldots, \mathbf{s}_r) = \bar{\mathbf{C}}\bar{\mathbf{A}}^t(\bar{\mathbf{s}}_1, \bar{\mathbf{s}}_2, \ldots, \bar{\mathbf{s}}_r) = \bar{\mathbf{C}}\bar{\mathbf{A}}^t\mathbf{P}$$

Suppose, with some α_i from $GF(p)$, $\alpha_1\bar{\mathbf{s}}_1 + \alpha_2\bar{\mathbf{s}}_2 + \ldots + \alpha_r\bar{\mathbf{s}}_r = \mathbf{0}$. Since the state $\alpha_1\bar{\mathbf{s}}_1 + \alpha_2\bar{\mathbf{s}}_2 + \ldots + \alpha_r\bar{\mathbf{s}}_r$ of $\bar{\mathcal{A}}$ is equivalent to state $\alpha_1\mathbf{s}_1 + \alpha_2\mathbf{s}_2 + \ldots + \alpha_r\mathbf{s}_r$ of $\mathcal{A}$, we must have $\alpha_1\mathbf{s}_1 + \alpha_2\mathbf{s}_2 + \ldots + \alpha_r\mathbf{s}_r = \mathbf{0}$; but—from **16–9**—this is possible only when $\alpha_1 = \alpha_2 = \ldots = \alpha_r = 0$. Thus $\bar{\mathbf{s}}_1, \bar{\mathbf{s}}_2, \ldots, \bar{\mathbf{s}}_r$ are linearly independent, which implies that $\mathbf{P}$ is nonsingular. Also, for all $t \geq 0$ and $\mathbf{s}$, $\mathbf{CA}^t\mathbf{s} = \bar{\mathbf{C}}\bar{\mathbf{A}}^t\mathbf{Ps}$, which implies that every state $\mathbf{s}$ of $\mathcal{A}$ is equivalent to state $\mathbf{Ps}$ of $\bar{\mathcal{A}}$.

Combining **16–1** and **16–8**, we now have:

16–11 *Assertion:* Equivalent minimal LSCs are similar.

That equivalent nonminimal LSCs are not necessarily similar is demonstrated in **11–8.**

In conclusion, the minimal form of an LSC is unique up to similarity, as well as up to isomorphism. To determine whether or not two LSCs are equivalent, one can construct their minimal forms and test these forms either for isomorphism or for similarity.

The relations of isomorphism, equivalence and similarity, as applied to minimal and nonminimal LSCs, are summarized in Table 2.1.

Table 2.1. Isomorphism, equivalence, and similarity

Relation	For nonminimal LSCs implies:	For minimal LSCs implies:
Isomorphism	equivalence	equivalence, similarity
Equivalence	—	isomorphism, similarity
Similarity	isomorphism, equivalence	isomorphism, equivalence

17. Canonical LSCs

Let $\breve{\mathcal{A}}$ be a minimal form of an LSC $\mathcal{A}$. If $\breve{\mathcal{A}}$ is characterized by $\breve{\mathbf{A}}$, $\breve{\mathbf{B}}$, $\breve{\mathbf{C}}$ and $\breve{\mathbf{D}}$, an LSC $\mathcal{A}^*$ exists which is equivalent to $\breve{\mathcal{A}}$ and characterized by

17–1 $$\mathbf{A}^* = \mathbf{P}\breve{\mathbf{A}}\mathbf{P}^{-1} \qquad \mathbf{B}^* = \mathbf{P}\breve{\mathbf{B}} \qquad \mathbf{C}^* = \breve{\mathbf{C}}\mathbf{P}^{-1} \qquad \mathbf{D}^* = \breve{\mathbf{D}}$$

where $\mathbf{A}^*$ is the rational canonical form of $\mathbf{A}$. $\mathcal{A}^*$ is called a *canonical realization* of $\mathcal{A}$. This realization features the useful properties of being minimal and of having an internal circuit which consists of the union of shift registers. An LSC already in a canonical form is called a *canonical* LSC. Thus, every LSC is equivalent to a canonical LSC.

Fig. 2.15 shows the general form of a canonical LSC.

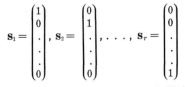

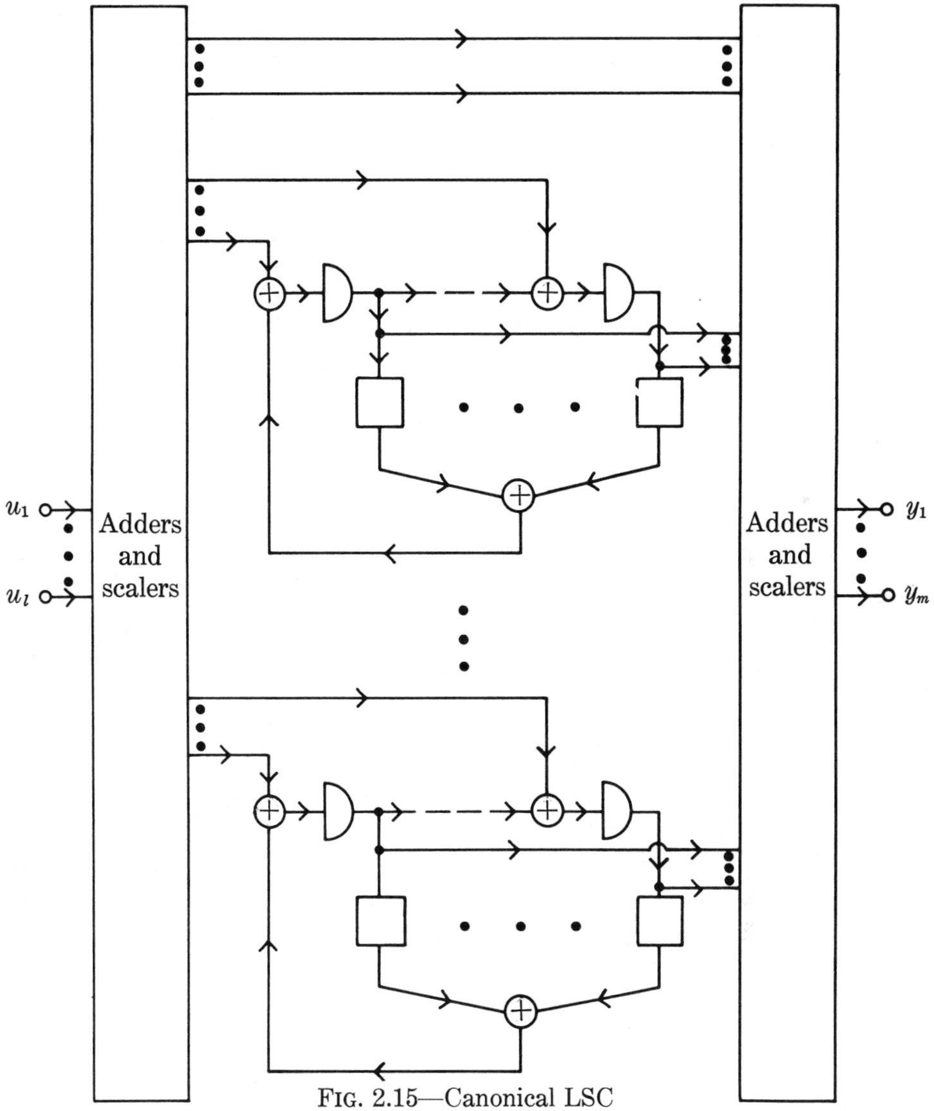

FIG. 2.15—Canonical LSC

17–2 *Example:* Consider a 2-dimensional LSC $\mathcal{A}$ over $GF(2)$, characterized by

17–3 $$\mathbf{A} = \begin{pmatrix} 1 & 1 \\ 0 & 1 \end{pmatrix} \qquad \mathbf{B} = \begin{pmatrix} 0 \\ 1 \end{pmatrix} \qquad \mathbf{C} = \begin{pmatrix} 1 & 0 \\ 0 & 1 \end{pmatrix} \qquad \mathbf{D} = \begin{pmatrix} 1 \\ 0 \end{pmatrix}$$

Carrying out the minimization procedure described in Sec. **14**, we have $\mathbf{T} = \mathbf{C} = \mathbf{I}$ and $\mathbf{R} = \mathbf{I}$. Hence $\mathcal{A}$ is minimal and, in fact, the minimal form $\check{\mathcal{A}}$ is identical with $\mathcal{A}$:

17–4 $$\check{\mathbf{A}} = \mathbf{A} \qquad \check{\mathbf{B}} = \mathbf{B} \qquad \check{\mathbf{C}} = \mathbf{C} \qquad \check{\mathbf{D}} = \mathbf{D}$$

The rational canonical form $\mathbf{A}^*$ of $\check{\mathbf{A}}$ and the corresponding similarity transformation matrix can be found by the methods outlined in Chap. 1:

17–5 $$\mathbf{A}^* = \mathbf{P}\breve{\mathbf{A}}\mathbf{P}^{-1} = \begin{pmatrix} 0 & 1 \\ 1 & 0 \end{pmatrix} \qquad \mathbf{P} = \begin{pmatrix} 1 & 0 \\ 1 & 1 \end{pmatrix} = \mathbf{P}^{-1}$$

The other characterizing matrices of the canonical realization $\mathcal{A}^*$ of $\mathcal{A}$ are given by

17–6 $$\mathbf{B}^* = \mathbf{P}\breve{\mathbf{B}} = \begin{pmatrix} 0 \\ 1 \end{pmatrix} \qquad \mathbf{C}^* = \breve{\mathbf{C}}\mathbf{P}^{-1} = \begin{pmatrix} 1 & 0 \\ 1 & 1 \end{pmatrix} \qquad \mathbf{D}^* = \breve{\mathbf{D}} = \begin{pmatrix} 1 \\ 0 \end{pmatrix}$$

$\mathcal{A}^*$ is shown in Fig. 2.16.

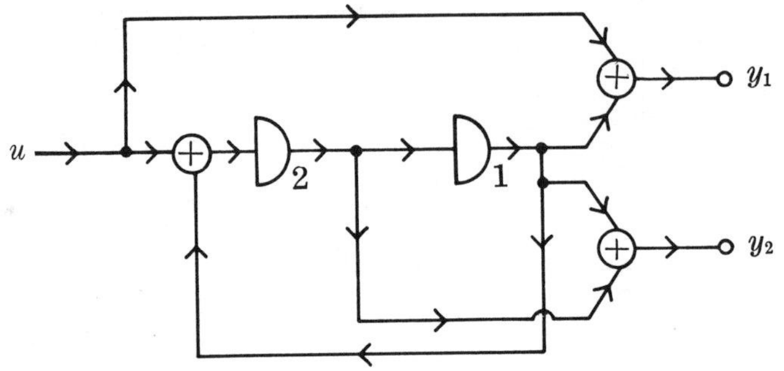

FIG. 2.16—Canonical form of LSC of Example **17–2**

18. Single-Output LSCs

Let $\breve{\mathcal{A}}$ be an r-dimensional minimal LSC with a single output terminal, characterized by $\breve{\mathbf{A}}$, $\breve{\mathbf{B}}$, $\breve{\mathbf{C}}$ and $\breve{\mathbf{D}}$ and obtained by the method of Sec. **14.** In this case $\breve{\mathbf{C}}\breve{\mathbf{A}}^t$ is an r-dimensional row vector, and the diagnostic matrix $\breve{\mathbf{K}}$ of $\breve{\mathcal{A}}$ is an $r \times r$ matrix. Since $\breve{\mathcal{A}}$ is minimal, the r rows of $\breve{\mathbf{K}}$ must be linearly independent and hence—by **15–7**—we have

18–1 $$\breve{\mathbf{K}} = \breve{\mathbf{T}} = \mathbf{I}_r$$

Denoting the ith row of $\breve{\mathbf{A}}$ by $\mathbf{a}_i$, **18–1** implies:

18–2 $$\breve{\mathbf{C}} = (1, 0, 0, \ldots, 0)$$

18–3 $$\begin{aligned} \breve{\mathbf{C}}\breve{\mathbf{A}} = \mathbf{a}_1 &= (0, 1, 0, \ldots, 0) \\ \breve{\mathbf{C}}\breve{\mathbf{A}}^2 = \mathbf{a}_2 &= (0, 0, 1, \ldots, 0) \\ &\vdots \\ \breve{\mathbf{C}}\breve{\mathbf{A}}^{r-1} = \mathbf{a}_{r-1} &= (0, 0, 0, \ldots, 1) \end{aligned}$$

The identities **18–3** imply that $\breve{\mathbf{A}}$ has the form of a companion matrix and, hence, that the internal circuit of $\breve{\mathcal{A}}$ consists of a single shift register. By **18–2**, the output of $\breve{\mathcal{A}}$ is tapped directly from delayer 1, the "last" delayer in the shift register. Due to the simplicity of its internal circuit and its output connection, this realization (which is not necessarily canonical) is highly desirable from a practical standpoint. It will be referred to as a *simple* LSC. The general form of a simple LSC [corresponding to $\breve{\mathbf{A}}$ whose last row is $(-\alpha_0, -\alpha_1, \ldots, -\alpha_{r-1})$] is shown in Fig. 2.17. Summarizing, we have:

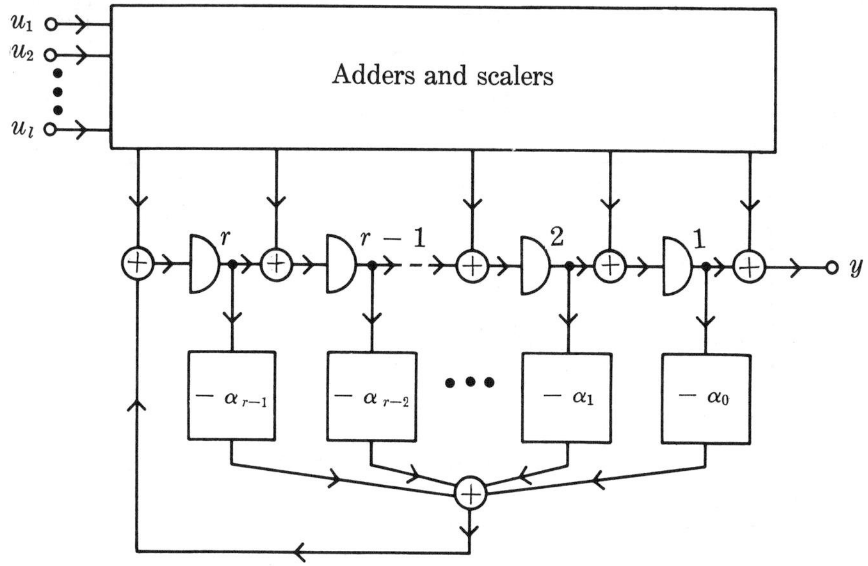

FIG. 2.17—Simple LSC

18–4 *Assertion:* Every single-output LSC is equivalent to a minimal simple LSC (obtainable by the minimization procedure of Sec. **14**).

When a given LSC $\mathcal{A}$ has m output terminals ($m > 1$), a minimal simple LSC can be constructed with respect to each output terminal individually; the resulting m simple LSCs can subsequently be connected to the same input lines to form an LSC $\tilde{\mathcal{A}}$ such as shown in Fig. 2.18, which has the following property: For every state $\mathbf{s}$ in $\mathcal{A}$ there is at least one state $\tilde{\mathbf{s}}$ in $\tilde{\mathcal{A}}$ equivalent to $\mathbf{s}$ (but not necessarily conversely). Thus, although $\mathcal{A}$ does not generally simulate $\tilde{\mathcal{A}}$, $\tilde{\mathcal{A}}$ always simulates $\mathcal{A}$. $\tilde{\mathcal{A}}$, called the *pseudocanonical realization* of $\mathcal{A}$, has the advantage of extremely simple output connections. Its disadvantage is that, generally, it is of higher dimension than $\check{\mathcal{A}}$.

18–5 *Example:* Consider the LSC $\mathcal{A}$ of Example **17–2**. The simple LSC $\mathcal{A}_1$ corresponding to output terminal 1 can be obtained by replacing **C** and **D** with their first rows,

18–6 $$\mathbf{C}' = (1, 0) \qquad \mathbf{D}' = (1)$$

and proceeding as prescribed in Sec. **14**:

18–7 $$\mathbf{K}' = \begin{pmatrix} \mathbf{C}' \\ \mathbf{C}'\mathbf{A} \end{pmatrix} = \begin{pmatrix} 1 & 0 \\ 1 & 1 \end{pmatrix} = \mathbf{T}' = \mathbf{R}'$$

$\mathcal{A}_1$, then, is characterized by

18–8 $$\mathbf{A}_1 = \mathbf{T}'\mathbf{A}\mathbf{R}' = \begin{pmatrix} 0 & 1 \\ 1 & 0 \end{pmatrix} \qquad \mathbf{B}_1 = \mathbf{T}'\mathbf{B} = \begin{pmatrix} 0 \\ 1 \end{pmatrix}$$
$$\mathbf{C}_1 = \mathbf{C}'\mathbf{R}' = (1, 0) \qquad \mathbf{D}_1 = \mathbf{D}' = (1)$$

The simple LSC $\mathcal{A}_2$ corresponding to output terminal 2 can be obtained by replacing **C** and **D** with their second rows,

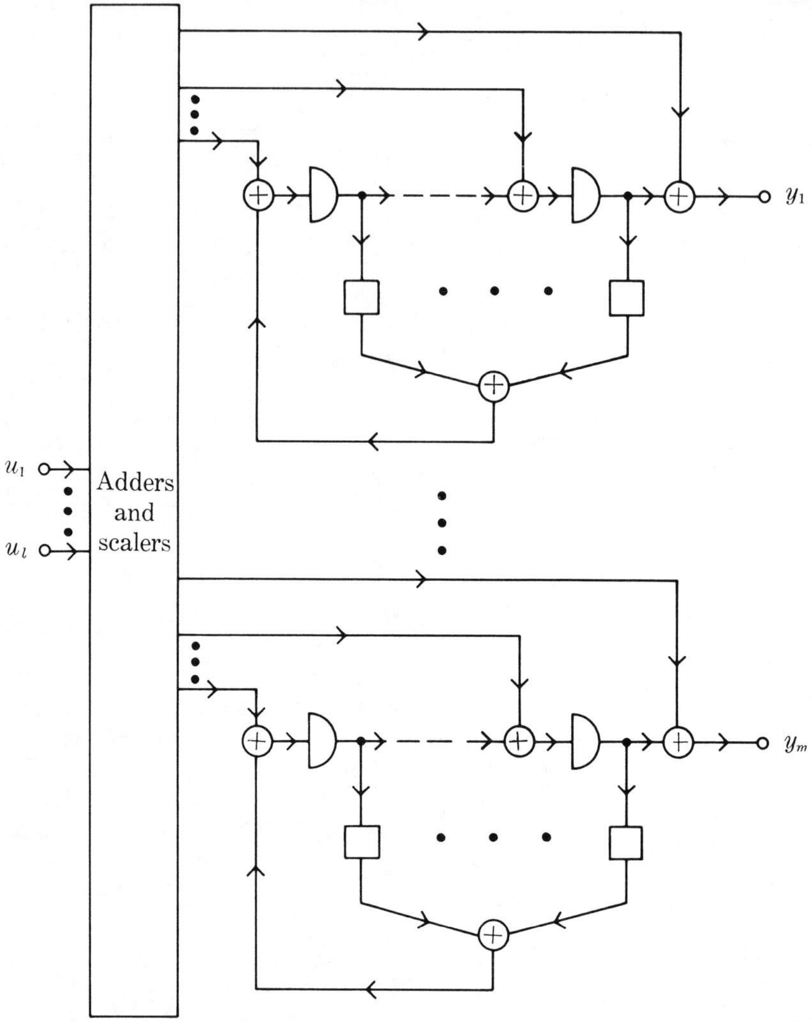

FIG. 2.18—Pseudocanonical realization of LSC

18–9 $$\mathbf{C}'' = (0, 1) \qquad \mathbf{D}'' = (0)$$

Accordingly:

18–10 $$\mathbf{K}'' = \begin{pmatrix} \mathbf{C}'' \\ \mathbf{C}''\mathbf{A} \end{pmatrix} = \begin{pmatrix} 0 & 1 \\ 0 & 1 \end{pmatrix} \qquad \mathbf{T}'' = (0, 1) \qquad \mathbf{R}'' = \begin{pmatrix} 0 \\ 1 \end{pmatrix}$$

$\mathcal{A}_2$, then, is characterized by

18–11 $$\begin{aligned} \mathbf{A}_2 &= \mathbf{T}''\mathbf{A}\mathbf{R}'' = (1) & \mathbf{B}_2 &= \mathbf{T}''\mathbf{B} = (1) \\ \mathbf{C}_2 &= \mathbf{C}''\mathbf{R}'' = (1) & \mathbf{D}_2 &= \mathbf{D}'' = (0) \end{aligned}$$

$\mathcal{A}_1$ and $\mathcal{A}_2$, connected "in parallel" to form the pseudocanonical realization of $\mathcal{A}$, are shown in Fig. 2.19.

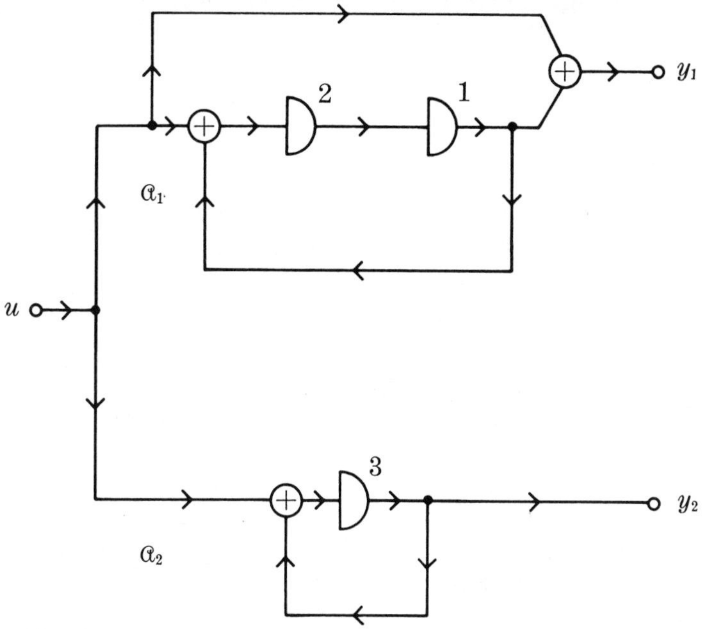

FIG. 2.19—Pseudocanonical realization of LSC of Fig. 2.16

19. Multi-Channel Analogs of Two-Terminal LSCs

A *two-terminal* LSC $\mathcal{A}$ is an LSC with one input terminal and one output terminal ($l = m = 1$). An *f-channel analog* of $\mathcal{A}$, denoted by $\mathcal{A}_{(f)}$, is an LSC with f input terminals and f output terminals, whose input and output vectors correspond to input and output subsequences (of length f) in $\mathcal{A}$. More pre-

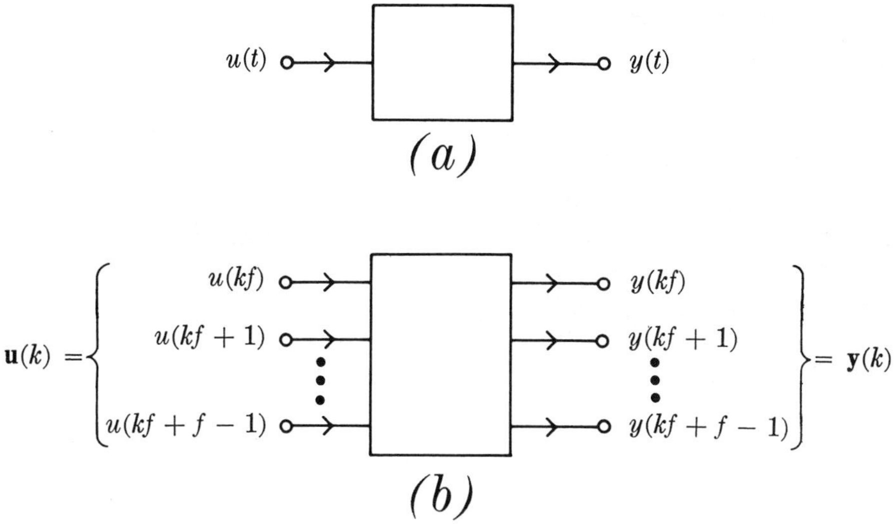

FIG. 2.20— (*a*) Two-terminal LSC; (*b*) its *f*-channel analog

cisely (see Fig. 2.20), let the initial state of $\mathcal{A}$ be $\mathbf{s}(0)$, its input $u(t)$ and its output $y(t)$. Let the input of $\mathcal{A}_{(f)}$ at time k ($k = 0, 1, 2, \ldots$) be

19–1
$$\mathbf{u}(k) = \begin{pmatrix} u(kf) \\ u(kf+1) \\ \cdot \\ \cdot \\ \cdot \\ u(kf+f-1) \end{pmatrix}$$

Then, with a suitable initial state $\bar{\mathbf{s}}(0)$, the output of $\mathcal{A}_{(f)}$ at time k is

19–2
$$\mathbf{y}(k) = \begin{pmatrix} y(kf) \\ y(kf+1) \\ \cdot \\ \cdot \\ \cdot \\ y(kf+f-1) \end{pmatrix}$$

Thus, by employing f "channels" instead of one, $\mathcal{A}_{(f)}$ is capable of operating f times faster than $\mathcal{A}$. The following establishes that $\mathcal{A}_{(f)}$ can be constructed for any $f \geq 1$; moreover, an $\mathcal{A}_{(f)}$ can be constructed whose dimension is the same as that of $\mathcal{A}$ and whose initial state $\bar{\mathbf{s}}(0)$ (as defined above) is precisely $\mathbf{s}(0)$.

19–3 *Assertion:* Let $\mathcal{A}$ be an LSC characterized by **A, B, C** and **D**. Then an f-channel analog of $\mathcal{A}$ is the LSC $\mathcal{A}_{(f)}$ characterized by

$$\bar{\mathbf{A}} = \mathbf{A}^f \qquad \bar{\mathbf{B}} = (\mathbf{A}^{f-1}\mathbf{B},\quad \mathbf{A}^{f-2}\mathbf{B},\quad \mathbf{A}^{f-3}\mathbf{B},\quad \ldots,\quad \mathbf{AB}, \mathbf{B})$$

19–4
$$\bar{\mathbf{C}} = \begin{pmatrix} \mathbf{C} \\ \mathbf{CA} \\ \mathbf{CA}^2 \\ \cdot \\ \cdot \\ \cdot \\ \mathbf{CA}^{f-1} \end{pmatrix} \qquad \bar{\mathbf{D}} = \begin{pmatrix} \mathbf{D} & & & & & \\ \mathbf{CB} & \mathbf{D} & & & & \\ \mathbf{CAB} & \mathbf{CB} & \mathbf{D} & & & \\ \cdot & & & & & \\ \cdot & & & & & \\ \cdot & & & & & \\ \mathbf{CA}^{f-2}\mathbf{B} & \mathbf{CA}^{f-3}\mathbf{B} & \mathbf{CA}^{f-4}\mathbf{B} & \ldots & \mathbf{CB} & \mathbf{D} \end{pmatrix}$$

Proof: Following **9–7**, the output of $\mathcal{A}$ (for all $t \geq 0$), is given by

19–5
$$y(t) = \mathbf{CA}^t\mathbf{s}(0) + \left[\sum_{\nu=0}^{t-1} \mathbf{CA}^{t-\nu-1}\mathbf{B}u(\nu)\right] + \mathbf{D}u(t)$$

Let $t = kf + i - 1$, where $1 \leq i \leq f$. The sum in the brackets can be decomposed into partial sums involving $u(\mu f)$, $u(\mu f + 1)$, . . . , $u(\mu f + f - 1)$ ($\mu = 0, 1, \ldots, k-1$) and terms involving $u(kf)$, $u(kf+1)$, . . . , $u(kf + i - 2)$; hence

19–6
$$\begin{aligned} y(kf+i-1) = \mathbf{CA}^{kf+i-1}\mathbf{s}(0) &+ \sum_{\mu=0}^{k-1} \mathbf{CA}^{(kf+i-1)-\mu f-1}\mathbf{B}u(\mu f) \\ &+ \sum_{\mu=0}^{k-1} \mathbf{CA}^{(kf+i-1)-\mu f-2}\mathbf{B}u(\mu f+1) \\ &\cdot \\ &\cdot \\ &\cdot \\ &+ \sum_{\mu=0}^{k-1} \mathbf{CA}^{(kf+i-1)-\mu f-f}\mathbf{B}u(\mu f+f-1) \end{aligned}$$

$$\begin{aligned}
&+ \mathbf{CA}^{(kf+i-1)-kf-1}\mathbf{B}u(kf)\\
&+ \mathbf{CA}^{(kf+i-1)-kf-2}\mathbf{B}u(kf+1)\\
&\cdot\\
&\cdot\\
&\cdot\\
&+ \mathbf{CA}^{(kf+i-1)-kf-i+1}\mathbf{B}u(kf+i-2)\\
&+ \mathbf{D}u(kf+i-1)
\end{aligned}$$

or

$$y(kf+i-1) = (\mathbf{CA}^{i-1})(\mathbf{A}^f)^k\mathbf{s}(0) + \sum_{\mu=0}^{k-1}(\mathbf{CA}^{i-1})(\mathbf{A}^f)^{k-\mu-1}[\mathbf{A}^{f-1}\mathbf{B}u(\mu f)$$

19–7
$$\begin{aligned}
&+ \mathbf{A}^{f-2}\mathbf{B}u(\mu f+1) + \ldots + \mathbf{AB}u(\mu f+f-2)\\
&+ \mathbf{B}u(\mu f+f-1)] + \mathbf{CA}^{i-2}\mathbf{B}u(kf) + \mathbf{CA}^{i-3}\mathbf{B}u(kf+1)\\
&+ \ldots + \mathbf{CB}u(kf+i-2) + \mathbf{D}u(kf+i-1)
\end{aligned}$$

On the other hand, if the initial state of $\mathcal{A}_{(f)}$ is also $\mathbf{s}(0)$ and its input $\mathbf{u}(k)$ is as given in **19–1**, then its output, by **9–7**, is given by

19–8
$$\mathbf{y}(k) = \overline{\mathbf{C}}\overline{\mathbf{A}}^k\mathbf{s}(0) + \left[\sum_{\mu=0}^{k-1}\overline{\mathbf{C}}\overline{\mathbf{A}}^{k-\mu-1}\mathbf{Bu}(\mu)\right] + \overline{\mathbf{D}}\mathbf{u}(k)$$

Using **19–4**, the ith row of $\mathbf{y}(k)$ is seen to be precisely the expression **19–7**, and hence $\mathbf{y}(k)$ is precisely the vector shown in **19–2**.

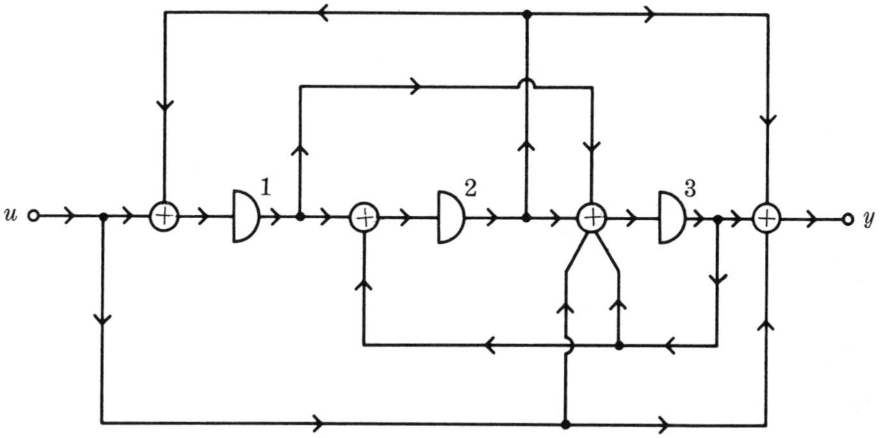

FIG. 2.21—LSC over $GF(2)$

19–9 *Example:* Fig. 2.21 shows a two-terminal LSC $\mathcal{A}$ over $GF(2)$, characterized by

19–10
$$\mathbf{A} = \begin{pmatrix} 0 & 1 & 0\\ 1 & 0 & 1\\ 1 & 1 & 1\end{pmatrix} \qquad \mathbf{B} = \begin{pmatrix}1\\0\\1\end{pmatrix} \qquad \mathbf{C} = (0, 1, 1) \qquad \mathbf{D} = (1)$$

$\mathcal{A}_{(2)}$, the two-channel analog of $\mathcal{A}$, is characterized by

19–11
$$\bar{\mathbf{A}} = \mathbf{A}^2 = \begin{pmatrix} 1 & 0 & 1 \\ 1 & 0 & 1 \\ 0 & 0 & 0 \end{pmatrix} \qquad \bar{\mathbf{B}} = (\mathbf{AB},\ \mathbf{B}) = \begin{pmatrix} 0 & 1 \\ 0 & 0 \\ 0 & 1 \end{pmatrix}$$
$$\bar{\mathbf{C}} = \begin{pmatrix} \mathbf{C} \\ \mathbf{CA} \end{pmatrix} = \begin{pmatrix} 0 & 1 & 1 \\ 0 & 1 & 0 \end{pmatrix} \qquad \bar{\mathbf{D}} = \begin{pmatrix} \mathbf{D} & \\ \mathbf{CB} & \mathbf{D} \end{pmatrix} \quad \begin{pmatrix} 1 & 0 \\ 1 & 1 \end{pmatrix}$$

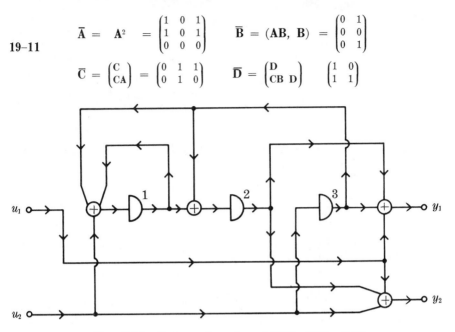

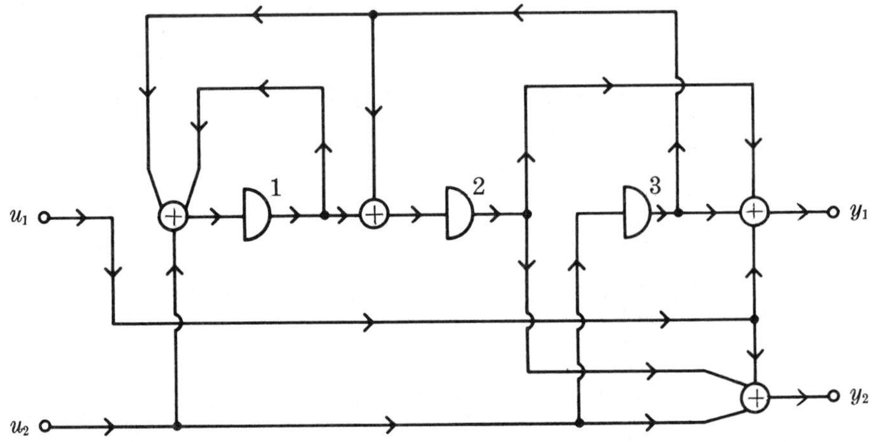

FIG. 2.22—2-channel analog of LSC of Fig. 2.21

$\mathcal{A}_{(2)}$ is shown in Fig. 2.22. For example, if

19–12
$$\mathbf{s}(0) = \begin{pmatrix} 1 \\ 0 \\ 1 \end{pmatrix}$$

and

19–13
$$u(t)\colon 1011000 \ldots$$

the outputs of $\mathcal{A}$ at $t = kf = 2$ and $t = kf + 1 = 3$ are given by

19–14
$$y(2) = \mathbf{CA}^2\mathbf{s}(0) + \mathbf{CAB}u(0) + \mathbf{CB}u(1) + \mathbf{D}u(2) = 1$$
$$y(3) = \mathbf{CA}^3\mathbf{s}(0) + \mathbf{CA}^2\mathbf{B}u(0) + \mathbf{CAB}u(1) + \mathbf{CB}u(2) + \mathbf{D}u(3) = 0$$

If the initial state of $\mathcal{A}_{(2)}$ is $\mathbf{s}(0)$ as given in **19–12**, and if the inputs to $\mathcal{A}_{(2)}$ are

19–15
$$u_1(k)\colon 11000 \ldots$$
$$u_2(k)\colon 01000 \ldots$$

then the output of $\mathcal{A}_{(2)}$ at $t = k = 1$ is given by

19–16
$$\mathbf{y}(1) = \bar{\mathbf{C}}\bar{\mathbf{A}}\mathbf{s}(0) + \bar{\mathbf{C}}\bar{\mathbf{B}}\mathbf{u}(0) + \bar{\mathbf{D}}\mathbf{u}(1) = \begin{pmatrix} 1 \\ 0 \end{pmatrix} = \begin{pmatrix} y(2) \\ y(3) \end{pmatrix}$$

20. Controllability of LSCs

Let $\mathcal{A}$ be an n-dimensional, l-input LSC, characterized by **A**, **B**, **C** and **D**. $\mathcal{A}$ is said to be *strongly connected* if, for all possible pairs of states $\mathbf{s}_i$ and $\mathbf{s}_j$ of $\mathcal{A}$, there is an input sequence which takes $\mathcal{A}$ from $\mathbf{s}_i$ to $\mathbf{s}_j$. $\mathcal{A}$ is said to be *k-controllable* if there exists a *fixed* integer k such that, for all possible $\mathbf{s}_i$ and $\mathbf{s}_j$, there is an input sequence of length k which takes $\mathcal{A}$ from $\mathbf{s}_i$ to $\mathbf{s}_j$. Clearly, if $\mathcal{A}$ is k-controllable it is strongly connected.

20–1 *Assertion:* $\mathcal{A}$ is k-controllable if and only if the $n \times kl$ matrix

20–2
$$\mathbf{L}_k = (\mathbf{A}^{k-1}\mathbf{B}, \mathbf{A}^{k-2}\mathbf{B}\ .\ .\ .\ , \mathbf{AB}, \mathbf{B})$$

is of rank n.

Proof: By **9–2**, $\mathcal{A}$ is k-controllable if and only if, for every $\mathbf{s}_i$ and $\mathbf{s}_j$ there is an input sequence $\mathbf{u}(t)$ such that

20–3
$$\mathbf{s}_j - \mathbf{A}^k\mathbf{s}_i = \sum_{\nu=0}^{k-1}\mathbf{A}^{k-\nu-1}\mathbf{Bu}(\nu) = \mathbf{L}^k\begin{pmatrix}\mathbf{u}(0)\\ \mathbf{u}(1)\\ \cdot\\ \cdot\\ \cdot\\ \mathbf{u}(k-1)\end{pmatrix}$$

Since $\mathbf{s}_j - \mathbf{A}^k\mathbf{s}_i$ can be an arbitrary n-dimensional vector $\mathbf{v}$, $\mathcal{A}$ is k-controllable if and only if $\mathbf{x}$ in $\mathbf{L}_k\mathbf{x} = \mathbf{v}$ is solvable for all $\mathbf{v}$, and hence if and only if $\mathbf{L}_k$ is of rank n.

20–4 *Assertion:* Let the minimum polynomial of $\mathbf{A}$ be of degree r. Then $\mathcal{A}$ is k-controllable for some k, if and only if it is r-controllable.

Proof: If the minimum polynomial is $m_{\mathbf{A}}(x) = \alpha_0 + \alpha_1 x + \ .\ .\ .\ + \alpha_{r-1}x^{r-1} + x_r$, then

20–5
$$\mathbf{A}^r\mathbf{B} = -\alpha_0\mathbf{B} - \alpha_1\mathbf{AB} - \ .\ .\ .\ - \alpha_{r-1}\mathbf{A}^{r-1}\mathbf{B}$$

and hence the columns of $\mathbf{A}^\nu\mathbf{B}$ are linearly dependent on columns of $\mathbf{L}_{r-1}$ for all $\nu \geq r$. Thus, if $\mathbf{L}_\nu$ has rank n for any ν, $\mathbf{L}_r$ must also have this rank.

Since the degree of the minimum polynomial does not exceed n, we have the following weaker version of **20–4**:

20–6 *Assertion:* $\mathcal{A}$ is k-controllable for some k if and only if it is n-controllable.

To determine the least k such that $\mathcal{A}$ is k-controllable, the least k has to be found such that $\mathbf{L}_k$ contains n linearly independent columns. If none of the integers $k = 1, 2, \ .\ .\ .\ , n$ satisfy this condition, $\mathcal{A}$ is not controllable for any k.

When $\mathcal{A}$ has only one input terminal ($l = 1$), $\mathbf{L}_k$ is $n \times k$, and **20–1** implies that $\mathcal{A}$ is k-controllable if and only if $\mathbf{L}_k$ is nonsingular. In this case, therefore, the least k must equal n.

20–7 *Assertion:* $\mathcal{A}$ is k-controllable if and only if it is strongly connected.

Proof: Suppose $\mathcal{A}$ is strongly connected. Let l_{ab} denote the length of the shortest input sequence taking $\mathcal{A}$ from $\mathbf{s}_a$ to $\mathbf{s}_b$. Denote $\mathbf{0} = \mathbf{s}_0$, and define

20–8
$$l' = \max_a l_{a0} \qquad l'' = \max_b l_{0b} \qquad k = l' + l''$$

$\mathcal{A}$ can be taken from any state $\mathbf{s}_i$ to any state $\mathbf{s}_j$ by an input sequence of length k, constructed as follows: The first l_{i0} inputs constitute the input sequence which takes $\mathbf{s}_i$ to $\mathbf{0}$; these are followed by $k - l_{i0} - l_{0j}$ zeros (since $l_{i0} \leq l'$ and $l_{0j} \leq l''$, $k - l_{i0} - l_{0j} \geq 0$) which takes $\mathbf{0}$ back to $\mathbf{0}$; the last l_{0j} inputs constitute the input sequence which takes $\mathbf{0}$ to $\mathbf{s}_j$.

20–9 *Assertion:* If state $\mathbf{s}$ is reachable from state $\mathbf{0}$, then $\mathbf{0}$ is reachable from $\mathbf{s}$.

Proof: If $\mathbf{s}$ is reachable from $\mathbf{0}$, by **9–2** $\mathbf{s}$ is some linear combination of columns of $\mathbf{B}$, $\mathbf{AB}$, $\mathbf{A}^2\mathbf{B}$, . . . , and hence $-\mathbf{A}^t\mathbf{s}$ must be some linear combination of columns of $-\mathbf{A}^t\mathbf{B}$, $-\mathbf{A}^{t+1}\mathbf{B}$, $-\mathbf{A}^{t+2}\mathbf{B}$, . . . Since $m_{\mathbf{A}}(x)$ is of degree at most n, $-\mathbf{A}^t\mathbf{s}$ is expressible as a linear combination of columns of $\mathbf{B}$, $\mathbf{AB}$, . . . , $\mathbf{A}^{n-1}\mathbf{B}$. Thus, for any t, an nl-dimensional vector $\mathbf{x}$ can be found such that

20–10 $$\mathbf{0} - \mathbf{A}^t\mathbf{s} = \mathbf{L}_n\mathbf{x}$$

which, by **20–3**, implies that **0** is reachable from any state $\mathbf{A}^t\mathbf{s}$—i.e., from any state reached from **0**.

20–11 *Example:* For the LSC over $GF(2)$ of Fig. 2.19, we have

20–12 $$\mathbf{A} = \begin{pmatrix} 0 & 1 & 0 \\ 1 & 0 & 0 \\ 0 & 0 & 1 \end{pmatrix} \quad \mathbf{B} = \begin{pmatrix} 0 \\ 1 \\ 1 \end{pmatrix}$$

20–13 $$\mathbf{L}_3 = (\mathbf{A}^2\mathbf{B}, \mathbf{AB}, \mathbf{B}) = \begin{pmatrix} 0 & 1 & 0 \\ 1 & 0 & 1 \\ 1 & 1 & 1 \end{pmatrix}$$

Since L_3 is singular, the LSC is not k-controllable for any k (this also signifies that the LSC is not strongly connected).

20–14 *Example:* Fig. 2.23 shows an LSC over $GF(3)$, where

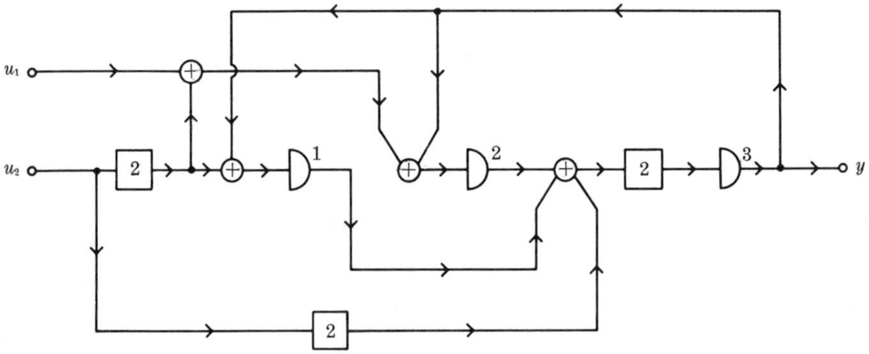

FIG. 2.23—LSC over $GF(3)$

20–15 $$\mathbf{A} = \begin{pmatrix} 0 & 0 & 1 \\ 0 & 0 & 1 \\ 2 & 2 & 0 \end{pmatrix} \quad \mathbf{B} = \begin{pmatrix} 0 & 2 \\ 1 & 2 \\ 0 & 1 \end{pmatrix}$$

20–16 $$\mathbf{L}_3 = (\mathbf{A}^2\mathbf{B},\ \mathbf{AB},\ \mathbf{B}) = \begin{pmatrix} 2 & 2 & \vdots & 0 & 1 & \vdots & 0 & 2 \\ 2 & 2 & \vdots & 0 & 1 & \vdots & 1 & 2 \\ 0 & 1 & \vdots & 2 & 2 & \vdots & 0 & 1 \end{pmatrix}$$

Conversion of $\mathbf{L}_3$ into the row-reduced echelon canonical form reveals that its rank is 3, and that the LSC is k-controllable with $k = 2$ (but with no smaller k). Suppose we wish to find the input sequence $\mathbf{u}(t)$ (of length 2) which takes $\mathbf{s}_i$ to $\mathbf{s}_j$, where

20–17 $$\mathbf{s}_i = \begin{pmatrix} 0 \\ 2 \\ 1 \end{pmatrix} \qquad \mathbf{s}_j = \begin{pmatrix} 0 \\ 1 \\ 2 \end{pmatrix}$$

20–18 $$\mathbf{s}_j - \mathbf{A}^2\mathbf{s}_i = \begin{pmatrix} 0 \\ 1 \\ 2 \end{pmatrix} - \begin{pmatrix} 2 & 2 & 0 \\ 2 & 2 & 0 \\ 0 & 0 & 1 \end{pmatrix} \begin{pmatrix} 0 \\ 2 \\ 1 \end{pmatrix} = \begin{pmatrix} 2 \\ 0 \\ 1 \end{pmatrix} = \mathbf{v}$$

Hence, $\begin{pmatrix} \mathbf{u}(0) \\ \mathbf{u}(1) \end{pmatrix}$ is any solution to $\mathbf{L}_2\mathbf{x} = \mathbf{v}$, or

2–19 $$\begin{pmatrix} 0 & 1 & \vdots & 0 & 2 \\ 0 & 1 & \vdots & 1 & 2 \\ 2 & 2 & \vdots & 0 & 1 \end{pmatrix} \mathbf{x} = \begin{pmatrix} 2 \\ 0 \\ 1 \end{pmatrix}$$

The set of possible solutions is given by

20–20 $$\mathbf{x} = \begin{pmatrix} 0 \\ \alpha \\ \hdashline 1 \\ 1 + \alpha \end{pmatrix}$$

One possible input sequence is obtained when we set $\alpha = 0$:

20–21 $$\mathbf{u}(0) = \begin{pmatrix} 0 \\ 0 \end{pmatrix} \qquad \mathbf{u}(1) = \begin{pmatrix} 1 \\ 1 \end{pmatrix}$$

21. Predictability in LSCs

An LSC is said to have *finite memory* if there is an integer μ such that the output at any time is uniquely determined by the input at that time and by the last μ inputs and outputs; i.e., for all t,

21–1 $$\mathbf{y}(t) = f(\mathbf{u}(t),\ \mathbf{u}(t-1),\ \ldots,\ \mathbf{u}(t-\mu),\ \mathbf{y}(t-1),\ \ldots,\ \mathbf{y}(t-\mu))$$

Thus, if an LSC has a finite memory, its output at any time can be predicted on the basis of its input at that time and on the basis of a finite number of observations of past inputs and outputs. The least integer μ satisfying **21–1** is called the *memory* of the LSC.

In what follows, $\mathcal{A}$ will be an n-dimensional, l-input LSC, characterized by **A, B, C** and **D**.

21–2 *Assertion:* Every LSC $\mathcal{A}$ has a finite memory. The memory of $\mathcal{A}$ equals at most the degree of the minimum polynominal of **A**.

Proof: Let the minimum polynominal of **A** be

21–3 $$m_{\mathbf{A}}(x) = \alpha_o + \alpha_1 x + \ldots + \alpha_{r-1}x^{r-1} + x^r$$

(where, necessarily, $r \leq n$). Following **9–5**, let

21–4 $$\mathbf{z}(t) = \mathbf{y}(t) - \sum_{\nu=0}^{t} \mathbf{H}(t-\nu)\mathbf{u}(\nu) = \mathbf{CA}^t\mathbf{s}(0)$$

By **21–3**,

21–5 $$\mathbf{CA}^r\mathbf{s}(0) = -\alpha_0\mathbf{Cs}(0) - \alpha_1\mathbf{CAs}(0) - \dots - \alpha_{r-1}\mathbf{CA}^{r-1}\mathbf{s}(0)$$

or

21–6 $$\mathbf{z}(r) = -\alpha_0\mathbf{z}(0) - \alpha_1\mathbf{z}(1) - \dots - \alpha_{r-1}\mathbf{z}(r-1)$$

Hence

21–7 $$\begin{aligned}\mathbf{y}(r) &= \sum_{\nu=0}^{r}\mathbf{H}(r-\nu)\mathbf{u}(\nu) + \sum_{t=0}^{r-1}\sum_{\nu=0}^{t}\alpha_t\mathbf{H}(t-\nu)\mathbf{u}(\nu) - \sum_{t=0}^{r-1}\alpha_t\mathbf{y}(t)\\ &= f(\mathbf{u}(r), \mathbf{u}(r-1), \dots, \mathbf{u}(0), \mathbf{y}(r-1), \dots, \mathbf{y}(0))\end{aligned}$$

As a direct corollary, we have:

21–8 *Assertion:* Every n-dimensional LSC has memory at most n.

When $\mathcal{A}$ is a two-terminal LSC, **21–7** implies that, for all t, we can write

21–9 $$\begin{aligned}y(t) &= \eta_0 u(t) + \eta_1 u(t-1) + \dots + \eta_r u(t-r)\\ &\quad + \eta_{r+1}y(t-1) + \dots + \eta_{2r}y(t-r)\end{aligned}$$

where $r \leq n$ is the degree of the minimum polynominal of **A**. Hence, $\mathcal{A}$ can be realized by means of at most $2n$ delayers and a single adder, as shown in Fig. 2.24.

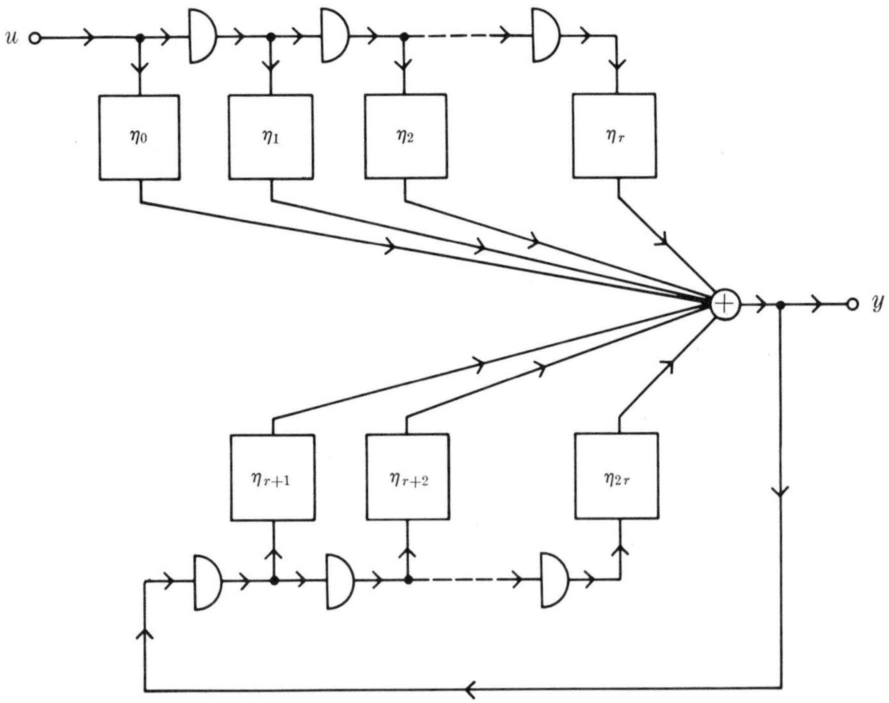

FIG. 2.24—Single-adder realization of two-terminal LSC with memory r

21–10 *Example:* Let $\mathcal{A}$ be a two-terminal LSC over GF(2), characterized by

21–11
$$\mathbf{A} = \begin{pmatrix} 0 & 1 & 0 & 0 \\ 1 & 1 & 0 & 0 \\ 0 & 0 & 0 & 1 \\ 0 & 0 & 1 & 1 \end{pmatrix} \qquad \mathbf{B} = \begin{pmatrix} 1 \\ 1 \\ 1 \\ 0 \end{pmatrix}$$
$$\mathbf{C} = (0, 1, 0, 1) \qquad \mathbf{D} = (1)$$

The minimum polynominal of **A** is $1 + x + x^2$, and hence

21–12
$$\mathbf{CA}^2\mathbf{s}(0) = -\mathbf{Cs}(0) - \mathbf{CAs}(0)$$

$$\mathbf{y}(2) = \mathbf{CA}^2\mathbf{s}(0) + \sum_{\nu=0}^{2} \mathbf{H}(2-\nu)u(\nu)$$
$$= -\mathbf{Cs}(0) - \mathbf{CAs}(0) + \sum_{\nu=0}^{2} \mathbf{H}(2-\nu)u(\nu)$$
$$= -\left[y(0) - \sum_{\nu=0}^{0}\mathbf{H}(0-\nu)u(\nu)\right] - \left[y(1) - \sum_{\nu=0}^{1}\mathbf{H}(1-\nu)u(\nu)\right]$$

21–13
$$+ \sum_{\nu=0}^{2}\mathbf{H}(2-\nu)u(\nu)$$
$$= -[y(0) - \mathbf{D}\mathrm{u}(0)] - [y(1) - \mathbf{CB}u(0) - \mathbf{D}u(1)] + \mathbf{CAB}u(0) + \mathbf{CB}u(1) + \mathbf{D}u(2)$$
$$= \mathbf{D}u(2) + (\mathbf{D} + \mathbf{CB})u(1) + (\mathbf{D} + \mathbf{CB} + \mathbf{CAB})u(0) - y(1) - y(0)$$
$$= u(2) + u(0) + y(1) + y(0)$$

Thus, for all t:

21–14
$$y(t) = u(t) + u(t-2) + y(t-1) + y(t-2)$$

The realization of $\mathcal{A}$ with a single adder is shown in Fig. 2.25.

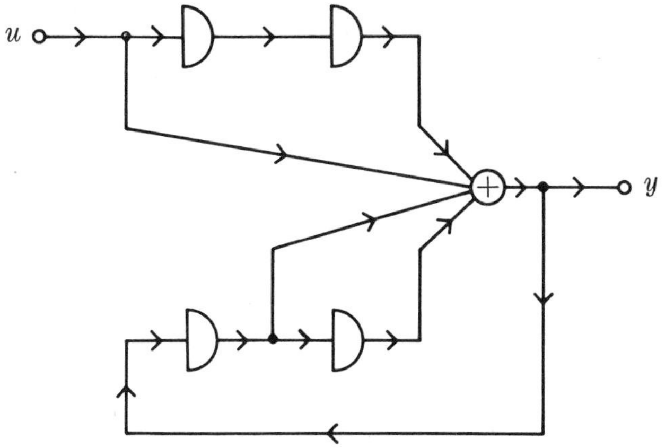

FIG. 2.25—LSC of Example **21–10**

A special case of a finite-memory LSC is an LSC where the output can be predicted on the basis of the inputs only:

21–15
$$\mathbf{y}(t) = f(\mathbf{u}(t), \mathbf{u}(t-1), \ldots, \mathbf{u}(t-\mu))$$

If μ is the least integer satisfying **21–15**, the LSC is called *μ-definite.*

21–16 *Assertion:* $\mathcal{A}$ is μ-definite if and only if μ is the least integer such that $\mathbf{CA}^{\mu} = \mathbf{0}$. If $\mathcal{A}$ is μ-definite, then μ equals at most the degree of the minimum polynominal of **A**.

Proof: From **9–5** it follows that $\mathbf{y}(\mu)$ depends on $\mathbf{u}(\mu)$, $\mathbf{u}(\mu-1)$, . . ., $\mathbf{u}(0)$ only, if and only if $\mathbf{CA}^{\mu}\mathbf{s}(0)$ assumes the same value for all $\mathbf{s}(0)$, hence if and only if $\mathbf{CA}^{\mu} = \mathbf{0}$. Let $m_{\mathrm{A}}(x)$ be as in **21–3**, and let α_j be the first nonzero coefficient. Assume $\mu > r$ is the least integer such that $\mathbf{CA}^{\mu} = \mathbf{0}$. We can write:

21–17 $$\mathbf{CA}^{\mu} = -\alpha_j\mathbf{CA}^{j+\mu-r} - \alpha_{j+1}\mathbf{CA}^{j+1+\mu-r} - \ . \ . \ . \ -\alpha_{r-1}\mathbf{CA}^{\mu-1} = \mathbf{0}$$

or

21–18 $$\begin{aligned} \mathbf{CA}^{\mu+r-j-1} &= -\alpha_j\mathbf{CA}^{\mu-1} - \alpha_{j+1}\mathbf{CA}^{\mu} - \alpha_{j+2}\mathbf{CA}^{\mu+1} - \ . \ . \ . -\alpha_{r-1}\mathbf{CA}^{\mu+r-j-2} \\ &= -\alpha_j\mathbf{CA}^{\mu-1} - \mathbf{CA}^{\mu}(\alpha_{j+1} + \alpha_{j+2}\mathbf{A} + \ . \ . \ . + \alpha_{r-1}\mathbf{A}^{r-j-2}) \\ &= -\alpha_j\mathbf{CA}^{\mu-1} + \mathbf{0} = \mathbf{0} \end{aligned}$$

Hence we must have $\mathbf{CA}^{\mu-1} = \mathbf{0}$. By contradtiction, $\mu \leq r$.

As a direct corollary, we have:

21–19 *Assertion:* If an n-dimensional LSC is μ-definite, then $\mu \leq n$.

An LSC is said to be *information lossless* if its initial state and output sequence uniquely determine the input sequence.

21–20 *Assertion:* $\mathcal{A}$ is information lossless if and only if **D** is of rank l.

Proof: We can write:

21–21 $$\mathbf{y}(0) - \mathbf{Cs}(0) = \mathbf{Du}(0)$$

Given $\mathbf{s}(0)$ and $\mathbf{y}(0)$, $\mathbf{u}(0)$ can be uniquely determined if and only if $\mathbf{Dx} = \mathbf{v}$ is uniquely solvable (for all consistent $\mathbf{v}$), and hence if and only if **D** is of rank l. If $\mathbf{u}(0)$ is determinable, $\mathbf{s}(1) = \mathbf{As}(0) + \mathbf{Bu}(0)$ can be computed and subsequently $\mathbf{u}(\mathbf{1})$ from $\mathbf{y}(1) - \mathbf{Cs}(1) = \mathbf{Du}(1)$. **21–20** then follows by induction.

When $\mathcal{A}$ has only one input terminal ($l = 1$), **21–20** implies that $\mathcal{A}$ is information lossless if and only if **D** is nonzero.

Chapter 3

Autonomous Linear Sequential Circuits

1. Introduction

In this chapter we shall consider LSCs whose output as well as state behavior is independent of the input. Such LSCs will be called *autonomous* LSCs (abbreviated ALSCs). ALSCs may be viewed as ordinary LSCs where the characterizing matrices **B** and **D** happen to be **0**, or, alternatively, where $\mathbf{u}(t)$ is stipulated to remain **0** for all $t \geq 0$. The study of such circuits is motivated by two factors: First, as seen in Sec. **2.9**, the free response of an LSC is obtainable by setting $\mathbf{u}(t) = \mathbf{0}$ for all $t \geq 0$ and, hence, by regarding the LSC as an autonomous one. The study of ALSCs, therefore, is an essential step in the evaluation of the total response of LSCs. Secondly, ALSCs may be regarded (and are indeed utilized extensively) as special devices which independently *generate* sequences of symbols, rather than transform externally applied sequences. The study of ALSCs, therefore, is also the study of the important class of LSCs employed as "sequence generators."

In subsequent sections it is shown how the behavior of ALSCs can be described algebraically. Algorithms are given for constructing ALSCs to yield specified families of outputs, and detailed discussion is presented of the characterization and properties of such families.

The material in this chapter is based in part on the work of Fitzpatrick,[34] Golomb,[49] Kwakernaak,[66] Peterson,[80] and Zierler.[101]

2. Sequences over $GF(p)$

In this and the following chapters we shall deal with time functions $f(t)$ which are defined for non-negative integers t only, and which assume values from $GF(p)$. Such functions will be referred to as *sequences* [over $GF(p)$].

A sequence $f(t) = \alpha_t$ will be displayed in the form

2–1 $$f(t)\colon \alpha_0\alpha_1\alpha_2 \ldots$$

If $f(t) = 0$ for all $t \geq 0$, it is called a *zero sequence*. If $f(t + T) = f(t)$ for all $t \geq \tau$, it is said to have *transience* τ and *period* T; it is displayed in the form

2–2 $$f(t)\colon \alpha_0\alpha_1 \ldots \alpha_{\tau-1}\ \alpha_\tau\alpha_{\tau+1} \ldots \alpha_{\tau+T-1}, \alpha_\tau\alpha_{\tau+1} \ldots \alpha_{\tau+T-1}, \ldots$$

When $\tau = 0$, $f(t)$ is *strictly periodic* (in this case the dot preceding α_τ is omitted). If τ is the least integer such that, for some T, $f(t + T) = f(t)$ for all $t \geq \tau$, then τ is called the *minimal transience* of $f(t)$. If T is the least integer such that, for some τ, $f(t + T) = f(t)$ for all $t \geq \tau$, T is called the *minimal period* of $f(t)$.

If $f(t) = \alpha$ for all $t \geq \tau$, it will be displayed in the form

2-3 $$f(t)\colon \alpha_0\alpha_1 \ . \ . \ . \ \alpha_{\tau-1}\alpha\alpha\alpha \ . \ . \ .$$

When $\alpha = 0$, $f(t)$ is referred to as an *ultimately-zero sequence.*

3. Pseudocanonical Realization of ALSCs

An ALSC over $GF(p)$ is any LSC over $GF(p)$ where $\mathbf{B} = \mathbf{D} = \mathbf{0}$. Its black box representation is shown in Fig. 3.1. In this chapter we shall concern ourselves with the performance of an ALSC at each of its m output terminals. Hence, we shall permit ourselves the replacement of any ALSC $\mathcal{A}$ with the pseudocanonical realization of $\mathcal{A}$, which (as a special case of Fig. 2.18) assumes the form shown in Fig. 3.2. Each subcircuit in this realization is a *simple* ALSC; the simple ALSC with the output y_i can be obtained directly by minimizing $\mathcal{A}$ with respect to the output y_i (i.e., with the ith row of $\mathbf{C}$ substituted for $\mathbf{C}$), using the method of Sec. **2.14**.

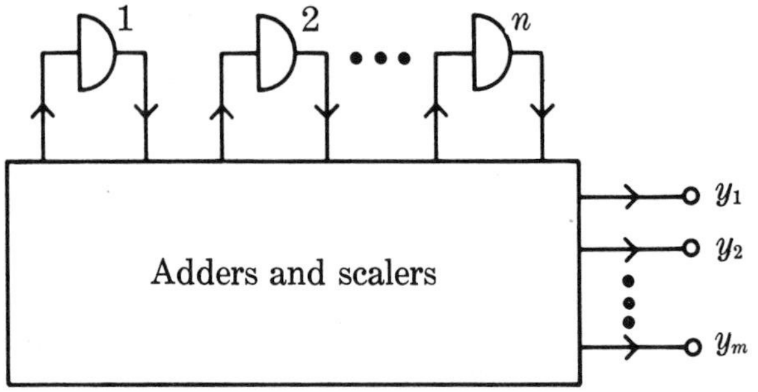

FIG. 3.1—n-dimensional ALSC

Inasmuch as every ALSC can be simulated by the union of simple ALSCs, both the analysis and synthesis of general ALSCs can be carried out most conveniently through the analysis and synthesis of simple ALSCs. From this point on, therefore, our discussion will be limited, by and large, to simple ALSCs.

4. Simple ALSCs

The characteristic matrix of every simple ALSC is the companion matrix of some nonconstant monic polynomial over $GF(p)$, say

4-1 $$\phi(x) = \alpha_0 + \alpha_1 x + \ . \ . \ . \ + \alpha_{n-1}x^{n-1} + x^n$$

(see Fig. 3.3). This polynomial uniquely determines the scaler constant in the feedback lines of the ALSC, and hence uniquely determines the entire structure and performance of the ALSC. It will be called the *feedback polynomial* of the ALSC. If the feedback polynomial $\phi(x)$ of an ALSC is indivisible by x (i.e., $\alpha_0 \neq 0$), the ALSC is said to be *nonsingular;* otherwise it is *singular.*

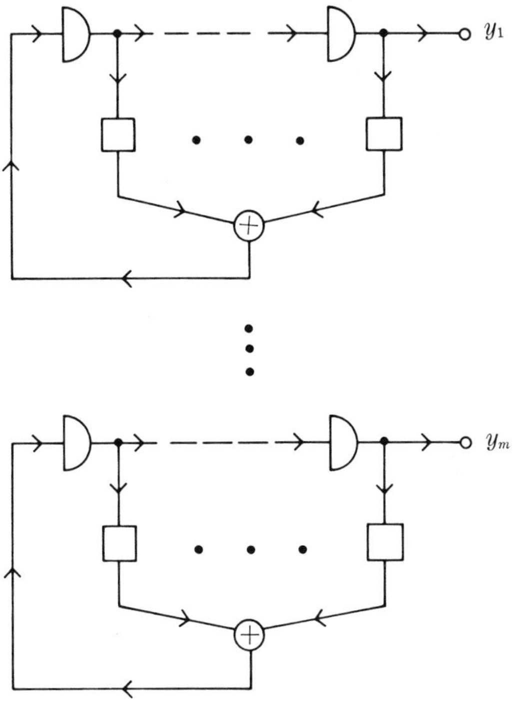

FIG. 3.2—Pseudocanonical realization of ALSC

4–2 *Assertion:* Let $\mathcal{A}$ be an ALSC with the feedback polynomial $\phi(x)$ of **4–1**. The sequence

4–3 $$y(t)\colon\ y_0y_1y_2y_3\ .\ .\ .$$

[over $GF(p)$] is an output sequence of $\mathcal{A}$ if and only if, for all $t \geq 0$,

4–4 $$y_{t+n} = -\alpha_0 y_t - \alpha_1 y_{t+1} - \ .\ .\ .\ - \alpha_{n-1} y_{t+n-1}$$

Proof: As is evident from Fig. 3.3, at any time $t + \nu$ $(0 \leq \nu \leq n - 1)$ the output of $\mathcal{A}$ is the output of delayer $\nu + 1$ as observed at time t. Hence, if $y(t)$ of **4–3** is an output sequence of $\mathcal{A}$, it must satisfy **4–4**. The solution of **4–4** is uniquely determined by the "initial conditions" $y_0, y_1, \ldots, y_{n-1}$, i.e., by the initial state of $\mathcal{A}$:

4–5 $$\mathbf{s}(0) = \begin{pmatrix} y_0 \\ y_1 \\ \cdot \\ \cdot \\ \cdot \\ y_{n-1} \end{pmatrix}$$

Since there are p^n distinct $\mathbf{s}(0)$, there are p^n distinct sequences $y(t)$ satisfying **4–4**. On the other hand, since the output of an ALSC is uniquely determined by its initial state, $\mathcal{A}$ generates p^n distinct output sequences $y(t)$. Hence, if $y(t)$ of **4–3** satisfies **4–4**, it must be an output sequence of $\mathcal{A}$.

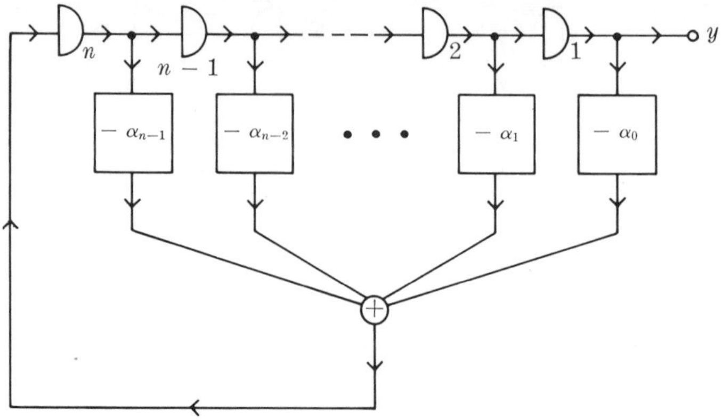

FIG. 3.3—Simple ALSC realizing $\mathbf{M}_{\alpha_0+\alpha_1 x+ \ldots +\alpha_{n-1}x^{n-1}+x^n}$

4–4 is called the *recurrence equation* of $\mathcal{A}$, and any of its solutions a *linear recursive sequence* corresponding to $\phi(x)$. Thus, **4–2** states that a sequence is an output sequence of $\mathcal{A}$ if and only if it is a linear recursive sequence corresponding to $\phi(x)$.

5. Output of Nonsingular Simple ALSC

In what follows, the ring of polynomials over $GF(p)$ modulo the polynomial $1 - x^T$ will be denoted by $R_{1-\xi^T}$ (see Sec. **1.9**). In accordance with our convention, the elements of $R_{1-\xi^T}$ will be written as polynomials in ξ. If $g(x)$ is a polynomial of degree $T - n$ $(0 < n \leq T)$, the ideal generated by $g(\xi)$ in $R_{1-\xi^T}$ is a vector space over $GF(p)$ with a basis $\{g(\xi), \xi g(\xi), \xi^2 g(\xi), \ldots, \xi^{n-1} g(\xi)\}$ (see **1.11–7**). This ideal will be denoted by $(g(\xi))_T$.

Let $y(t) = y_t$ be any purely periodic sequence over $GF(p)$ of period T:

5–1 $$y(t)\colon\ y_0 y_1 \ldots y_{T-1}, y_0 y_1 \ldots y_{T-1}, \ldots$$

Such a sequence can be uniquely associated with an element of $R_{1-\xi^T}$ given by

5–2 $$Y(\xi) = y_0\xi^{T-1} + y_1\xi^{T-2} + \ldots + y_{T-2}\xi + y_{T-1}$$

$Y(\xi)$ will be said to *ring-represent* $y(t)$.

Consider a nonsingular simple ALSC $\mathcal{A}$ with the feedback polynomial $\phi(x)$ as given in **4–1**. Since $\phi(x)$ is indivisible by x, one can always find an integer i such that $\phi(x)$ divides $1 - x^i$. The least such i, namely the *exponent* of $\phi(x)$ (see **1.8–1**), will be denoted by T. The polynomial

5–3 $$g(x) = \frac{1 - x^T}{\phi(x)}$$

will be called the *generator polynomial* of $\mathcal{A}$.

5–4 *Assertion:* Let $\mathcal{A}$ be a nonsingular simple ALSC with the feedback polynomial $\phi(x)$ and generator polynomial $g(x) = (1 - x^T)/\phi(x)$. Then all output sequences of $\mathcal{A}$ are purely periodic with period T. Moreover, a sequence is an output sequence of $\mathcal{A}$ if and only if it is ring-represented by an element of $(g(\xi))_T$.

Proof: Consider any sequence $y(t)$ as in **5–1**, such that $Y(\xi)$ of **5–2** is an element of $(g(\xi))_T$. Let $\phi(x)$ be given as in **4–1**, and compute

5–5
$$\begin{aligned}\phi(\xi)Y(\xi) &= (\alpha_0 + \alpha_1\xi + \ldots + \alpha_{n-1}\xi^{n-1} + \xi^n)\cdot(y_{T-1} + y_{T-2}\xi \\ &\qquad + \ldots + y_1\xi^{T-2} + y_0\xi^{T-1}) \\ &= \epsilon_0 + \epsilon_1\xi + \ldots + \epsilon_{T-2}\xi^{T-2} + \epsilon_{T-1}\xi^{T-1}\end{aligned}$$

Equating coefficients, for $n \le \nu \le T-1$ we have

5–6
$$\epsilon_\nu = \alpha_0 y_{T-1-\nu} + \alpha_1 y_{T-\nu} + \alpha_2 y_{T+1-\nu} + \ldots + \alpha_{n-1}y_{T+n-2-\nu} + y_{T+n-1-\nu}$$

Since $1 - \xi^T = 0$, $\xi^{T+\nu} = \xi^\nu$ and hence, for $0 \le \nu < n$ we have

5–7
$$\begin{aligned}\epsilon_\nu = {}& \alpha_0 y_{T-1-\nu} + \alpha_1 y_{T-\nu} + \alpha_2 y_{T+1-\nu} + \ldots + \alpha_\nu y_{T-1} \\ &+ \alpha_{\nu+1}y_0 + \alpha_{\nu+2}y_1 + \ldots + \alpha_{n-1}y_{n-\nu-2} + y_{n-\nu-1}\end{aligned}$$

Since $Y(\xi)$ is in $(g(\xi))_T$, it is a multiple of $g(\xi)$ and hence $\phi(\xi)Y(\xi)$ is a multiple of $\phi(\xi)g(\xi) = 1 - \xi^T = 0$. Thus, for all ν, $\epsilon_\nu = 0$ and **5–6** and **5–7** yield, respectively:

5–8
$$y_{T+n-1-\nu} = -\alpha_0 y_{T-1-\nu} - \alpha_1 y_{T-\nu} - \alpha_2 y_{T+1-\nu} - \ldots - \alpha_{n-1}y_{T+n-2-\nu}$$
$$(\nu = n, n+1, \ldots, T-1)$$

5–9
$$\begin{aligned}y_{n-\nu-1} = {}& -\alpha_0 y_{T-1-\nu} - \alpha_1 y_{T-\nu} - \alpha_2 y_{T+1-\nu} - \ldots - \alpha_\nu y_{T-1} \\ &- \alpha_{\nu+1}y_0 - \alpha_{\nu+2}y_1 - \ldots - \alpha_{n-1}y_{n-\nu-2}\end{aligned}$$
$$(\nu = 0, 1, \ldots, n-1)$$

Substituting t for $T - 1 - \nu$ in **5–8**, and for $-\nu - 1$ in **5–9**, we have, respectively:

5–10
$$y_{t+n} = -\alpha_0 y_t - \alpha_1 y_{t+1} - \ldots - \alpha_{n-1}y_{t+n-1}$$
$$(t = 0, 1, \ldots, T-n-1)$$

5–11
$$\begin{aligned}y_{t+n} = {}& -\alpha_0 y_{T+t} - \alpha_1 y_{T+t+1} - \ldots - \alpha_{-t-1}y_{T-1} \\ &- \alpha_{-t}y_0 - \alpha_{-t+1}y_1 - \ldots - \alpha_{n-1}y_{n+t-1}\end{aligned}$$
$$(t = -n, -n+1, \ldots, -1)$$

Since $y(t)$ is purely periodic with period T, t can be replaced with $t \pm T$, and **5–11** can be written as

5–12
$$y_{t+n} = -\alpha_0 y_t - \alpha_1 y_{t+1} - \ldots - \alpha_{n-1}y_{t+n-1}$$
$$(t = T-n, T-n+1, \ldots, T-1)$$

Combining **5–10** and **5–12**, it follows that $y(t)$ satisfies the recurrence equation corresponding to $\phi(x)$ for $t = 0, 1, \ldots, T-1$, and hence—by the periodicity of $y(t)$—for all $t \ge 0$. Thus, if $Y(\xi)$ is an element of $(g(\xi))_T$, $y(t)$ is an output sequence of $\mathcal{A}$. Since the order of $(g(\xi))_T$ is the same as the number of distinct output sequences of $\mathcal{A}$ (namely p^n), it follows that if $y(t)$ is an output sequence of $\mathcal{A}$ then $Y(\xi)$ must be an element of $(g(\xi))_T$.

$(g(\xi))_T$ is called the *output ideal* of $\mathcal{A}$; it uniquely represents the set of output sequences generated by $\mathcal{A}$.

5–13 *Example:* $\mathcal{A}$ is a 4-dimensional nonsingular simple ALSC over $GF(2)$, with the feedback polynomial

5–14
$$\phi(x) = 1 + x + x^3 + x^4 = (1-x)^2(1 + x + x^2)$$

(see Fig. 3.4). The exponent of $(1 + x)^2$ is 2, while the exponent of $1 + x + x^2$ is 3; the exponent T of $\phi(x)$, therefore, is 6 (see **1.8–2**). Hence, the generator polynomial of $\mathcal{A}$ is

5–15 $$g(x) = \frac{1 + x^6}{1 + x + x^3 + x^4} = 1 + x + x^2$$

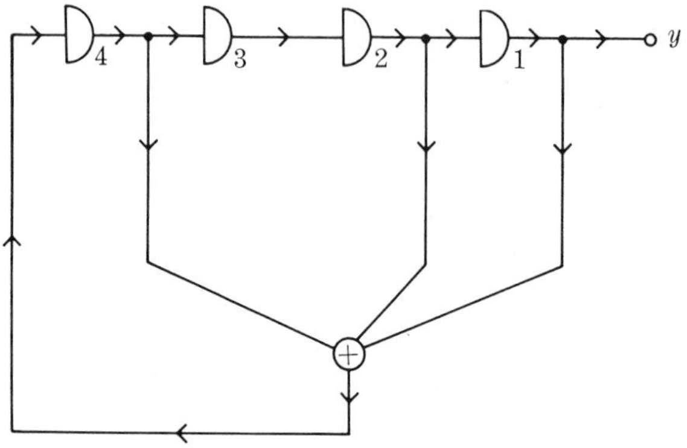

FIG. 3.4—ALSC over $GF(2)$

The output ideal of $\mathcal{A}$ is $(1 + \xi + \xi^2)_6$, with a basis

5–16
$$\begin{aligned} \xi^3 g(\xi) &= \xi^5 + \xi^4 + \xi^3 \\ \xi^2 g(\xi) &= \xi^4 + \xi^3 + \xi^2 \\ \xi g(\xi) &= \xi^3 + \xi^2 + \xi \\ g(\xi) &= \xi^2 + \xi + 1 \end{aligned}$$

The $2^4 = 16$ linear combinations of the polynomials in **5–16** ring-represent the 16 possible output sequences of $\mathcal{A}$. For example,

5–17 $$Y(\xi) = g(\xi) + \xi^2 g(\xi) + \xi^3 g(\xi) = \xi^5 + \xi + 1$$

ring-represents the output sequence

5–18 $$y(t)\colon\ 100011,\ 100011,\ \ldots$$

6. The Generator Matrix

Let $\mathcal{A}$ be a nonsingular simple ALSC with the feedback polynomial $\phi(x)$ of degree n, and the generator polynomial

6–1 $$g(x) = \frac{1 - x^T}{\phi(x)} = \gamma_0 x^{T-n} + \gamma_1 x^{T-n-1} + \ldots + \gamma_{T-n-1} x + \gamma_{T-n}$$

The *generator matrix* of $\mathcal{A}$ is an $n \times T$ matrix $\mathbf{G}$ whose (i,j) element is the coefficient of ξ^{T-j} in $\xi^{n-i} g(\xi)$:

6–2 $$\mathbf{G} = \begin{pmatrix} \gamma_0 & \gamma_1 & \ldots & \gamma_{T-n-1} & \gamma_{T-n} & & & \\ & \gamma_0 & \gamma_1 & \ldots & \gamma_{T-n-1} & \gamma_{T-n} & & \\ & & \cdot & & & & & \\ & & & \cdot & & & & \\ & & & & \cdot & & & \\ & & & \gamma_0 & \gamma_1 & \ldots & \gamma_{T-n-1} & \gamma_{T-n} \end{pmatrix}$$

Since $\xi^{n-1}g(\xi), \xi^{n-2}g(\xi), \ldots, \xi g(\xi), g(\xi)$ form a basis for $(g(\xi))_T$, it follows that the sequence

6–3 $$y(t)\colon y_0y_1 \ldots y_{T-1}, y_0y_1 \ldots y_{T-1}, \ldots$$

is an output sequence of $\mathcal{A}$ if and only if the vector $(y_0, y_1, \ldots, y_{T-1})$ is in the row space of **G**.

The generator matrix can be partitioned as follows:

6–4 $$\mathbf{G} = (\mathbf{G}_1, \mathbf{G}_2)$$

where $\mathbf{G}_1$ is $n \times n$. Since $\gamma_0 \neq 0$, $\mathbf{G}_1$ is triangular with nonzero elements on the principal diagonal; hence $\mathbf{G}_1$ is nonsingular.

6–5 *Assertion:* Let $\mathcal{A}$ be a nonsingular ALSC with the $n \times T$ generator matrix **G**. If the initial state of $\mathcal{A}$ is $\mathbf{s}(0)$, then the ith output of $\mathcal{A}$ ($i = 1, 2, \ldots, T$) is given by the ith element of

6–6 $$[\mathbf{s}(0)]^{\mathrm{TR}}(\mathbf{I}_n, \mathbf{G}_1^{-1}\mathbf{G}_2)$$

Proof: The ith output of $\mathcal{A}$ ($i = 1, 2, \ldots, n$) is given by the ith element of $[\mathbf{s}(0)]^{\mathrm{TR}}$. Hence, $[\mathbf{s}(0)]^{\mathrm{TR}}$ must be some linear combination of rows of $\mathbf{G}_1$, say

6–7 $$[\mathbf{s}(0)]^{\mathrm{TR}} = \mathbf{v}\mathbf{G}_1$$

Explicitly:

6–8 $$\mathbf{v} = [\mathbf{s}(0)]^{\mathrm{TR}}\mathbf{G}_1^{-1}$$

The ith output of $\mathcal{A}$ ($i = 1, 2, \ldots, T$) must be the same linear combination of **G**:

6–9 $$\mathbf{v}\mathbf{G} = [\mathbf{s}(0)]^{\mathrm{TR}}\mathbf{G}_1^{-1}(\mathbf{G}_1, \mathbf{G}_2) = [\mathbf{s}(0)]^{\mathrm{TR}}(\mathbf{I}_n, \mathbf{G}_1^{-1}\mathbf{G}_2)$$

6–5 facilitates the determination of the particular output of $\mathcal{A}$ corresponding to any specified initial state. The converse problem—determining the initial state for any specified output sequence (realizable by $\mathcal{A}$)—can be trivially solved via **4–5**.

6–10 *Example:* For the ALSC of Example **5–13**, we have:

6–11 $$\mathbf{G} = \underbrace{\begin{pmatrix} 1 & 1 & 1 & \\ & 1 & 1 & 1 \\ & & 1 & 1 \\ & & & 1 \end{pmatrix}}_{\mathbf{G}_1}\underbrace{\begin{matrix} & \\ & \\ 1 & \\ 1 & 1 \end{matrix}}_{\mathbf{G}_2} \qquad \mathbf{G}_1^{-1} = \begin{pmatrix} 1 & 1 & 0 & 1 \\ 0 & 1 & 1 & 0 \\ 0 & 0 & 1 & 1 \\ 0 & 0 & 0 & 1 \end{pmatrix}$$

If

6–12 $$\mathbf{s}(0) = \begin{pmatrix} 0 \\ 1 \\ 0 \\ 1 \end{pmatrix}$$

then

6–13 $$[\mathbf{s}(0)]^{\mathrm{TR}}(\mathbf{I}_n, \mathbf{G}_1^{-1}\mathbf{G}_2) = (0, 1, 0, 1)\left(\begin{array}{cccc|cc} 1 & & & & 1 & 1 \\ & 1 & & & 1 & 0 \\ & & 1 & & 0 & 1 \\ & & & 1 & 1 & 1 \end{array}\right)$$
$$= (0, 1, 0, 1, 0, 1)$$

Hence, the output sequence is

6–14 $$y(t)\colon 010101, 010101, \ldots$$

7. Periods of Output Sequences

Let $\mathcal{A}$ be an n-dimensional nonsingular simple ALSC with the feedback polynomial $\phi(x)$ and generator polynomial $g(x) = (1 - x^T)/\phi(x)$. By **5–4**, all output sequences of $\mathcal{A}$ have period T; they may, however, have minimal periods which properly divide T. The following shows that at least one output sequence has minimal period not less than T:

7–1 *Assertion:* The output sequence which is ring-represented by $g(\xi)$ has minimal period T.

Proof: Let $y(t)$ be the output sequence ring-represented by $g(\xi)$, and assume that $y(t)$ has period T', a proper divisor of T. Hence we can write

7–2 $$g(\xi) = g'(\xi)(1 + \xi^{T'} + \xi^{2T'} + \ldots + \xi^{T-T'})$$

where $g'(\xi)$ is of degree at most $T' - 1$. Since both sides of **7–2** are of degree less than T, **7–2** implies

7–3 $$g(x) = g'(x)(1 + x^{T'} + x^{2T'} + \ldots + x^{T-T'}) = g'(x)\frac{1 - x^T}{1 - x^{T'}}$$

or

7–4 $$1 - x^{T'} = g'(x)\frac{1 - x^T}{g(x)} = g'(x)\phi(x)$$

7–4 implies that there exists an integer $T' < T$ such that $\phi(x)$ divides $1 - x^{T'}$. This contradicts the definition of T and hence invalidates the assumption that T' is a proper divisor of T.

Note that the output sequences ring-represented by $g(\xi)$ has $00 \ldots 0\gamma_0$ for the first n symbols ($\gamma_0 \neq 0$). Hence, an output sequence of minimal period T can always be generated by imposing on $\mathcal{A}$ an initial state which is 0 in all coordinates except the nth.

The following facilitates the determination of all output sequences of $\mathcal{A}$ which have any specified period T' dividing T.

7–5 *Assertion:* Let T' be any divisor of T, and define

7–6 $$\phi'(x) = \gcd(1 - x^{T'}, \phi(x))$$

A sequence of period T' is an output sequence of $\mathcal{A}$ if and only if it is ring-represented by an element of $(g'(\xi)(1 + \xi^{T'} + \xi^{2T'} + \ldots + \xi^{T-T'}))_T$, where

7–7 $$g'(x) = \frac{1 - x^{T'}}{\phi'(x)}$$

Proof: Let $y(t)$ be a sequence over $GF(p)$, ring-represented by $Y(\xi)$ in $R_{1-\xi^T}$. If the period of $y(t)$ is T' (some divisor of T), then we can write

7–8 $$Y(\xi) = Y'(\xi)(1 + \xi^{T'} + \xi^{2T'} + \ldots + \xi^{T-T'})$$

where $Y'(\xi)$ is of degree at most $T' - 1$. By **5–4**, $y(t)$ is an output sequence of $\mathcal{A}$ if and only if $Y(\xi)$ is a multiple of $g(\xi)$; hence if and only if

7–9 $$\begin{aligned} Y(x) &= Y'(x)(1 + x^{T'} + x^{2T'} + \ldots + x^{T-T'}) \\ &= Y'(x)\frac{1 - x^T}{1 - x^{T'}} = Y'(x)\frac{\phi(x)}{1 - x^{T'}}\,\frac{1 - x^T}{\phi(x)} \\ &= Y'(x)\frac{\phi(x)}{1 - x^{T'}}g(x) = Y'(x)\frac{q(x)}{g'(x)}g(x) \end{aligned}$$

(where $q(x) = \phi(x)/\phi'(x)$) is a polynomial of degree at most $n - 1$; hence if and only if $Y'(x)$ is a multiple of $g'(x)$ of degree at most $T' - 1$; hence if and only if $Y(x)$ is a multiple of $g'(x)(1 + x^{T'} + x^{2T'} + \dots + x^{T-T'})$ of degree at most $T - 1$, which, by **1.11–7**, implies **7–5**. (Note that when $T' = T$, $\phi'(x) = \phi(x)$ and $g'(x) = g(x)$, as expected in view of **7–1**).

7–10 *Assertion:* If $\phi(x)$ is irreducible, then all nonzero output sequences of $\mathcal{A}$ have minimal period T.

Proof: By definition of T, $\phi(x)$ does not divide $1 - x^{T'}$ for any $T' < T$. Thus, if $\phi(x)$ is irreducible, we must have $\phi'(x) = \gcd\,(1 - x^{T'}, \phi(x)) = 1$ and $g'(x) = 1 - x^{T'}$. By **7–5**, all output sequences of period T' are included in $((1 - \xi^{T'})(1 + \xi^{T'} + \dots + \xi^{T-T'}))_T = (0)_T$. Since $(0)_T$ ring-represents the zero sequence only, **7–10** follows.

7–11 *Example.* Let $\mathcal{A}$ be a 5-dimensional nonsingular simple ALSC over $GF(2)$, with the feedback polynomial

7–12 $$\phi(x) = 1 + x + x^2 + x^3 + x^4 + x^5 = (1 + x)(1 + x + x^2)^2$$

The exponent of $1 + x$ is 1, the exponent of $1 + x + x^2$ is 3, and hence the exponent T of $\phi(x)$ is 6. For $T' = T = 6$, $\phi'(x) = \phi(x)$ and

7–13 $$g'(x) = g(x) = \frac{1 + x^6}{1 + x + x^2 + x^3 + x^4 + x^5} = 1 + x$$

Hence $(g'(\xi)(1 + \xi^{T'} + \dots + \xi^{T-T'}))_T = (1 + \xi)_6$. The output sequences of period 6 can be represented by the generator matrix

7–14 $$\mathbf{G}' = \mathbf{G} = \begin{pmatrix} 1 & 1 & & & & \\ & 1 & 1 & & & \\ & & 1 & 1 & & \\ & & & 1 & 1 & \\ & & & & 1 & 1 \end{pmatrix}$$

For $T' = 3$,

7–15 $$\phi'(x) = \gcd\,(1 + x^3, 1 + x + \dots + x^5) = 1 + x^3$$

7–16 $$g'(x) = \frac{1 + x^3}{1 + x^3} = 1$$

7–17 $$(g'(\xi)(1 + \xi^3))_6 = (1 + \xi^3)_6$$

The output sequences of period 3 can be represented by

7–18 $$\mathbf{G}' = \begin{pmatrix} 1 & & & 1 & & \\ & 1 & & & 1 & \\ & & 1 & & & 1 \end{pmatrix}$$

For $T' = 2$,

7–19 $$\phi'(x) = \gcd\,(1 + x^2, 1 + x + \dots + x^5) = 1 + x$$

7–20 $$g'(x) = \frac{1 + x^2}{1 + x} = 1 + x$$

7–21 $$(g'(\xi)(1 + \xi^2 + \xi^4))_6 = (1 + \xi + \xi^2 + \xi^3 + \xi^4 + \xi^5)_6$$

The output sequences of period 2 can be represented by

7–22 $$\mathrm{G}' = (1, 1, 1, 1, 1, 1)$$

For $T' = 1$,

7–23 $$\phi'(x) = \gcd(1 + x, 1 + x + \ldots + x^5) = 1 + x$$

7–24 $$g'(x) = \frac{1 + x}{1 + x} = 1$$

7–25 $$(g'(\xi)(1 + \xi + \xi^2 + \xi^3 + \xi^4 + \xi^5))_6 = (1 + \xi + \xi^2 + \xi^3 + \xi^4 + \xi^5)_6$$

which is the same as the ideal found for $T' = 2$.

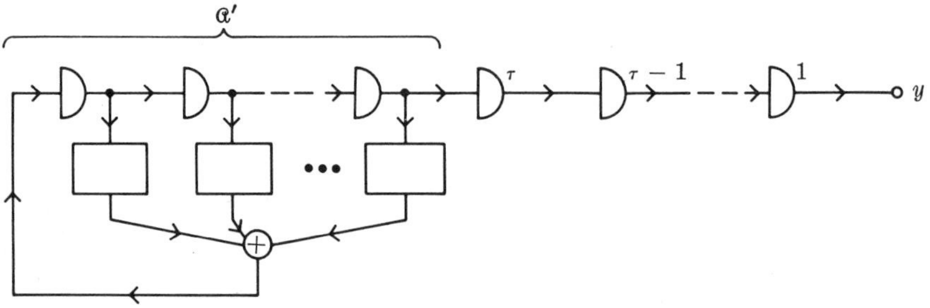

FIG. 3.5—Arbitrary simple ALSC

8. Output of Arbitrary Simple ALSC

If $\mathcal{A}$ is an arbitrary simple ALSC, its feedback polynomial has the general form

8–1 $$\phi(x) = x^\tau \phi'(x)$$

where $\phi'(x)$ is indivisible by x. $\mathcal{A}$, therefore, consists, in general, of a nonsingular ALSC $\mathcal{A}'$ whose feedback polynomial is $\phi'(x)$, feeding into a feedback-free string of τ delayers, as shown in Fig. 3.5 ($\mathcal{A}'$ is absent when $\phi'(x) = 1$; the string is absent when $\tau = 0$). Thus, the output sequences of $\mathcal{A}$ are those of $\mathcal{A}'$, prefixed by a string of τ symbols; the prefix can assume any of the p^τ possible forms, depending on the initial contents of delayers $1, 2, \ldots, \tau$. The generalization of **5–4** follows immediately:

8–2 *Assertion:* Let $\mathcal{A}$ be a simple ALSC with the feedback polynomial $x^\tau\phi'(x)$, where $\phi'(x)$ is indivisible by x and of exponent T. Let $g'(x) = (1 - x^T)/\phi'(x)$. Then the sequence

8–3 $$y(t)\colon\ y_0y_1 \ldots y_{\tau-1}\cdot y'_0y'_1 \ldots y'_{T-1},\ y'_0y'_1 \ldots y'_{T-1}, \ldots$$

[over $GF(p)$] is an output sequence of $\mathcal{A}$ if and only if the sequence

8–4 $$y'(t)\colon\ y'_0y'_1 \ldots y'_{T-1},\ y'_0y'_1 \ldots y'_{T-1}, \ldots$$

is ring-represented by an element of $(g'(\xi))_T$.

If $\mathcal{A}$ is n-dimensional, the knowledge of $y(0), y(1), \ldots, y(n - 1)$ yields—via **4–5**—the corresponding initial state of $\mathcal{A}$. When the initial state is known, the prefix $y_0y_1 \ldots y_{\tau-1}$ can be found directly from the first τ elements of the state; $y'(t)$ can be found from the remaining $n - \tau$ elements and the generating matrix of $\mathcal{A}'$, as shown in **6–5**.

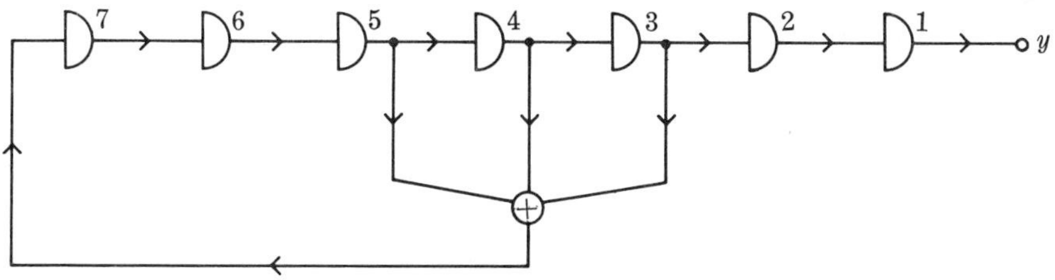

FIG. 3.6—ALSC over $GF(2)$

8–5 *Example:* The ALSC $\mathcal{A}$ over $GF(2)$ shown in Fig. 3.6 has the feedback polynomial

8–6 $$\phi(x) = x^2 + x^3 + x^4 + x^7 = x^2(1 + x + x^2 + x^5)$$

In this case,

8–7 $$\phi'(x) = 1 + x + x^2 + x^5 = (1 + x)^2(1 + x + x^3),\ T = 14$$

8–8 $$g'(x) = \frac{1 + x^{14}}{1 + x + x^2 + x^5} = 1 + x + x^3 + x^4 + x^5 + x^6 + x^9$$

and hence every output sequence of $\mathcal{A}$ consists of a prefix of 2 symbols from $GF(2)$, followed by a purely periodic sequence of period 14 which is ring-represented by an element in $(1 + \xi + \xi^3 + \xi^4 + \xi^5 + \xi^6 + \xi^9)_{14}$.

9. ALSCs for Specified Purely Periodic Sequences

The following shows that, given any finite set of purely periodic sequences over $GF(p)$, a simple ALSC (of least dimension) can be found which generates this set.

9–1 *Assertion:* Let $y^1(t), y^2(t), \ldots, y^r(t)$ be purely periodic sequences over $GF(p)$, where $y^i(t)$ has the minimal period T_i. Let $T = \text{lcm}\,(T_1, T_2, \ldots, T_r)$, and let $y^i(t)$ be ring-represented by the polynomial $Y^i(\xi)$ in $R_{1-\xi^T}$. Let

9–2 $$g(x) = \text{gcd}\,(1 - x^T, Y^1(x), Y^2(x), \ldots, Y^r(x))$$

Then an ALSC of least dimension generating $y^1(t), y^2(t), \ldots, y^r(t)$ is a nonsingular simple ALSC whose feedback polynomial is $\phi(x) = (1 - x^T)/g(x)$.

Proof: Let $\mathcal{A}'$ be a least-dimensional ALSC generating the sequences $y^i(t)$. Without loss in generality it may be assumed that $\mathcal{A}'$ is simple. Since the $y^i(t)$ are purely periodic, $\mathcal{A}'$ (being least-dimensional) must be nonsingular. If $\phi'(x)$ is the feedback polynomial of $\mathcal{A}'$, the exponent T' of $\phi'(x)$ must be a multiple of every T_i, and hence a multiple of $\text{lcm}\,(T_1, T_2, \ldots, T_r) = T$. Let $g'(x) = (1 - x^{T'})/\phi'(x)$. Then every polynomial

9–3 $$\overline{Y}^i(\xi) = Y^i(\xi)(1 + \xi^T + \xi^{2T} + \ldots + \xi^{T'-T})$$

(of degree at most T', ring-representing $y^i(t)$ in $R_{1-\xi^{T'}}$) must be an element of $(g'(\xi))_{T'}$, and hence a multiple of $g'(\xi)$. Thus, $g'(x)$ must divide all polynomials

9–4 $$\overline{Y}^i(x) = Y^i(x)(1 + x^T + x^{2T} + \ldots + x^{T'-T})$$

as well as

9–5 $$1 - x^{T'} = (1 - x^T)(1 + x^T + x^{2T} + \ldots + x^{T'-T})$$

Hence, $g'(x)$ must divide

9–6
$$\begin{aligned}&\gcd\,((1 - x^T)(1 + \ldots + x^{T'-T}),\ Y^1(x)(1 + \ldots + x^{T'-T}),\\ &\quad Y^2(x)(1 + \ldots + x^{T'-T}),\ \ldots,\ Y^r(x)(1 + \ldots + x^{T'-T}))\\ &= (1 + \ldots + x^{T'-T})\gcd\,(1 - x^T,\ Y^1(x),\ Y^2(x),\ \ldots,\ Y^r(x))\\ &= (1 + x^T + x^{2T} + \ldots + x^{T'-T})g(x)\end{aligned}$$

(where $g(x)$ is as defined in **9–2**). Thus, we must have, with an arbitrary $a(x)$,

9–7
$$\begin{aligned}\phi'(x) &= \frac{1 - x^{T'}}{g'(x)} = \frac{1 - x^{T'}}{(1 + x^T + x^{2T} + \ldots + x^{T'-T})g(x)/a(x)}\\ &= \frac{1 - x^T}{g(x)/a(x)} = a(x)\phi(x)\end{aligned}$$

Since $\phi'(x)$ is of least degree (and $\mathfrak{A}'$ of least dimension) when $a(x) = 1$, we have $\phi'(x) = \phi(x)$, and hence $\mathfrak{A}'$ is precisely the ALSC specified in **9–1**.

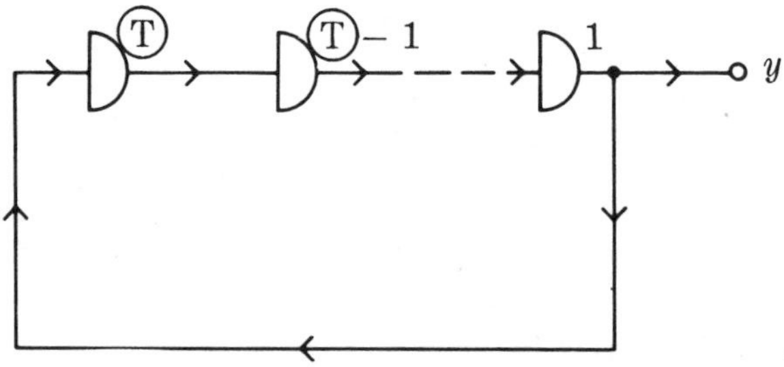

FIG. 3.7—Circulating shift register

When $g(x) = 1$ (the "worst" case), $\phi(x) = 1 - x^T$. Equivalently, we may take $\phi(x) = -1 + x^T$, which corresponds to a simple ALSC such as shown in Fig. 3.7 (and commonly known as a "circulating shift register").

9–8 *Example:* Consider the following purely periodic sequences (of minimal periods 7 and 14, respectively) over $GF(2)$:

9–9 $y^1(t)$: 0101110,0101110, . . .
$y^2(t)$: 11101100001001,11101100001001, . . .

In this case $T = 14$, and

9–10
$$\begin{aligned}Y^1(\xi) &= \xi^{12} + \xi^{10} + \xi^9 + \xi^8 + \xi^5 + \xi^3 + \xi^2 + \xi\\ Y^2(\xi) &= \xi^{13} + \xi^{12} + \xi^{11} + \xi^9 + \xi^8 + \xi^3 + 1\end{aligned}$$

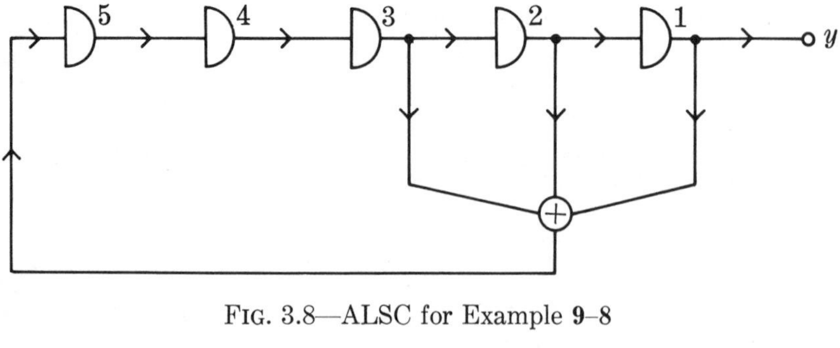

FIG. 3.8—ALSC for Example **9–8**

9–11
$$g(x) = \gcd\,(1 + x^{14}, Y^1(x), Y^2(x)) = 1 + x + x^3 + x^4 + x^5 + x^6 + x^9$$

9–12
$$\phi(x) = \frac{1 + x^{14}}{g(x)} = 1 + x + x^2 + x^5$$

The ALSC whose feedback polynomial is $1 + x + x^2 + x^5$ is shown in Fig. 3.8.

10. ALSCs for Specified Periodic Sequences

The generalization of **9–1** to periodic (but not necessarily purely periodic) sequences follows directly from **8–2**:

10–1 *Assertion:* Let $y^1(t), y^2(t), \ldots, y^r(t)$ be periodic sequences over $GF(p)$, where $y^i(t)$ has the minimal transience τ_i and minimal period T_i. Let $T = \text{lcm}\,(T_1, T_2, \ldots, T_r)$ and $\tau = \max\,(\tau_1, \tau_2, \ldots, \tau_r)$. If

10–2
$$y^i(t):\ y_0^i y_1^i \ldots y_{\tau-1}^i \cdot \bar{y}_0^i \bar{y}_1^i \ldots \bar{y}_{T-1}^i,\ \bar{y}_0^i \bar{y}_1^i \ldots \bar{y}_{T-1}^i, \ldots$$

let

10–3
$$\bar{y}^i(t):\ \bar{y}_0^i \bar{y}_1^i \ldots \bar{y}_{T-1}^i,\ \bar{y}_0^i \bar{y}_1^i \ldots \bar{y}_{T-1}^i, \ldots$$

be ring-represented by the polynomial $\bar{Y}^i(\xi)$ in $R_{1-\xi^T}$. Let

10–4
$$g'(x) = \gcd\,(1 - x^T, \bar{Y}^1(x), \bar{Y}^2(x), \ldots, \bar{Y}^r(x))$$

Then an ALSC of least dimension generating $y^1(t), y^2(t), \ldots, y^r(t)$ is a simple ALSC whose feedback polynomial is $x^\tau \phi'(x)$, where $\phi'(x) = (1 - x^T)/g'(x)$.

Thus, given any finite set of periodic sequences over $GF(p)$, a simple ALSC can be found (of least dimension) which generates this set.

10–5 *Example:* Consider the following periodic sequences (of minimal transiences 2 and 1, respectively, and minimal periods 7 and 14, respectively) over $GF(2)$:

10–6
$$y^1(t):\ 01.0101110,0101110, \ldots$$
$$y^2(t):\ 1.11110110000100,11110110000100, \ldots$$

In this case $\tau = 2$, $T = 14$, and $\bar{y}^1(t)$ and $\bar{y}^2(t)$ become the purely periodic sequences displayed in **9–9**. By **9–12**, a least-dimensional ALSC generating the sequences of **10–6** is a simple ALSC whose feedback polynomial is $x^2(1 + x + x^2 + x^5)$ (see Fig. 3.6).

11. Coverage of Simple ALSCs

An ALSC $\mathfrak{A}$ is said to *cover* an ALSC $\tilde{\mathfrak{A}}$ if all output sequences generated by $\tilde{\mathfrak{A}}$ can be generated by $\mathfrak{A}$.

11–1 *Assertion:* Let $\mathfrak{A}$ and $\tilde{\mathfrak{A}}$ be simple ALSCs with the feedback polynomials $\phi(x)$ and $\tilde{\phi}(x)$, respectively. Then $\mathfrak{A}$ covers $\tilde{\mathfrak{A}}$ if and only if $\phi(x)$ is a multiple of $\tilde{\phi}(x)$.

Proof: Suppose $\mathfrak{A}$ and $\tilde{\mathfrak{A}}$ have the feedback polynomials $\phi(x) = x^\tau \phi'(x)$ and $\tilde{\phi}(x) = x^{\tilde{\tau}} \tilde{\phi}'(x)$, respectively, where $\phi'(x)$ and $\tilde{\phi}'(x)$ are indivisible by x and are associated with the nonsingular ALSCs $\mathfrak{A}'$ and $\tilde{\mathfrak{A}}'$, respectively (see Fig. 3.5). Since $\mathfrak{A}$ must be capable of generating all $p^{\tilde{\tau}}$ ultimately-zero sequences generated by $\tilde{\mathfrak{A}}$, we must have $\tau \geq \tilde{\tau}$. Also, $\mathfrak{A}'$ must be capable of generating every purely periodic sequence generated by $\tilde{\mathfrak{A}}'$ and delayed $\tau - \tilde{\tau}$ dits. Now, let $g(x) = (1 - x^T)/\phi'(x)$ and $\tilde{g}(x) = (1 - x^{\tilde{T}})/\tilde{\phi}'(x)$, where $\tilde{T}$ must be a divisor of T. The output sequence ring-represented by $\xi^{\tau-\tilde{\tau}}\tilde{g}(\xi)$ in $R_{1-\xi^T}$ is also ring-represented by

11–2 $$\xi^{\tau-\tilde{\tau}}\tilde{g}(\xi)(1 + \xi^{\tilde{T}} + \xi^{2\tilde{T}} + \ldots + \xi^{T-\tilde{T}})$$

in $R_{1-\xi^T}$. Thus, $\mathcal{A}$ covers $\tilde{\mathcal{A}}$ if and only if the polynomial **11–2** is a multiple of $g(\xi)$ in $R_{1-\xi^T}$; hence if and only if, for some $a(x)$ and $b(x)$,

11–3 $$x^{\tau-\tilde{\tau}}\tilde{g}(x)(1 + x^{\tilde{T}} + x^{2\tilde{T}} + \ldots + x^{T-\tilde{T}}) = a(x)g(x) + b(x)(1 - x^T)$$

or, multiplying both sides by $x^{\tilde{\tau}}(1 - x^{\tilde{T}})/g(x)\tilde{g}(x)$,

11–4 $$x^{\tau}\frac{1 - x^T}{g(x)} = a(x)x^{\tilde{\tau}}\frac{1 - x^{\tilde{T}}}{\tilde{g}(x)} + b(x)\frac{1 - x^T}{g(x)}x^{\tilde{\tau}}\frac{1 - x^{\tilde{T}}}{\tilde{g}(x)}$$

or

11–5 $$\phi(x) = a(x)\tilde{\phi}(x) + b(x)\phi'(x)\tilde{\phi}(x) = [a(x) + b(x)\phi'(x)]\tilde{\phi}(x)$$

Hence, $\mathcal{A}$ covers $\tilde{\mathcal{A}}$ if and only if $\phi(x)$ is a multiple of $\tilde{\phi}(x)$.

12. Application of Results to Arbitrary ALSCs

In view of the observations made in Sec. **3**, the results obtained for simple ALSCs can be applied to arbitrary ALSCs in a straightforward manner.

To analyze the output y_i of an arbitrary ALSC $\mathcal{A}$ such as shown in Fig. 3.1, first construct its minimal form $\check{\mathcal{A}}_i$ with respect to the output y_i (i.e., with the ith row of **C** substituted for **C**), using the method of Sec. **2.14**. As $\mathcal{A}_i$ is a simple ALSC, its output y_i can be characterized by means of an output ideal or a generator matrix, as shown in the preceding sections. Suppose the characteristic matrices of $\mathcal{A}$ and $\check{\mathcal{A}}_i$ are **A** and **TAR**, respectively. Then, by **2.14—2**, every state **s** of $\mathcal{A}$ (restricted to output y_i only) is equivalent to **Ts** of $\check{\mathcal{A}}_i$, and every state $\check{\mathbf{s}}$ of $\check{\mathcal{A}}_i$ to $\mathbf{R}\check{\mathbf{s}}$ of $\mathcal{A}$. Hence, to find the output sequence generated by output terminal y_i when the initial state of $\mathcal{A}$ is **s**, find the corresponding initial state **Ts** of $\check{\mathcal{A}}_i$ and then use the method of **6–5** to find the output. Conversely, to find an initial state of $\mathcal{A}$ resulting in a specified output sequence at terminal y_i, first find the initial state $\check{\mathbf{s}}$ of $\check{\mathcal{A}}_i$ resulting in this sequence; the desired state of $\mathcal{A}$ is then $\mathbf{R}\check{\mathbf{s}}$.

To synthesize an m-output ALSC to generate m specified sets of periodic sequences, construct m simple ALSCs, as shown in **10–1**, to generate the different sets. The desired ALSC is then the union of the m simple ALSCs. As this ALSC is not necessarily minimal, one can employ the method of Sec. **2.14** to obtain the minimal realization.

13. Basis Matrices for Cyclic Spaces

For the remainder of this chapter we shall be concerned solely with the set of output sequences producible by a nonsingular simple ALSC. This set will be referred to as a *cyclic space*. We have seen that a cyclic space can be uniquely characterized by a feedback polynomial $\phi(x)$, or by an ideal $(g(\xi))_T$, or by a generator matrix **G**. In this and the following sections, other possible characterizations will be described.

A *basis matrix* of a cyclic space is any matrix **Z** for which the following holds: The sequence

13–1 $$y(t)\colon\ y_0y_1 \ldots y_{T-1},\ y_0y_1 \ldots y_{T-1}, \ldots$$

is in the cyclic space if and only if $(y_0, y_1, \ldots, y_{T-1})$ is in the row space of $\mathbf{Z}$. Thus, a basis matrix is any matrix row-equivalent to the generator matrix $\mathbf{G}$. If $\mathbf{Z}$ and $\phi(x)$ represent the same cyclic space, we shall say that $\mathbf{Z}$ *corresponds to* $\phi(x)$.

13–2 *Assertion:* Let $\phi(x) = \phi_1(x)\phi_2(x)$ have the exponent T. Let $\phi_1(x)$ and $\phi_2(x)$ be relatively prime, with the exponents T_1 and T_2, respectively. Let $\mathbf{Z}_1$ and $\mathbf{Z}_2$ be basis matrices corresponding to $\phi_1(x)$ and $\phi_2(x)$, respectively. Then

13–3 $$\mathbf{Z} = \begin{pmatrix} \mathbf{Z}_1 & \mathbf{Z}_1 & \cdots & \mathbf{Z}_1 \\ \mathbf{Z}_2 & \mathbf{Z}_2 & \cdots & \mathbf{Z}_2 \end{pmatrix}$$

(where $\mathbf{Z}_1$ repeats T/T_1 times and $\mathbf{Z}_2$ repeats T/T_2 times) is a basis matrix corresponding to $\phi(x)$.

Proof: By **1.8–2**, $T = \text{lcm}\,(T_1, T_2)$. Let

13–4 $$g(x) = \frac{1 - x^T}{\phi(x)}$$

13–5 $$g_1(x) = \frac{1 - x^{T_1}}{\phi_1(x)}(1 + x^{T_1} + x^{2T_1} + \cdots + x^{T-T_1}) = \frac{1 - x^T}{\phi_1(x)}$$

13–6 $$g_2(x) = \frac{1 - x^{T_2}}{\phi_2(x)}(1 + x^{T_2} + x^{2T_2} + \cdots + x^{T-T_2}) = \frac{1 - x^T}{\phi_2(x)}$$

Define $\mathbf{G}_1$, $\mathbf{G}_2$ and $\mathbf{G}$ as the generator matrices corresponding to $\phi_1(x)$, $\phi_2(x)$ and $\phi(x)$, respectively. To prove **13–3** it will suffice to prove that

13–7 $$\begin{pmatrix} \mathbf{G}_1 & \mathbf{G}_1 & \cdots & \mathbf{G}_1 \\ \mathbf{G}_2 & \mathbf{G}_2 & \cdots & \mathbf{G}_2 \end{pmatrix}$$

(where $\mathbf{G}_1$ and $\mathbf{G}_2$ repeat T/T_1 and T/T_2 times, respectively) is row-equivalent to $\mathbf{G}$. Hence, it will suffice to prove that an element is in $(g(\xi))_T$ if and only if it is expressible as a sum of elements from $(g_1(\xi))_T$ and $(g_2(\xi))_T$. Let $a(\xi)$ be any element in $(g(\xi))_T$:

13–8 $$a(\xi) = u(\xi)g(\xi)$$

Since $\phi_1(x)$ and $\phi_2(x)$ are relatively prime, by **1.7–8** we can write

13–9 $$1 = v_1(x)\phi_1(x) + v_2(x)\phi_2(x)$$

and hence, multiplying both sides by $a(x)$,

13–10 $$a(x) = a_1(x)g(x)\phi_1(x) + a_2(x)g(x)\phi_2(x) = a_1(x)g_2(x) + a_2(x)g_1(x)$$

Hence, $a(\xi)$ is expressible as a sum of elements from $(g_1(\xi))_T$ and $(g_2(\xi))_T$. Conversely, let $b(\xi)$ be expressible as

13–11 $$b(\xi) = b_1(\xi)g_1(\xi) + b_2(\xi)g_2(\xi)$$

Then $$b(x) = b_1(x)\frac{1 - x^T}{\phi_1(x)} + b_2(x)\frac{1 - x^T}{\phi_2(x)} + c(x)(1 - x^T)$$

13–12 $$= [b_1(x)\phi_2(x) + b_2(x)\phi_1(x)]\frac{1 - x^T}{\phi(x)} + c(x)(1 - x^T)$$

$$= d(x)g(x) + c(x)(1 - x^T)$$

and hence $b(\xi)$ is in $(g(\xi))_T$.

13–2 can be generalized by induction to the following:

13–13 *Assertion:* Let $\phi(x)$ have the exponent T and the prime factors $[p_1(x)]^{e_1}$, $[p_2(x)]^{e_2}, \ldots, [p_r(x)]^{e_r}$. Let T_i denote the exponent of $[p_i(x)]^{e_i}$, and $\mathbf{Z}_i$ a basis matrix corresponding to $[p_i(x)]^{e_i}$. Then

13–14
$$\mathbf{Z} = \begin{pmatrix} \mathbf{Z}_1 & \mathbf{Z}_1 & \ldots & \mathbf{Z}_1 \\ \mathbf{Z}_2 & \mathbf{Z}_2 & \ldots & \mathbf{Z}_2 \\ \cdot & & & \\ \cdot & & & \\ \cdot & & & \\ \mathbf{Z}_r & \mathbf{Z}_r & \ldots & \mathbf{Z}_r \end{pmatrix}$$

(where $\mathbf{Z}_i$ repeats T/T_i times) is a basis matrix corresponding to $\phi(x)$.

14. Basis Matrix Derived from Polynominal Ring

Let $\mathcal{A}$ be a nonsingular simple ALSC whose feedback polynomial is

14–1
$$\phi(x) = \alpha_0 + \alpha_1 x + \ldots + \alpha_{n-1}x^{n-1} + x^n \qquad (\alpha_0 \neq 0)$$

of exponent T. In $R_{\phi(\xi)}$, $\phi(\xi) = 0$ and, for any $t \geq 0$,

14–2
$$-\alpha_0\xi^t - \alpha_1\xi^{t+1} - \ldots - \alpha_{n-1}\xi^{t+n-1} = \xi^t(-\alpha_0 - \alpha_1\xi - \ldots - \alpha_{n-1}\xi^{n-1}) = \xi^t[\xi^n - \phi(\xi)] = \xi^{t+n}$$

Thus, the sequence $1\xi\xi^2\xi^3 \ldots$ satisfies the recurrence equation of $\mathcal{A}$ (see **4–4**). In particular, since the order of ξ is T, this equation is satisfied by the sequence

14–3
$$1\xi\xi^2 \ldots \xi^{T-1}, 1\xi\xi^2 \ldots \xi^{T-1}, \ldots$$

Suppose, in $R_{\phi(\xi)}$,

14–4
$$\xi^{j-1} = \eta_{1j} + \eta_{2j}\xi + \ldots + \eta_{nj}\xi^{n-1} \qquad (j = 1, 2, \ldots, T)$$

Since **14–3** must satisfy the recurrence equation component-wise, the same equation is also satisfied by the sequences

14–5
$$\eta_{i1}\eta_{i2} \ldots \eta_{iT}, \eta_{i1}\eta_{i2} \ldots \eta_{iT}, \ldots$$

(for $i = 1, 2, \ldots, n$) or by any linear combination of these sequences.

14–6 *Assertion:* The matrix

14–7
$$\mathbf{Z} = \begin{pmatrix} \eta_{11} & \eta_{12} & \ldots & \eta_{1T} \\ \eta_{21} & \eta_{22} & \ldots & \eta_{2T} \\ \cdot & & & \\ \cdot & & & \\ \cdot & & & \\ \eta_{n1} & \eta_{n2} & \ldots & \eta_{nT} \end{pmatrix}$$

is a basis matrix corresponding to $\phi(x)$.

Proof: From the preceding remarks it follows that if $(y_0, y_1, \ldots, y_{T-1})$ is in the row space of $\mathbf{Z}$ (as given in **14–7**), then it is in the cyclic space represented by $\phi(x)$. Since $c_0 + c_1\xi + \ldots + c_{n-1}\xi^{n-1} = 0$ if and only if $c_0 = c_1 = \ldots = c_{n-1} = 0$, the first n columns of $\mathbf{Z}$ are linearly independent. Thus, $\mathbf{Z}$ is of rank n and spans the entire cycle space.

Note that, for $j = 1, 2, \ldots, n$, $\eta_{jj} = 1$ while $\eta_{ij} = 0$ $(i \neq j)$. Hence, **Z** of **14–7** is of the form $(\mathbf{I}_n, \mathbf{Q})$, which is the row-reduced echelon canonical form of **G**.

14–8 *Example:* Consider the following polynomial over $GF(2)$:

14–9 $$\phi(x) = 1 + x + x^2 + x^4 = (1 + x)(1 + x^2 + x^3)$$

(with the exponent 7). In $R_{1+\xi+\xi^2+\xi^4}$ we have

14–10
$$\begin{aligned}
\xi_0 &= 1 \\
\xi^1 &= \quad\;\; \xi \\
\xi^2 &= \qquad\quad \xi^2 \\
\xi^3 &= \qquad\qquad\quad \xi^3 \\
\xi^4 &= 1 + \xi + \xi^2 \\
\xi^5 &= \quad\;\; \xi + \xi^2 + \xi^3 \\
\xi^6 &= 1 + \xi \qquad\; + \xi^3
\end{aligned}$$

Hence, a basis matrix corresponding to $\phi(x) = 1 + x + x^2 + x^4$ is given by

14–11
$$\mathbf{Z} = \left(\begin{array}{cccc|ccc}
1 & 0 & 0 & 0 & 1 & 0 & 1 \\
0 & 1 & 0 & 0 & 1 & 1 & 1 \\
0 & 0 & 1 & 0 & 1 & 1 & 0 \\
0 & 0 & 0 & 1 & 0 & 1 & 1
\end{array}\right)$$

which, as can be verified, is the row-reduced echelon canonical form of **G**. Alternatively, a basis matrix can be constructed from $\mathbf{Z}_1$, corresponding to $\phi_1(x) = 1 + x$, and $\mathbf{Z}_2$, corresponding to $\phi_2(x) = 1 + x^2 + x^3$, as indicated in **13–2**. In $R_{1+\xi}$ we have $\xi^0 = 1$. In $R_{1+\xi^2+\xi^3}$ we have:

14–12
$$\begin{aligned}
\xi^0 &= 1 \\
\xi^1 &= \quad\;\; \xi \\
\xi^2 &= \qquad\quad \xi^2 \\
\xi^3 &= 1 \qquad\; + \xi^2 \\
\xi^4 &= 1 + \xi + \xi^2 \\
\xi^5 &= 1 + \xi \\
\xi^6 &= \quad\;\; \xi + \xi^2
\end{aligned}$$

Hence, a basis matrix corresponding to $\phi(x) = 1 + x + x^2 + x^4$ is given by

14–13
$$\mathbf{Z} = \left(\begin{array}{ccccccc}
1 & 1 & 1 & 1 & 1 & 1 & 1 \\
\hline
1 & 0 & 0 & 1 & 1 & 1 & 0 \\
0 & 1 & 0 & 0 & 1 & 1 & 1 \\
0 & 0 & 1 & 1 & 1 & 0 & 1
\end{array}\right)$$

15. Null Matrices for Cyclic Spaces

A *null matrix* of a cyclic space is any matrix **N** for which the following holds: The sequence

15–1 $$y(t)\colon\ y_0y_1 \ldots y_{T-1},\ y_0y_1 \ldots y_{T-1}, \ldots$$

is in the cyclic space if and only if

15–2 $$(y_0, y_1, \ldots, y_{T-1})\mathbf{N} = \mathbf{0}$$

Hence, if the cyclic space has a basis matrix **Z**, **N** is any matrix such that **ZN** = **0**. By **1.13–1**, if **Z** is of rank n, **N** must be of rank $T - n$.

Consider the cyclic space corresponding to the feedback polynomial $\phi(x)$ of degree n and exponent T, and let $g(x) = (1 - x^T)/\phi(x)$. For $i = T - 1, T - 2, \ldots, T - n$, divide x^i by $g(x)$:

15–3 $$x^i = q_i(x)g(x) + r_i(x) \qquad (\partial(r_i(x)) < T - n)$$

The polynomials

15–4 $$f_i(\xi) = \xi^i - r_i(\xi) = q_i(\xi)g(\xi) \qquad (i = T - 1, T - 2, \ldots, T - n)$$

are, clearly, in $(g(\xi))_T$. The degree of $f_i(\xi)$ is i, but the coefficients of $\xi^{i-1}, \xi^{i-2}, \ldots, \xi^{T-n}$ are all 0 (since the degree of $r_i(\xi)$ is at most $T - n - 1$). Hence, if the coefficients of $f_{T-1}(\xi), f_{T-2}(\xi), \ldots, f_{T-n}(\xi)$ are arranged in n consecutive rows (with coefficient of ξ^{T-1} first, constant last), the resulting array is an $n \times T$ matrix of the form $(\mathbf{I}_n, \mathbf{Q})$. Since this matrix is of rank n, it can serve as a basis matrix of the cyclic space. Like the matrix given by **14–7**, it equals the row-reduced echelon canonical form of **G**. Once it is evaluated, **N** can be constructed by inspection, following **1.13–3**:

15–5 $$\mathbf{N} = \begin{pmatrix} -\mathbf{Q} \\ \mathbf{I}_{T-n} \end{pmatrix}$$

15–6 *Assertion:* Let

15–7 $$\phi(x) = \alpha_0 + \alpha_1 x + \ldots + \alpha_{n-1}x^{n-1} + x^n$$

and define the $(T - n) \times T$ matrix

15–8 $$\mathbf{\Phi} = \begin{pmatrix} \alpha_0 & \alpha_1 & \cdots & \alpha_{n-1} & 1 & & & & \\ & \alpha_0 & \alpha_1 & \cdots & \alpha_{n-1} & 1 & & & \\ & & \cdot & & & & & & \\ & & & \cdot & & & & & \\ & & & & \cdot & & & & \\ & & & & \alpha_0 & \alpha_1 & \cdots & \alpha_{n-1} & 1 \end{pmatrix}$$

$\mathbf{\Phi}^{\mathrm{TR}}$ is a null matrix of the cyclic space corresponding to $\phi(x)$.

Proof: Let $y(t)$ of **15–1** be any sequence in the cyclic space. By **5–6**, for $\nu = n, n + 1, \ldots, T - 1$:

15–9 $$y_{T-1-\nu}\alpha_0 + y_{T-\nu}\alpha_1 + \ldots + y_{T+n-2-\nu}\alpha_{n-1} + y_{T+n-1-\nu}\cdot 1 = 0$$

or, for $\nu = 0, 1, \ldots, T - n - 1$:

15–10 $$y_\nu\alpha_0 + y_{\nu+1}\alpha_1 + \ldots + y_{\nu+n-1}\alpha_{n-1} + y_{\nu+n}\cdot 1 = 0$$

which implies $(y_0, y_1, \ldots, y_{T-1})\mathbf{\Phi}^{\mathrm{TR}} = \mathbf{0}$.

15–11 *Example:* Let $\mathcal{A}$ be the ALSC of **5–13**. Here:

15–12 $$\phi(x) = 1 + x + x^3 + x^4 \qquad (n = 4, T = 6)$$

15–13 $$g(x) = 1 + x + x^2$$

Computing **15–3** for $i = 5, 4, 3, 2$:

15–14 $$\begin{aligned} x^5 &= (x^3 + x^2 + 1)(x^2 + x + 1) + x + 1 \\ x^4 &= (x^2 + x)(x^2 + x + 1) + x \\ x^3 &= (x + 1)(x^2 + x + 1) \qquad + 1 \\ x^2 & \qquad 1\,(x^2 + x + 1) + x + 1 \end{aligned}$$

we have

15–15
$$\begin{aligned} f_5(x) &= x^5 + x + 1 \\ f_4(x) &= x^4 + x \\ f_3(x) &= x^3 + 1 \\ f_2(x) &= x^2 + x + 1 \end{aligned}$$

and hence

15–16
$$\mathbf{Z} = \left(\begin{array}{cccc|cc} 1 & 0 & 0 & 0 & 1 & 1 \\ 0 & 1 & 0 & 0 & 1 & 0 \\ 0 & 0 & 1 & 0 & 0 & 1 \\ 0 & 0 & 0 & 1 & 1 & 1 \end{array}\right)$$

15–17
$$\mathbf{N} = \left(\begin{array}{cc} 1 & 1 \\ 1 & 0 \\ 0 & 1 \\ 1 & 1 \\ \hline 1 & 0 \\ 0 & 1 \end{array}\right)$$

Alternatively, following **15–6**:

15–18
$$\mathbf{N} = \mathbf{\Phi}^{\mathrm{TR}} = \begin{pmatrix} 1 & 1 & 0 & 1 & 1 & \\ & 1 & 1 & 0 & 1 & 1 \end{pmatrix}^{\mathrm{TR}}$$

16. Root Specification of Cyclic Spaces

Let $\rho_1, \rho_2, \ldots, \rho_r$ be distinct elements in a Galois field $GF(p^n)$. Let $m_i(x)$ be the minimum function of ρ_i (found as shown in **1.10–14**), and T_i the order of ρ_i $(i = 1, 2, \ldots, r)$ in this field. Define:

16–1
$$g(x) = \operatorname{lcm}\,(m_1(x), m_2(x), \ldots, m_r(x))$$

16–2
$$T = \operatorname{lcm}\,(T_1, T_2, \ldots, T_r)$$

16–3 *Assertion:* $Y(\xi)$ is an element in $(g(\xi))_T$ if and only if $Y(\rho_i) = 0$ for $i = 1, 2, \ldots, r$.

Proof: By **1.10–9**, $Y(\rho_i) = 0$ $(i = 1, 2, \ldots, r)$ if and only if $Y(x)$ is a multiple of every $m_i(x)$, and hence a multiple of $g(x)$. On the other hand, $(g(\xi))_T$ consists of all polynomials $Y(\xi)$ such that, for some $a(x)$ and $b(x)$,

16–4
$$Y(x) = a(x)g(x) + b(x)(1 - x^T)$$

By **1.8–2**, $g(x)$ divides $1 - x^T$, and hence $(g(\xi))_T$ consists of all polynomials $Y(\xi)$ such that $Y(x)$ is a multiple of $g(x)$.

Thus, a cyclic space (where $g(x)$ has no repeated factors) can be specified by a set of elements out of $GF(p^n)$ in the following manner: A polynomial ring-represents a sequence in the cyclic space if and only if it has all these elements as roots in the field.

Consider a cyclic space specified by the roots $\rho_1, \rho_2, \ldots, \rho_r$, and let

16–5
$$Y(\xi) = y_0\xi^{T-1} + y_1\xi^{T-2} + \ldots + y_{T-2}\xi + y_{T-1}$$

ring-represent an input sequence $y(t)$. If this sequence belongs to the space, then (by **16–3**), for $i = 1, 2, \ldots, r$:

16–6
$$Y(\rho_i) = y_0\rho_i^{T-1} + y_1\rho_i^{T-2} + \ldots + y_{T-2}\rho_i + y_{T-1} = 0$$

Suppose, in $GF(p^n)$,

16–7 $$\rho_i = \rho_{1i} + \rho_{2i}\xi + \cdots + \rho_{ni}\xi^{n-1}$$

since **16–6** must be satisfied component-wise,

16–8 $$y_0\rho_{ki}^{T-1} + y_1\rho_{ki}^{T-2} + \cdots + y_{T-2}\rho_{ki} + y_{T-1} = 0$$
$$(k = 1, 2, \ldots, n;\ i = 1, 2, \ldots, r)$$

Thus, the sequence is in the space if and only if

16–9 $$(y_0, y_1, \ldots, y_{T-1})\mathbf{\Psi}^{\text{TR}} = \mathbf{0}$$

where

16–10 $$\mathbf{\Psi} = \begin{pmatrix} \rho_{11}^{T-1} & \rho_{11}^{T-2} & \cdots & \rho_{11} & 1 \\ \cdot & & & & \\ \cdot & & & & \\ \cdot & & & & \\ \rho_{n1}^{T-1} & \rho_{n1}^{T-2} & \cdots & \rho_{n1} & 1 \\ \hdashline \cdot & & & & \\ \cdot & & & & \\ \cdot & & & & \\ \hdashline \rho_{1r}^{T-1} & \rho_{1r}^{T-2} & \cdots & \rho_{1r} & 1 \\ \cdot & & & & \\ \cdot & & & & \\ \cdot & & & & \\ \rho_{nr}^{T-1} & \rho_{nr}^{T-2} & \cdots & \rho_{nr} & 1 \end{pmatrix}$$

$\mathbf{\Psi}$, then, can serve as a null matrix for the cyclic space specified by $\rho_1, \rho_2, \ldots, \rho_r$.

16–11 *Example:* Consider the cyclic space specified by the roots 1 and ξ^7 in the field $GF(3^2)$ whose modulus polynomial is $1 + x + 2x^2$. The minimum function of 1 is (clearly) $2 + x$, and that of ξ^7 is (see **1.10–14**) $2 + x + x^2$. The orders of 1 and ξ^7 are 1 and 8, respectively. Hence, $g(x) = (2 + x)(2 + x + x^2) = 1 + x + x^3$ and $T = 8$. The cyclic space is that represented by $(1 + \xi + \xi^3)_8$. Using the identities **1.10–11**, the $\mathbf{\Psi}$ matrix for this space can be computed to be

16–12 $$\mathbf{\Psi} = \begin{pmatrix} 1 & 1 & 1 & 1 & 1 & 1 & 1 & 1 \\ 0 & 0 & 0 & 0 & 0 & 0 & 0 & 0 \\ \hdashline 0 & 1 & 1 & 2 & 0 & 2 & 2 & 1 \\ 1 & 1 & 2 & 0 & 2 & 2 & 1 & 0 \end{pmatrix}$$

(where the second row is redundant).

17. Maximum-Period Sequences

When the feedback polynomial of a nonsingular simple ALSC $\mathcal{A}$ over $GF(p)$ is a maximum-exponent polynomial of degree n, then (by **7–10**) all its nonzero output sequences are of minimal period $p^n - 1$. In this case $\mathcal{A}$ is called a *maximum-period ALSC* and each output sequence a *maximum-period sequence.*

In what follows, a *truncate* of a sequence $y(t)$ will refer to a sequence obtained by deleting any number (possibly 0) of successive elements from $y(t)$, starting with $y(0)$. If $y(t)$ is purely periodic with minimal period T, then it has exactly T distinct truncates.

17–1 *Assertion:* The set of $p^n - 1$ distinct truncates of any sequence generated by a maximum-period ALSC $\mathcal{A}$, is the set of all nonzero output sequences of $\mathcal{A}$.

Proof: **17–1** follows immediately from the fact that each truncate of an output sequence is also an output sequence, and that $\mathcal{A}$ generates exactly $p^n - 1$ distinct nonzero output sequences.

17–2 *Assertion:* The first $p^n - 1$ subsequences of length n in a maximum-period sequence constitute all distinct nonzero subsequences of length n over $GF(p)$.

Proof: Any n successive elements in the sequence uniquely determine all subsequent elements. Moreover, the sequence—being a nonzero sequence—cannot contain n successive zeros. **17–2** then follows from the fact that the minimal period of the sequence is $p^n - 1$.

17–3 *Assertion:* In a minimal period of a maximum-period sequence, every nonzero field element appears p^{n-1} times, and 0 appears $p^{n-1} - 1$ times.

Proof: In the set of all subsequences of length n over $GF(p)$, every field element appears the same number of times, and hence $np^n/p = np^{n-1}$ times. Thus, in the set of all nonzero such subsequences, every nonzero field element appears np^{n-1} times. By **17–2**, a minimal period of a maximum-period sequence initiates all nonzero subsequences of length n over $GF(p)$, where each element is shared by n such subsequences. Hence, every nonzero field element appears $np^{n-1}/n = p^{n-1}$ times in a minimal period. The number of zeros in a minimal period is given by

17–4 $$(p^n - 1) - (p - 1)p^{n-1} = p^{n-1} - 1$$

17–5 *Assertion*: Let r_h denote the number of runs of length exactly h of a (fixed) field element α, initiated in a minimal period of a maximum-period sequence. Then:

17–6 $$r_h = 0 \qquad (h > n)$$

17–7 $$r_n = 1 \qquad (\alpha \neq 0), \qquad r_n = 0 \qquad (\alpha = 0)$$

17–8 $$r_{n-1} = p - 2 \qquad (\alpha \neq 0), \qquad r_{n-1} = p - 1 \qquad (\alpha = 0)$$

17–9 $$r_h = (p - 1)^2 p^{n-h-2} \qquad (h = 1, 2, \ldots, n - 2)$$

Proof: **17–6** and **17–7** follow from **17–2.** Also, by **17–2,** a minimal period contains exactly $p - 1$ α-subsequences of length $n - 1$ (each subsequence followed by a different non-α element). To obtain r_{n-1}, one should subtract from $p - 1$ the number of all α-subsequences of length $n - 1$ *preceded* by α, which is 1 when $\alpha \neq 0$ and 0 when $\alpha = 0$. The result is as given in **17–8.** Finally, for any $h < n - 1$, r_h can be computed by counting all distinct ways in which an α-subsequence of length h can be preceded by a non-α element ($p - 1$ ways), followed by a non-α element ($p - 1$ ways) which is in turn followed by $n - h - 2$ arbitrary elements (p^{n-h-2} ways). The result is **17–9.**

The total number of runs of any fixed element initiated in a minimal period is given by

17–10 $$p - 1 + (p - 1)^2 \sum_{k=2}^{n-1} p^{k-2} = p - 1 + (p - 1)^2 \frac{p^{n-2} - 1}{p - 1} = (p - 1)p^{n-2}$$

For any $h < n - 1$, the ratio of runs of length h to the total number of runs is

17–11 $$\frac{(p-1)^2 p^{n-h-2}}{(p-1)p^{n-2}} = \frac{p-1}{p^h}$$

In particular, when $p = 2$, this ratio equals 2^{-h}.

17–12 *Assertion:* In a maximum-period sequence

17–13 $$y(t+\theta) = \alpha y(t) \qquad (\alpha \neq 0)$$

for all $t \geq 0$, if and only if

17–14 $$\theta = 0 \bmod 1 + p + p^2 + \ldots + p^{n-1}$$

Proof: By Fermat's theorem (see **1.5–8**), $\alpha^{p-1} = 1$. Hence, if **17–13** holds,

17–15 $$y(t + (p-1)\theta) = \alpha^{p-1}y(t) = y(t)$$

and hence, for some integer k,

17–16 $$(p-1)\theta = k(p^n - 1)$$

17–17 $$\theta = k\,\frac{p^n - 1}{p - 1} = k(1 + p + p^2 + \ldots + p^{n-1})$$

which implies **17–14**. Now, by recursive application of **4–4**, for any $\theta > 0$ and all $t \geq 0$ we can write:

17–18 $$y(t+\theta) = \alpha_0 y(t) + \alpha_1(t+1) + \ldots + \alpha_{n-1}y(t+n-1)$$

Let $y(t_1)y(t_1+1)\ldots y(t_1+n-1)$ be a subsequence of length n in $y(t)$. By **17–2**, for any $\alpha \neq 0$ and some θ $(0 < \theta < p^n)$, $y(t)$ must also contain the subsequence

17–19 $$\begin{aligned} &y(t_1+\theta)y(t_1+1+\theta)\ldots y(t_1+n-1+\theta) \\ &\quad = [\alpha y(t_1)][\alpha y(t_1+1)]\ldots[\alpha y(t_1+n-1)] \end{aligned}$$

Hence, by **17–18**, for any $\alpha \neq 0$ there is θ $(0 < \theta < p^n)$ such that $y(t+\theta) = \alpha y(t)$ for *all* $t \geq 0$. Since α can assume exactly $p - 1$ distinct values and since θ, as just shown, must satisfy **17–14**, **17–13** must be true for *all* values of θ satisfying **17–14**.

17–20 *Example:* Let $\mathcal{A}$ be a simple ALSC over $GF(3)$ with the feedback polynomial $\phi(x) = 1 + 2x^2 + x^3$ $(n = 3)$. The exponent of $\phi(x)$ is $26 = 3^3 - 1$, and hence $\mathcal{A}$ is a maximum-period ALSC. The generating polynomial of $\mathcal{A}$ is

17–21 $$\begin{aligned} g(x) = \frac{1 - x^{26}}{1 + 2x^2 + x^3} &= 1 + x^2 + 2x^3 + x^4 + x^5 + 2x^6 \\ &+ x^8 + x^9 + x^{10} + 2x^{13} + 2x^{15} + x^{16} + 2x^{17} \\ &+ 2x^{18} + x^{19} + 2x^{21} + 2x^{22} + 2x^{23} \end{aligned}$$

A maximum-period sequence is one ring-represented in $(g(\xi))_T$ by $g(\xi)$:

17–22 $$y(t)\colon 00222012212020011102112101, \ldots$$

The first 26 subsequences of length 3 in $y(t)$ are

17–23
002, 022, 222, 220, 201, 012, 122,
221, 212, 120, 202, 020, 200, 001,
011, 111, 110, 102, 021, 211, 112,
121, 210, 101, 010, 100

which are all nonzero subsequences of length 3 over $GF(3)$. A period of $y(t)$ contains $3^{3-1} = 9$ ones, 9 twos, and $3^{3-1} - 1 = 8$ zeros. For any nonzero field element (1 or 2) it contains 1 run of length 3, $3 - 2 = 1$ run of length 2, and $(3 - 1)^2 3^{2-2} = 4$ runs of length 1. It contains $3 - 1 = 2$ runs of zeros of length 2, and 4 runs of length 1. In conformity with **17–12**, $y(t + 13) = 2y(t)$ for all $t \geq 0$.

18. Autocorrelation of Maximum-Period Sequences

In this section we shall regard maximum-period sequences as sequences over the field of real numbers. If $y(t)$ is such a sequence, its average value is given by (see **17–3**):

18–1
$$\frac{p^{n-1}[1 + 2 + \cdots + (p - 1)]}{p^n - 1} = \frac{p^n(p - 1)}{2(p^n - 1)}$$

When $p^n >> 1$, this average is approximately $\tilde{y} = \frac{1}{2}(p - 1)$. The *normalized* sequence $\bar{y}(t)$ is defined by

18–2
$$\bar{y}(t) = y(t) - \tilde{y} = y(t) - \tfrac{1}{2}(p - 1)$$

The *autocorrelation function* of $y(t)$ is given by

18–3
$$R(\theta) = \frac{\sum_{t=0}^{p^n-2} \bar{y}(t)\bar{y}(t + \theta)}{\sum_{t=0}^{p^n-2} [\bar{y}(t)]^2}$$

$R(\theta)$ is seen to be periodic with θ, with the period $p^n - 1$. Setting $\theta = 0$ in **18–3**, we have:

18–4
$$R(0) = 1$$

Note that

18–5
$$\begin{aligned}
&= \sum_{t=0}^{p^n-2} \bar{y}(t)\bar{y}(t + \theta) = \sum_{t=0}^{p^n-2} [y(t) - \tfrac{1}{2}(p - 1)][y(t + \theta) - \tfrac{1}{2}(p - 1)] \\
&= \sum_{t=0}^{p^n-2} y(t)y(t + \theta) - \left[(p - 1)\sum_{t=0}^{p^n-2} y(t)\right] + \tfrac{1}{4}(p^n - 1)(p - 1)^2 \\
&= \left[\sum_{t=0}^{p^n-2} y(t)y(t + \theta)\right] - \tfrac{1}{2}p^n(p - 1)^2 + \tfrac{1}{4}(p^n - 1)(p - 1)^2 \\
&= \left[\sum_{t=0}^{p^n-2} y(t)y(t + \theta)\right] - \tfrac{1}{4}(p^n + 1)(p - 1)^2
\end{aligned}$$

18–6 *Assertion:* For all $\theta \not\equiv 0 \bmod 1 + p + p^2 + \cdots + p^{n-1}$,

18–7
$$R(\theta) = \frac{-3(p - 1)}{p^n(p + 1) - 3(p - 1)}$$

Proof: By **17–3**,

18–8
$$\sum_{t=0}^{p^n-2}[y(t)]^2 = p^{n-1}[1^2 + 2^2 + \ldots + (p-1)^2]$$
$$= p^{n-1}\tfrac{1}{6}p(p-1)(2p-1)$$
$$= \tfrac{1}{6}p^n(p-1)(2p-1)$$

Hence,

18–9
$$\sum_{t=0}^{p^n-2}[\bar{y}(t)]^2 = \left\{\sum_{t=0}^{p^n-2}[y(t)]^2\right\} - \tfrac{1}{4}(p^n+1)(p-1)^2$$
$$= \tfrac{1}{6}p^n(p-1)(2p-1) - \tfrac{1}{4}(p^n+1)(p-1)^2$$
$$= \tfrac{1}{12}p^n(p^2-1) - \tfrac{1}{4}(p-1)^2$$

Now, consider the relation **17–18**. Here, at least one of the α_i must be nonzero. Suppose the only nonzero coefficient is α_0. Then $y(t+\theta) = \alpha_0 y(t)$ and, by **17–12**,

18–10
$$\theta = 0 \bmod 1 + p + p^2 + \ldots + p^{n-1}$$

This case is of no interest in the present assertion. Next, suppose α_i $(i \neq 0)$ is one of the nonzero coefficients in **17–18**. Consider all p distinct subsequences $y(t-n+1)y(t-n+2)\ldots y(t)$ having the following properties: $y(t)$ is a fixed element $\alpha \neq 0$; $y(t-i)$ assumes the values $0, 1, \ldots, p-1$; all other $n-2$ elements are fixed but arbitrary. The corresponding values of $y(t+\theta)$ $(\theta > 0)$, are given by

18–11
$$y(t+\theta) = \beta + \alpha_i y(t-i)$$

[computed over $GF(p)$] where β is constant. Since $\alpha_i \neq 0$, as $y(t-i)$ assumes all values in $GF(p)$, so does $y(t+\theta)$. Hence, the contribution of the subsequences just described to $\Sigma y(t)y(t+\theta)$ is

18–12
$$\alpha[0 + 1 + \ldots + (p-1)] = \tfrac{1}{2}\alpha p(p-1)$$

Assigning all possible values to the $n-2$ arbitrary elements, yields the contribution due to all subsequences $y(t-n+1)y(t-n+2)\ldots y(t)$ where $y(t) = \alpha$:

18–13
$$\tfrac{1}{2}\alpha p(p-1)p^{n-2} = \tfrac{1}{2}\alpha p^{n-1}(p-1)$$

Finally, counting the contribution due to all possible α's, we have:

18–14
$$\sum_{t=0}^{p^n-2} y(t)y(t+\theta) = \tfrac{1}{2}p^{n-1}(p-1)[1 + 2 + \ldots + (p-1)]$$
$$= \tfrac{1}{4}p^n(p-1)^2$$

Hence:

18–15
$$\sum_{t=0}^{p^n-2}\bar{y}(t)\bar{y}(t+\theta) = \tfrac{1}{4}p^n(p-1)^2 - \tfrac{1}{4}(p^n+1)(p-1)^2$$
$$= -\tfrac{1}{4}(p-1)^2$$

18–16
$$R(\theta) = \frac{-\tfrac{1}{4}(p-1)^2}{\tfrac{1}{12}p^n(p^2-1) - \tfrac{1}{4}(p-1)^2} = \frac{-3(p-1)}{p^n(p+1) - 3(p-1)}$$

18–6 shows that, "almost everywhere" (except for values of θ satisfying **18–10**) the autocorrelation function of a maximum-period sequence of large period ($p^n >> 1$) is much smaller than 1. For example (see Fig. 3.9), the maximum-period sequence **17–22** has $R(\theta) = -\frac{1}{17}$ for all θ except when θ is an even multiple of 13 (in which case $R(\theta) = 1$) or an odd multiple of 13 (in which case $R(\theta) = \frac{8}{17}$).

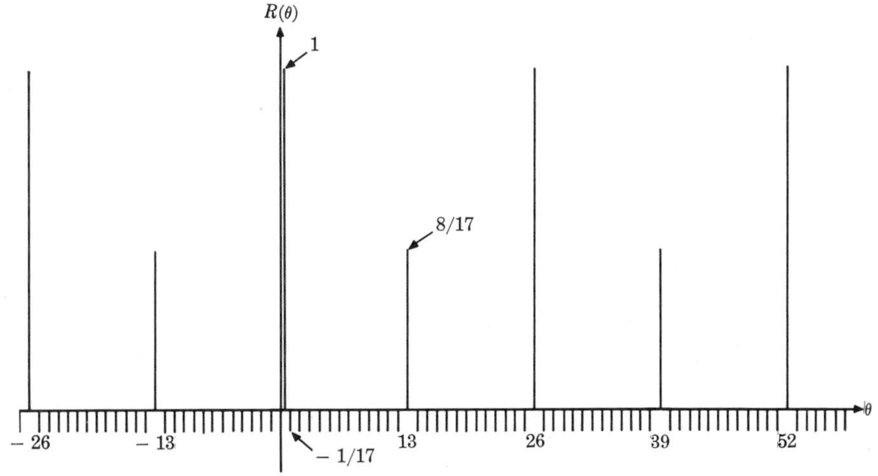

FIG. 3.9—Autocorrelation function of 00222012212020011102112101, . . .

When $p = 2$, $1 + p + p^2 + \ldots + p^{n-1} = 2^n - 1$, and **18–4** and **18–6** yield

18–17
$$R(\theta) = \begin{cases} 1 & (\theta = 0 \bmod 2^n - 1) \\ \dfrac{-1}{2^n - 1} & \text{(otherwise)} \end{cases}$$

In this case, for all θ except at the start of each period, $R(\theta)$ is inversely proportional to the period.

Note that, when $p = 2$, all elements of the normalized sequence are either $\frac{1}{2}$ or $-\frac{1}{2}$. Also, when $p = 2$, the sum in **18–15** becomes $-\frac{1}{4}$. This implies that, if a sequence is compared, element by element, with any of its truncates (except the truncate where an integral number of periods has been deleted), the number of disagreements minus the number of agreements per period is exactly 1.

Chapter 4

Quiescent Linear Sequential Circuits

1. Introduction

In this chapter we shall consider LSCs whose initial state (at $t = 0$) is $\mathbf{0}$. Such LSCs are called *quiescent* LSCs (abbreviated QLSCs). The study of such circuits is motivated by two factors. First, as seen in Sec. **2.9**, the forced response of an LSC is obtainable by setting $\mathbf{s}(0) = \mathbf{0}$ and, hence, by regarding the LSC as a quiescent one. The study of QLSCs, therefore, is an essential step in the evaluation of the total response of LSCs. Secondly, QLSCs may be regarded (and are indeed employed extensively) as special devices which transform input sequences into output sequences in accordance with some fixed rule (which implies a fixed initial state—$\mathbf{0}$ for convenience). The study of QLSCs, therefore, is also the study of the important class of LSCs employed as "sequence transformers."

In subsequent sections, concepts and properties peculiar to QLSCs are introduced. A transform method is described, in terms of which all problems concerned with the analysis and synthesis of QLSCs are readily treated.

The material in this chapter is based in part on the work of Bacon,[2] Booth,[12] Friedland,[35] and Huffman.[60]

2. Two-Terminal QLSCs

Throughout this chapter we shall regard every LSC as a QLSC; i.e., we shall assume $\mathbf{s}(0) = \mathbf{0}$. In addition, we shall assume that only zero input is applied to an LSC prior to $t = 0$ (i.e., $\mathbf{u}(t) = \mathbf{0}$ for all $t < 0$), with the implication that all variables associated with the LSC are taken as $\mathbf{0}$ for all $t < \mathbf{0}$.

In accordance with **2.9–5**, the output of a QLSC characterized by **A**, **B**, **C** and **D**, can be written as

2–1
$$\mathbf{y}(t) = \sum_{\nu=0}^{t} \mathbf{H}(t - \nu)\mathbf{u}(\nu)$$

where

2–2
$$\mathbf{H}(t) = \begin{cases} \mathbf{D} & (t = 0) \\ \mathbf{C}\mathbf{A}^{t-1}\mathbf{B} & (t > 0) \end{cases}$$

If $h_{ij}(t)$ denotes the (i,j) element of $\mathbf{H}(t)$, and $\mathbf{u}(t)$ and $\mathbf{y}(t)$ are as defined in Sec. **2.4**, the ith element of $\mathbf{y}(t)$ can be written in the form

2–3
$$y_i(t) = \sum_{j=1}^{l} \left[\sum_{\nu=0}^{t} h_{ij}(t-\nu)u_j(\nu) \right]$$

Hence, the output appearing at each output terminal of a QLSC can be most conveniently computed by adding up components of the form

2–4
$$y_{ij}(t) = \sum_{\nu=0}^{t} h_{ij}(t-\nu)u_j(\nu)$$

2–4, in turn, is the form that **2–1** assumes for QLSCs with a single input terminal and a single output terminal, i.e., for *two-terminal QLSCs*. From this point on, therefore, our discussion will be limited, by and large, to two-terminal QLSCs, where **B** and **C** are vectors, **D** is a scalar, and $\mathbf{H}(t)$ is a scalar function of time. $\mathbf{H}(t)$ will be written as $h(t)$, and **2–1** as

2–5
$$y(t) = \sum_{\nu=0}^{t} h(t-\nu)u(\nu)$$

3. The Superposition Property

3–1 *Assertion:* Let the output of a two-terminal QLSC resulting from input $u^i(t)$ be $y^i(t)$ $(i = 1, 2, \ldots, r)$. Then the output resulting from input

3–2
$$u(t) = \sum_{i=1}^{r} \alpha_i u^i(t)$$

[where the α_i are from $GF(p)$] is given by

3–3
$$y(t) = \sum_{i=1}^{r} \alpha_i y^i(t)$$

Proof: By **2–5**,

3–4
$$y(t) = \sum_{\nu=0}^{t} h(t-\nu) \sum_{i=1}^{r} \alpha_i u^i(\nu)$$
$$= \sum_{i=1}^{r} \alpha_i \sum_{\nu=0}^{t} h(t-\nu)u^i(\nu) = \sum_{i=1}^{r} \alpha_i y^i(t)$$

The property of two-terminal QLSCs described in **3–1** is referred to as the *superposition property* of QLSCs. It implies that if the response of a QLSC is known to a number of inputs, the response to any linear combination of these inputs is also known.

4. The Impulsive Response

A *unit impulse* $i(t)$ is a function defined by

4–1
$$i(t) = \begin{cases} 1 & (t = 0) \\ 0 & (t \neq 0) \end{cases}$$

The *impulsive response* of a QLSC is its output when the input is $i(t)$. Substituting $i(\nu)$ for $u(\nu)$ in **2–5**, it follows that $h(t)$ is precisely the impulsive response. We thus have:

4–2 *Assertion:* Let $\mathcal{A}$ be a QLSC characterized by **A**, **B**, **C** and **D**. Then the impulsive response $h(t)$ of $\mathcal{A}$ is given by: $h(0) = \mathbf{D}$, $h(t) = \mathbf{CA}^{t-1}\mathbf{B}$ $(t > 0)$.

From **2–5** it is apparent that the output of a QLSC to an arbitrary input can be computed by adding up impulsive responses, appropriately scaled and delayed.

4–3 *Example:* Consider the QLSC over $GF(3)$, characterized by

4–4
$$\mathbf{A} = \begin{pmatrix} 0 & 2 & 0 & 0 \\ 1 & 0 & 2 & 1 \\ 0 & 1 & 1 & 0 \\ 2 & 0 & 1 & 1 \end{pmatrix} \qquad \mathbf{B} = \begin{pmatrix} 1 \\ 0 \\ 0 \\ 0 \end{pmatrix}$$
$$\mathbf{C} = (0, 0, 2, 1) \qquad \mathbf{D} = (0)$$

(this is the LSC of Fig. 2.3, with output y_2 deleted). The impulsive response of this QLSC can be computed as follows:

4–5
$$\begin{aligned} h(0) &= \mathbf{D} = 0, & h(1) &= \mathbf{CB} = 0 \\ h(2) &= \mathbf{CAB} = 2, & h(3) &= \mathbf{CA}^2\mathbf{B} = 1 \\ h(4) &= \mathbf{CA}^3\mathbf{B} = 1, & h(5) &= \mathbf{CA}^4\mathbf{B} = 0 \\ h(6) &= \mathbf{CA}^5\mathbf{B} = 1, & h(7) &= \mathbf{CA}^6\mathbf{B} = 2 \\ h(8) &= \mathbf{CA}^7\mathbf{B} = 2, & \ldots \end{aligned}$$

Since $\mathbf{CA}^8 = \mathbf{C}$, $h(t + 8) = h(t)$ for all $t > 0$:

4–6 $h(t)$: 0.02110122,02110122, . . .

Now, suppose

4–7 $u(t)$: 1022000 . . .

By **2–5**, the corresponding output $y(t)$ can be computed as follows:

4–8

ν	$u(\nu)$	$u(\nu)h(t-\nu)$
0	1	0021101220211012 2021 . . .
1	0	0000000000000000000 . . .
2	2	001220211012202110 . . .
3	2	00122021101220211 . . .
	$y(t)$:	0021.20211012,20211012, . . .

5. The d-Transform

The *d-transform* of a sequence $f(t)$ over $GF(p)$ (where $f(t) = 0$ for all $t < 0$) is denoted by $\mathfrak{D}[f(t)]$ or F, and defined by

5–1
$$\mathfrak{D}[f(t)] = F = \sum_{t=0}^{\infty} f(t)d^t$$

$f(t)$ or $\mathfrak{D}^{-1}[F]$ is called the *inverse transform* of F.

Let $F = q(d)/r(d)$ be any ratio of two polynomials in d where, after cancelling all factors common to $q(d)$ and $r(d)$, the denominator is indivisible by d. Then F can be expressed as a power series in d, obtainable by arranging $q(d)$ and $r(d)$ in ascending powers of d and formally dividing $q(d)$ by $r(d)$:

5–2 $$F = \frac{q(d)}{r(d)} = f_0 + f_1 d + f_2 d^2 + f_3 d^3 + \dots$$

In this case F is said to be *invertible,* and $\mathfrak{D}^{-1}[F]$ is defined as $f(t) = f_t$ Clearly, if $q(d)/r(d)$ is invertible, so is

5–3 $$\frac{q'(d)}{r'(d)} = \frac{a(d)q(d)}{a(d)r(d)}$$

where $a(d)$ is any nonzero polynomial in d; in fact, the inverse transforms of $q(d)/r(d)$ and $q'(d)/r'(d)$ are the same.

Let $F^{(i)}$ be the ith derivative of F with respect to d, where F is treated as a ratio of two polynomials over the field of real numbers. $F^{(i)}(0)$ will denote the value assumed by $F^{(i)}$ when d is set to 0. From **5–2** it follows immediately that

5–4 $$f(t) = \frac{F^{(t)}(0)}{t!} \bmod p$$

5–5 *Example:* Consider the following ratio of polynomials over $GF(3)$:

5–6 $$F = \frac{2d^2}{1 + d + 2d^2}$$

$\mathfrak{D}^{-1}[F]$ can be computed as follows:

5–7 $$\begin{array}{r|l}
 & 2d^2 + d^3 + d^4 + d^6 + 2d^7 + 2d^8 + \dots \\
\hline
1 + d + 2d^2 & 2d^2 \\
 & 2d^2 + 2d^3 + d^4 \\
 & \quad d^3 + 2d^4 \\
 & \quad d^3 + d^4 + 2d^5 \\
 & \qquad d^4 + d^5 \\
 & \qquad d^4 + d^5 + 2d^6 \\
 & \qquad\quad d^6 \\
 & \qquad\quad d^6 + d^7 + 2d^8 \\
 & \qquad\qquad 2d^7 + d^8 \\
 & \qquad\qquad 2d^7 + 2d^8 + d^9 \\
 & \qquad\qquad\quad 2d^8 + 2d^9 \\
 & \qquad\qquad\quad \dots
\end{array}$$

Hence:

5–8 $$f(t)\colon 002110122 \dots$$

5–9 *Example:* Let $F = (1 + 3d)^6$ be a polynomial over $GF(5)$. Hence:

5–10 $$F^{(t)} = \begin{cases} (1 + 3d)^6 & (t = 0) \\ 3^t \cdot 6 \cdot 5 \dots (6 - t + 1)(1 + 3d)^{6-t} & (1 \le t \le 6) \\ 0 & (t > 6) \end{cases}$$

and, by **5–4**,

5–11 $$f(t) = \begin{cases} 1 & (t = 0) \\ \dfrac{3^t \cdot 6 \cdot 5 \dots (6 - t + 1)}{t!} \bmod 5 & (1 \le t \le 6) \\ 0 & (t > 6) \end{cases}$$

Thus,

5–12 $f(t)$: 1300034000 . . .

6. Transform Pairs

Table 4.1 Transform pairs

Pair	$f(t)$	F
1	$\sum_{i=1}^{r} \alpha_i f_i(t)$	$\sum_{i=1}^{r} \alpha_i F_i$
2	$f(t - t_0)$	$d^{t_0}F$
3	$(f_1 * f_2)(t)$	F_1F_2
4	$f(t) = f(t + T)$	$\dfrac{f(0) + f(1)d + \ldots + f(T-1)d^{T-1}}{1 - d^T}$
5	$\sum_{\nu=0}^{t} f(\nu)$	$\dfrac{F}{1-d}$
6	$\alpha^t f(t)\ (\alpha \neq 0)$	$F(\alpha d)$
7	$i(t)$	1
8	$\alpha^t \quad (\alpha \neq 0)$	$\dfrac{1}{1 - \alpha d}$
9	$\binom{r}{t}_p$	$(1 + d)^r$
10	$(-1)^t\binom{r+t-1}{t}_p$	$\dfrac{1}{(1+d)^r}$

A sequence $f(t)$ and its d-transform F are called a *transform pair*. Table 4.1 lists some commonly encountered transform pairs. The validity of these pairs is proved below, directly from the definition **5.1**.

Pair 1:

$$\sum_{t=0}^{\infty}\sum_{i=1}^{r}\alpha_i f_i(t)d^t = \sum_{i=1}^{r}\alpha_i\sum_{t=0}^{\infty}f_i(t)d^t = \sum_{i=1}^{r}\alpha_i F_i$$

Pair 2:

$$\sum_{t=0}^{\infty}f(t - t_0)d^t = \sum_{t=t_0}^{\infty}f(t - t_0)d^t = \sum_{t'=0}^{\infty}f(t')d^{t'+t_0} = d^{t_0}\sum_{t'=0}^{\infty}f(t')d^{t'} = d^{t_0}F$$

Pair 3: $(f_1 * f_2)(t)$, called the *convolution* of $f_1(t)$ and $f_2(t)$, is defined by

$$(f_1 * f_2)(t) = \sum_{\nu=0}^{t} f_1(\nu)f_2(t - \nu)$$

Hence, if $f_1(t) = \alpha_t$ and $f_2(t) = \beta_t$, then $(f_1 * f_2)(k)$ is the sum of all products $\alpha_i\beta_j$ such that $i + j = k$. On the other hand, the coefficient of d^k in

$$F_1F_2 = (\alpha_0 + \alpha_1 d + \alpha_2 d^2 + \ldots)(\beta_0 + \beta_1 d + \beta_2 d^2 + \ldots)$$

is also the sum of all products $\alpha_i\beta_j$ such that $i + j = k$.

Pair 4: [$f(t)$ is a purely periodic function with period T].

$$\sum_{t=0}^{\infty}f(t)d^t = [f(0) + f(1)d + \ldots + f(T-1)d^{T-1}]\cdot(1 + d^T + d^{2T} + \ldots)$$

$$= \frac{f(0) + f(1)d + \ldots + f(T-1)d^{T-1}}{1 - d^T}$$

Pair 5:

$$\sum_{t=0}^{\infty}\sum_{\nu=0}^{t} f(\nu)d^t = f(0) + [f(0) + f(1)]d + [f(0) + f(1) + f(2)]d^2 + \cdots$$

$$\begin{aligned} &= [f(0) + f(1)d + f(2)d^2 + \cdots] \\ &\quad + d[f(0) + f(1)d + f(2)d^2 + \cdots] \\ &\quad + d^2[f(0) + f(1)d + f(2)d^2 + \cdots] \\ &\quad + \cdots \\ &= F + dF + d^2F + \cdots = F(1 + d + d^2 + \cdots) = \frac{F}{1-d} \end{aligned}$$

Pair 6:

$$\sum_{t=0}^{\infty}\alpha^t f(t)d^t = \sum_{t=0}^{\infty} f(t)(\alpha d)^t = F(\alpha d)$$

Pair 7: [i(t) is a unit impulse].

$$\sum_{t=0}^{\infty} i(t)d^t = 1\cdot d^0 = 1$$

Pair 8:

$$\sum_{t=0}^{\infty}\alpha^t d^t = \sum_{t=0}^{\infty}(\alpha d)^t = \frac{1}{1-\alpha d}$$

In Pairs *9* and *10*, $\binom{k}{t}_p$ is defined as follows:

$$\binom{k}{t}_p = \begin{cases} 1 & (t = 0) \\ \dfrac{k(k-1)\cdots(k-t+1)}{t!} \bmod p & (t > 0) \end{cases}$$

Pair 9: By Newton's binomial theorem, the coefficient (modulo p) of d^t in the power series expansion of $(1 + d)^r$ is precisely $\binom{r}{t}_p$.

Pair 10: Since Newton's binomial theorem holds for negative powers, the coefficient (modulo p) of d^t in the power series expansion of $(1 + d)^{-r}$ is

$$\binom{-r}{t}_p = (-1)^t\binom{r+t-1}{t}_p$$

7. Use of Transform-Pairs Table

Inverse transformation of a ratio of two polynomials in d can be done by long division or by the derivative method illustrated in Sec. **5**. Alternatively, it can be done by a judicious use of a table of transform pairs such as Table 4.1.

7–1 *Example:* Consider $F = (1 + 3d)^6$ over $GF(5)$. Using Pairs *6* and *9* in succession, we obtain:

7–2 $$f(t) = \mathfrak{D}^{-1}[(1 + 3d)^6] = 3^t\mathfrak{D}^{-1}[(1 + d)^6] = 3^t\binom{6}{t} \bmod 5$$

Hence:

7–3 $$f(t)\colon 1300034000 \ldots$$

(which checks with **5–12**).

7–4 *Example:* Consider $F = (d^2 + d^3)/(1 + d^3)$ over $GF(3)$. Since

7–5 $$f(t) = \mathfrak{D}^{-1}\left[\frac{d^2 + d^3}{1 + d^3}\right] = \mathfrak{D}^{-1}\left[d^2\left(\frac{1+d}{1+d^3}\right)\right]$$

we have, using Pairs *2* and *6* in succession,

7-6 $$f(t+2) = \mathfrak{D}^{-1}\left[\frac{1+d}{1+d^3}\right] = \mathfrak{D}^{-1}\left[\frac{1+2(2d)}{1-(2d)^3}\right] = 2^t\mathfrak{D}^{-1}\left[\frac{1+2d}{1-d^3}\right]$$

Using Pair *4*:

7-7 $$\mathfrak{D}^{-1}\left[\frac{1+2d}{1-d^3}\right]: \quad 120,120,120, \ldots$$

Since

7-8 $$2^t: \ 12,12,12, \ldots$$

we have, by **7-6** and **7-7**:

7-9 $$f(t+2): \ 110220,110220, \ldots$$

and hence

7-10 $$f(t): \ 00.110220,110220, \ldots$$

8. Periodic Functions

8-1 *Assertion:* $f(t)$ is periodic if and only if F is an invertible ratio of two polynomials in d.

Proof: Let $f(t)$ be a periodic function, given by

8-2 $$f(t): \ \alpha_0\alpha_1 \ldots \alpha_{\tau-1}\cdot\alpha_\tau\alpha_{\tau+1} \ldots \alpha_{\tau+T-1}, \ldots$$

Using Pairs *2* and *4*,

8-3 $$F = \alpha_0 + \alpha_1 d + \ldots + \alpha_{\tau-1}d^{\tau-1} + d^\tau\left(\frac{\alpha_\tau + \alpha_{\tau+1}d + \ldots + \alpha_{\tau+T-1}d^{T-1}}{1-d^T}\right)$$

$$= \frac{(1-d^T)(\alpha_0 + \alpha_1 d + \ldots + \alpha_{\tau-1}d^{\tau-1}) + d^\tau(\alpha_\tau + \alpha_{\tau+1}d + \ldots + \alpha_{\tau+T-1}d^{T-1})}{1-d^T}$$

which is an invertible ratio of two polynomials in d. Conversely, let $F = q(d)/r(d)$, where $r(0) \neq 0$. F can always be written in the form

8-4 $$F = P(d) + \frac{a(d)}{r(d)}$$

where $P(d)$ is a polynomial in d and where $\partial(a(d)) < \partial(r(d))$. When $a(d) = 0$, F is a polynomial and hence $f(t)$ is ultimately zero; thus, $f(t)$ is periodic with period 1. Otherwise, let T be the exponent of $r(x)$; we can write:

8-5 $$r(d)b(d) = 1 - d^T$$

Hence, 8-4 can be written in the form

8-6 $$F = P(d) + \frac{a(d)b(d)}{1-d^T}$$

where $\partial(a(d)b(d)) < T$. By Pair *4*, then, $f(t)$ is periodic with period T.

8-7 *Assertion:* Let $F = q(d)/r(d)$, where $q(d)$ and $r(d)$ are relatively prime ($r(0) \neq 0$). Then the minimal period of $f(t)$ is the exponent of $r(x)$.

Proof: From the proof to **8-1** it follows that the minimal period must divide the exponent of $r(x)$. Let the exponent be T and the minimal period $T' < T$. Then we can write $F = q(d)/r(d) = q'(d)/(1 - d^{T'})$, or

8-8 $$q(d)(1 - d^{T'}) = r(d)q'(d)$$

Since $q(d)$ and $r(d)$ are relatively prime, $r(d)$ must divide $1 - d^{T'}$. This, however, contradicts the definition of T, and hence we must have $T' \geq T$. Since T' divides T, we finally have $T' = T$.

The following is a direct corollary of **8–7**:

8–9 *Assertion:* Let $F = q(d)/r(d)$ be an invertible ratio of two polynomials in d. Then the minimal period of $f(t)$ is the exponent of $r(x)/\gcd(q(x), r(x))$.

9. Partial Fraction Expansion

Consider a ratio of two polynomials in d,

9–1
$$\frac{q(d)}{r(d)} = \frac{q(d)}{b_1(d)b_2(d)}$$

where $b_1(d)$ and $b_2(d)$ are relatively prime. By **1.7–8**, we can write, with some $a_1(d)$ and $a_2(d)$:

9–2
$$1 = a_1(d)b_1(d) + a_2(d)b_2(d)$$

Multiplying **9–2** by $q(d)/r(d)$, we have:

9–3
$$\frac{q(d)}{r(d)} = \frac{a_2(d)q(d)}{b_1(d)} + \frac{a_1(d)q(d)}{b_2(d)}$$

9–3 can be generalized by induction to the following:

9–4 *Assertion:* Let

9–5
$$\frac{q(d)}{r(d)} = \frac{q(d)}{b_1(d)b_2(d)\ \ldots\ b_r(d)}$$

where every $b_i(d)$ and $b_j(d)$ $(j \neq i)$ are relatively prime. Then we can write:

9–6
$$\frac{q(d)}{r(d)} = \frac{q_1(d)}{b_1(d)} + \frac{q_2(d)}{b_2(d)} + \ldots + \frac{q_r(d)}{b_r(d)}$$

Now, consider the ratio

9–7
$$\frac{q'(d)}{r'(d)} = \frac{q'(d)}{[b(d)]^e}$$

Using the division algorithm (see **1.7–3**), the following equations can be successively constructed:

9–8
$$\begin{aligned} q'(d) &= f_0(d)b(d) + r_0(d) \\ f_0(d) &= f_1(d)b(d) + r_1(d) \\ f_1(d) &= f_2(d)b(d) + r_2(d) \\ &\ldots \\ f_{e-2}(d) &= f_{e-1}(d)b(d) + r_{e-1}(d) \end{aligned}$$

where

9–9
$$\partial(r_i(d)) < \partial(b(d)) \qquad (i = 0, 1, \ldots, e-1)$$

By successive substitution we obtain:

9–10
$$\begin{aligned} q'(d) &= f_0(d)b(d) + r_0(d) \\ &= f_1(d)[b(d)]^2 + r_1(d)b(d) + r_0(d) \\ &= f_2(d)[b(d)]^3 + r_2(d)[b(d)]^2 + r_1(d)b(d) + r_0(d) \\ &\ldots \\ &= f_{e-1}(d)[b(d)]^e + r_{e-1}(d)[b(d)]^{e-1} + r_{e-2}(d)[b(d)]^{e-2} \\ &\qquad + \ldots + r_1(d)b(d) + r_0(d) \end{aligned}$$

Dividing **9–10** by $r'(d)$, we obtain:

9–11 $$\frac{q'(d)}{r'(d)} = f_{e-1}(d) + \frac{r_{e-1}(d)}{b(d)} + \frac{r_{e-2}(d)}{[b(d)]^2} + \cdots + \frac{r_0(d)}{[b(d)]^e}$$

where, by **9–9**, each denominator $[b(d)]^i$ is of degree greater than the corresponding numerator $r_{e-i}(d)$.

Combining **9–4** and **9–11**, the following can now be stated:

9–12 *Assertion:* Let $q(d)/r(d)$ be a ratio of two polynomials in d, where $r(d)$ has the prime factors $[p_1(d)]^{e_1}, [p_2(d)]^{e_2}, \ldots, [p_r(d)]^{e_r}$. Then $q(d)/r(d)$ can always be expanded in *partial fractions,* in the form

9–13 $$\frac{q(d)}{r(d)} = P(d) + \sum_{i=1}^{r} \sum_{j=1}^{e_i} \frac{q_{ij}(d)}{[p_i(d)]^j}$$

where $P(d)$ is a polynomial and where $\partial(q_{ij}(d)) < \partial([p_i(d)]^j)$.

9–14 *Example:* Consider the following ratio of polynomials over $GF(2)$:

9–15 $$F = \frac{d + d^2 + d^5}{1 + d^6} = \frac{d + d^2 + d^5}{(1 + d)^2(1 + d + d^2)^2}$$

Following **9–2**, we have:

9–16 $$\begin{aligned} 1 &= a_1(d)(1 + d)^2 + a_2(d)(1 + d + d^2)^2 \\ &= a_1(d)(1 + d^2) + a_2(d)(1 + d^2 + d^4) \end{aligned}$$

By inspection (or by the method illustrated in **1.7–9**), $a_1(d) = d^2$ and $a_2(d) = 1$. Hence, we can write:

9–17 $$\mathrm{F} = \frac{d + d^2 + d^5}{(1 + d)^2} + \frac{d^3 + d^4 + d^7}{(1 + d + d^2)^2}$$

Performing **9–8** for the first ratio, we have:

9–18 $$\begin{aligned} d + d^2 + d^5 &= (1 + d^2 + d^3 + d^4)(1 + d) + 1 \\ 1 + d^2 + d^3 + d^4 &= (1 + d + d^3)(1 + d) \end{aligned}$$

Now **9–10** becomes:

9–19 $$d + d^2 + d^5 = (1 + d + d^3)(1 + d)^2 + 1$$

Dividing by $(1 + d)^2$, we obtain:

9–20 $$\frac{d + d^2 + d^5}{(1 + d)^2} = 1 + d + d^3 + \frac{1}{(1 + d)^2}$$

Performing **9–8** for the second ratio in **9–17**:

9–21 $$\begin{aligned} d^3 + d^4 + d^7 &= (1 + d + d^4 + d^5)(1 + d + d^2) + 1 \\ 1 + d + d^4 + d^5 &= (1 + d + d^3)(1 + d + d^2) + d \end{aligned}$$

Now **9–10** becomes

9–22 $$d^3 + d^4 + d^7 = (1 + d + d^3)(1 + d + d^2)^2 + d(1 + d + d^2) + 1$$

Dividing by $(1 + d + d^2)^2$, we obtain

9–23 $$\frac{d^3 + d^4 + d^7}{(1 + d + d^2)^2} = 1 + d + d^3 + \frac{d}{1 + d + d^2} + \frac{1}{(1 + d + d^2)^2}$$

Thus, the partial fraction expansion of F is given by

9–24 $$F = \frac{d + d^2 + d^5}{1 + d^6} = \frac{1}{(1+d)^2} + \frac{d}{1 + d + d^2} + \frac{1}{(1 + d + d^2)^2}$$

10. The Transfer Function

Let $\mathcal{A}$ be a two-terminal n-dimensional QLSC, characterized by **A**, **B**, **C** and **D**. The state and output equations of $\mathcal{A}$ can be written in the form

10–1 $$\mathbf{s}(t) = \mathbf{A}\mathbf{s}(t-1) + \mathbf{B}u(t-1)$$

10–2 $$y(t) = \mathbf{C}\mathbf{s}(t) + \mathbf{D}u(t)$$

Let **S** be an n-dimensional column vector whose ith coordinate is the d-transform of the ith coordinate of $\mathbf{s}(t)$. When the d-transform of **10–1** and **10–2** is taken, the result is

10–3 $$\mathbf{S} = d\mathbf{A}\mathbf{S} + d\mathbf{B}U$$

10–4 $$Y = \mathbf{C}\mathbf{S} + \mathbf{D}U$$

[where U and Y are the d-transforms of $u(t)$ and $y(t)$, respectively]. From **10–3**:

10–5 $$(d\mathbf{A} - \mathbf{I})\mathbf{S} = -d\mathbf{B}\mathrm{U}$$

$|d\mathbf{A} - \mathbf{I}|$ is some polynominal in d of degree at most n:

10–6 $$|d\mathbf{A} - \mathbf{I}| = \alpha_0' + \alpha_1' d + \ldots + \alpha_n' d^n$$

When $d = 0$, $|d\mathbf{A} - \mathbf{I}| = |-\mathbf{I}| = (-1)^n$. Hence $\alpha_0' \neq 0$ and one can define

10–7 $$(d\mathbf{A} - \mathbf{I})^{-1} = \frac{(d\mathbf{A} - \mathbf{I})^{AD}}{|d\mathbf{A} - \mathbf{I}|}$$

From **10–5**, then,

10–8 $$\mathbf{S} = -\frac{(d\mathbf{A} - \mathbf{I})^{AD} d\mathbf{B}}{|d\mathbf{A} - \mathbf{I}|} U$$

Substituting in **10–4**,

10–9 $$Y = \left(\mathbf{D} - \frac{\mathbf{C}(d\mathbf{A} - \mathbf{I})^{AD} d\mathbf{B}}{|d\mathbf{A} - \mathbf{I}|}\right) U$$

The ratio Y/U, i.e., the ratio of the d-transforms of the output and input of $\mathcal{A}$, is seen to depend only on the parameters of the circuit itself. This ratio is called the *transfer function* of the QLSC, denoted by $\mathfrak{T}$:

10–10 $$\mathfrak{T} = \frac{Y}{U} = \frac{\mathfrak{D}[y(t)]}{\mathfrak{D}[u(t)]} = \mathbf{D} - \frac{\mathbf{C}(d\mathbf{A} - \mathbf{I})^{AD} d\mathbf{B}}{|d\mathbf{A} - \mathbf{I}|}$$

Since $\mathbf{C}(d\mathbf{A} - \mathbf{I})^{AD} d\mathbf{B}$, like $|d\mathbf{A} - \mathbf{I}|$, is a polynominal in d of degree at most n, $\mathfrak{T}$ can be written in the form

10–11 $$\mathfrak{T} = \frac{\beta_0' + \beta_1' d + \ldots + \beta_n' d^n}{\alpha_0' + \alpha_1' d + \ldots + \alpha_n' d^n}$$

Since $\alpha_0' \neq 0$, $\mathfrak{T}$ can be multiplied and divided by $(\alpha_0')^{-1}$ to yield the *normalized form* of the transfer function:

10–12 $$\mathfrak{T} = \frac{\beta_0 + \beta_1 d + \ldots + \beta_n d^n}{1 + \alpha_1 d + \ldots + \alpha_n d^n}$$

(where any of the α_i or β_i may be 0).

Note that

10–13
$$\begin{aligned} 1 + \alpha_1 + \ldots + \alpha_n x^n &= (\alpha_0')^{-1}(\alpha_0' + \alpha_1' x + \ldots + \alpha_n' x^n) \\ &= (\alpha_0')^{-1}|x\mathbf{A} - \mathbf{I}| = (\alpha_0')^{-1}x^n\left|\mathbf{A} - \frac{1}{x}\mathbf{I}\right| \\ &= (\alpha_0')^{-1}[\phi_A(x)]^* \end{aligned}$$

where $\phi_A(x)$ is the characteristic polynominal of **A**. Thus, within a constant multiplier, the denominator of $\mathfrak{J}$ and the reciprocal of $\phi_A(d)$ (see **1.7–15**) are the same. Consequently, the factors of the denominator of $\mathfrak{J}$ are all reciprocals of factors of $\phi_A(d)$; moreover (by **1.8–1**), the exponents of the denominator of $\mathfrak{J}$ and of $\phi_A(x)$ are identical. (These conclusions should be modified in cases where the numerator and denominator of $\mathfrak{J}$ have common factors.)

11. Computation of Forced Response

11–1 We can now formulate a procedure for computing the forced response of a two-terminal QLSC $\mathfrak{A}$:

(i) Compute the transfer function $\mathfrak{J}$ of $\mathfrak{A}$.
(ii) Compute the d-transform of the input, $U = \mathfrak{D}[u(t)]$.
(iii) The output of $\mathfrak{A}$ is given by

11–2
$$y(t) = \mathfrak{D}^{-1}[U\mathfrak{J}]$$

11–3 *Assertion:* The response of a two-terminal QLSC to a periodic input is periodic.

Proof: By **10–12**, $\mathfrak{J}$ is an invertible ratio of two polynominals in d and, by **8–1**, so is U; hence, so is $U\mathfrak{J}$. **11–3** then follows from **8–1**.

11–4 *Example:* For the QLSC of Example **4–3**,

11–5
$$\begin{aligned} \frac{\mathbf{S}}{U} &= \frac{-1}{|d\mathbf{A} - \mathbf{I}|}(d\mathbf{A} - \mathbf{I})^{\mathrm{AD}}d\mathbf{B} \\ &= \frac{-1}{1 + d + d^3 + 2d^4}\begin{pmatrix} -d(1 + d + 2d^2 + d^3) \\ -d^2(1 + 2d^2) \\ -d^3(1 + d) \\ -d^2(2 + d) \end{pmatrix} \end{aligned}$$

and hence

11–6
$$\mathfrak{J} = \frac{2d^2}{1 + d + 2d^2}$$

The response of the QLSC to the input 1022000 . . . is given by

11–7
$$\begin{aligned} y(t) &= \mathfrak{D}^{-1}\left[(1 + 2d^2 + 2d^3)\frac{2d^2}{1 + d + 2d^2}\right] \\ &= \mathfrak{D}^{-1}\left[\frac{2d^2 + d^4 + d^5}{1 + d + 2d^2}\right] \\ &= \mathfrak{D}^{-1}\left[2 + d^2 + 2d^3 + \frac{1 + d}{1 + d + 2d^2}\right] \\ &= \mathfrak{D}^{-1}\left[2 + d^2 + 2d^3 + \frac{1 + d^2 + 2d^3 + 2d^4 + 2d^6 + d^7}{1 - d^8}\right] \end{aligned}$$

or

11–8
$$y(t)\colon 0021.20211012,20211012, \ldots$$

(which checks with **4–8**).

12. Transfer Function and Impulsive Response

Since $\mathfrak{D}[i(t)] = 1$, we have:

12–1 $$h(t) = \mathfrak{D}^{-1}[\mathfrak{Z}] \qquad H = \mathfrak{Z}$$

Thus, given the transfer function of a QLSC, the impulsive response can be readily determined, and conversely.

12–2 *Assertion:* The transfer function of a two-terminal n-dimensional QLSC can be identified by observing the first $n + p^n$ symbols of the impulsive response.

Proof: By **10–12**, the transfer function can be written as

12–3 $$\mathfrak{Z} = H = P(d) + \frac{q(d)}{r(d)}$$

where $P(d)$ and $r(d)$ are polynominals of degree at most n, and where $\partial(q(d)) < \partial(r(d))$. If T is the exponent of $r(x)$ (and hence a divisor of $p^n - 1$), we can write

12–4 $$H = P(d) + \frac{q'(d)}{1 - d^T}$$

Hence, $h(t)$ has minimal transience of at most $n + 1$ and minimal period of at most $p^n - 1$. Thus, $h(t)$ and hence $H = \mathfrak{Z}$, can be determined on the basis of the first $n + p^n$ symbols of $h(t)$.

That the bound $n + p^n$ is sometimes met with equality can be verified by comparing the impulsive responses of the QLSCs over $GF(2)$ with the transfer functions d and $d/(1 + d)$.

12–5 *Example:* A two-terminal QLSC over $GF(3)$ is known to be 2-dimensional ($n + 1 = 3$, $3^n - 1 = 8$); the first 11 symbols of its impulsive response are given by 00211012202. Since the minimal period is evidently not 4, it must be 8, and hence the transfer function of the QLSC is given by

12–6 $$\mathfrak{Z} = H = 2d^2 + d^3\left(\frac{1 + d + d^3 + 2d^4 + 2d^5 + 2d^7}{1 - d^8}\right) = \frac{2d^2}{1 + d + 2d^2}$$

(which checks with **11–6**).

13. Signal-Flow Graph Techniques

A signal applied to the input terminal of a two-terminal QLSC can reach the output terminal by traversing a number of distinct paths consisting of adders, scalers and delayers (this number is infinite whenever any of the paths contains a closed loop). Let the distinct paths be labeled $\pi_1, \pi_2, \pi_3, \ldots$; if π_i contains k_i delayers and if the product of scaler constants encountered along π_i is α_i, let $\mathfrak{Z}_i = \alpha_i d^{k_i}$. Thus, if the input is $u(t)$, we have

13–1 $$Y = (\mathfrak{Z}_1 + \mathfrak{Z}_2 + \mathfrak{Z}_3 + \ldots)U$$

and hence

13–2 $$\mathfrak{Z} = \mathfrak{Z}_1 + \mathfrak{Z}_2 + \mathfrak{Z}_3 + \ldots$$

Techniques for expressing $\mathfrak{Z}$ in a closed form when the number of paths is infinite, are known as *signal-flow graph* techniques. As there are excellent textbooks available on signal-flow graphs, we shall not delve into them in this book. The following sources are suggested:

Y. Chow and E. Cassignol, "Linear Signal-Flow Graphs and Applications," John Wiley & Sons, Inc., New York, 1962.

C. S. Lorens, "Flowgraphs," McGraw-Hill Book Co., Inc., New York, 1964.

L. P. A. Robichaud, M. Boisvert, and J. Robert, "Signal Flow Graphs and Applications," Prentice-Hall, Inc., Englewood Cliffs, N. J., 1962.

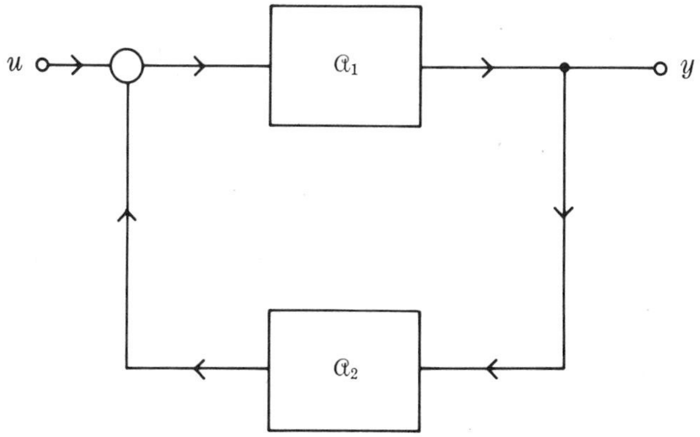

FIG. 4.1—QLSC for Example **13–3**

13–3 *Example:* Fig. 4.1 shows a general QLSC, where the circuits labeled $\mathcal{A}_1$ and $\mathcal{A}_2$ have the transfer functions $\mathfrak{J}_1$ and $\mathfrak{J}_2$, respectively. The transfer function of the overall QLSC is given by

13–4
$$\begin{aligned}\mathfrak{J} &= \mathfrak{J}_1 + \mathfrak{J}_1\mathfrak{J}_2\mathfrak{J}_1 + \mathfrak{J}_1\mathfrak{J}_2\mathfrak{J}_1\mathfrak{J}_2\mathfrak{J}_1 + \mathfrak{J}_1\mathfrak{J}_2\mathfrak{J}_1\mathfrak{J}_2\mathfrak{J}_1\mathfrak{J}_2\mathfrak{J}_1 + \dots \\ &= \mathfrak{J}_1[1 + \mathfrak{J}_1\mathfrak{J}_2 + (\mathfrak{J}_1\mathfrak{J}_2)^2 + (\mathfrak{J}_1\mathfrak{J}_2)^3 + \dots] = \frac{\mathfrak{J}_1}{1 - \mathfrak{J}_1\mathfrak{J}_2}\end{aligned}$$

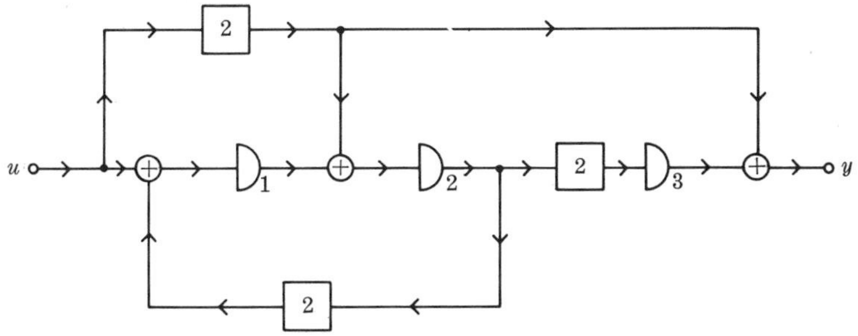

FIG. 4.2—QLSC over *GF*(3)

13–5 *Example:* Fig. 4.2 shows a QLSC over *GF*(3). Using **13–4**, the transfer function of the QLSC can be computed as follows:

13–6
$$\mathfrak{J} = 2 + \left(\frac{d^2}{1 - 2d^2}\right)2d + 2\left(\frac{d}{1 - 2d^2}\right)2d = \frac{2 + 2d^3}{1 + d^2}$$

14. Realization of Arbitrary QLSCs

A two-terminal QLSC whose transfer function is a prescribed ratio $\mathfrak{J}$ of two polynominals, will be referred to as a *realization* of $\mathfrak{J}$. It will be depicted schematically as shown in Fig. 4.3.

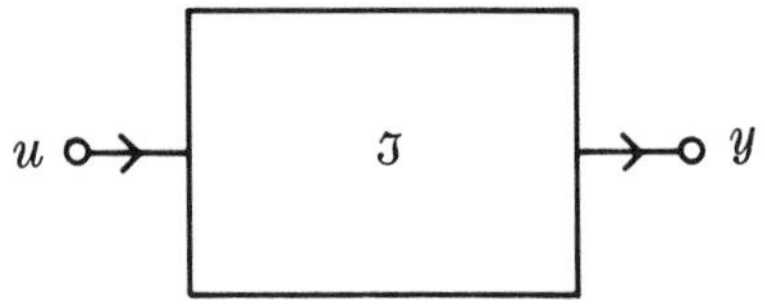

FIG. 4.3—Realization of $\mathfrak{J}$

A general QLSC with l input terminals and m output terminals can be specified by means of lm transfer functions $\mathfrak{J}_{ij}$ ($i = 1, 2, \ldots, l; j = 1, 2, \ldots, m$) defined as follows:

14–1 $$\mathfrak{J}_{ij} = \frac{Y_j}{U_i} = \left.\frac{\mathfrak{D}[y_j(t)]}{\mathfrak{D}[u_i(t)]}\right|_{u_\nu(t) \equiv 0 \text{ for all } \nu \neq i}$$

($\mathfrak{J}_{ij}$ is also the d-transform of $y_j(t)$ when $u_i(t)$ is a unit impulse and $u_\nu(t) \equiv 0$ for all $\nu \neq i$). A QLSC thus specified can be realized by realizing each $\mathfrak{J}_{ij}$ separately (as will be described in the following section) and interconnecting the resulting realizations as shown in Fig. 4.4.

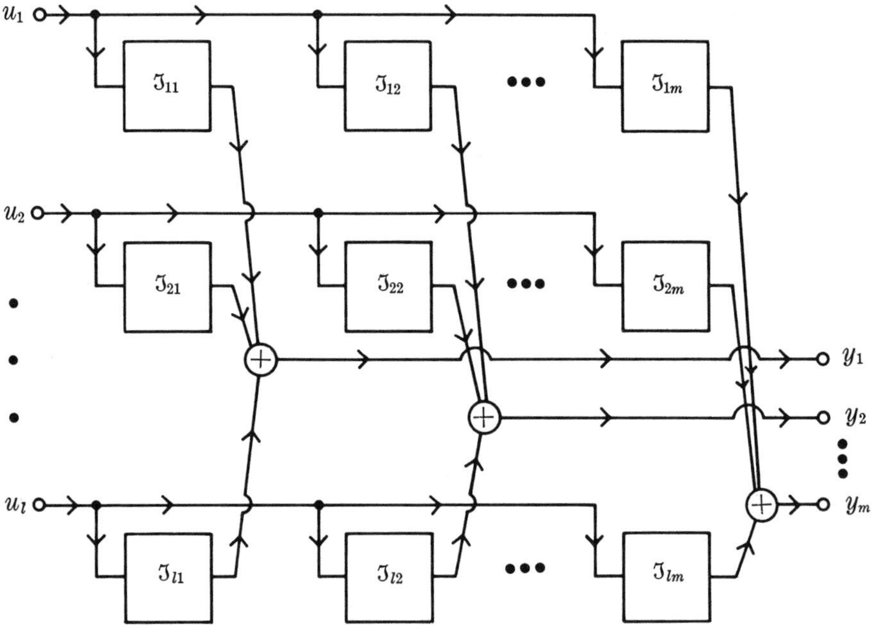

FIG. 4.4—Realization of arbitrary QLSC

15. Realization of Two-Terminal QLSCs

Consider the two-terminal n-dimensional QLSC shown in Fig. 4.5. If $s_i(t)$ denotes the output of delayer i, the following sequence of equations can be derived directly from the circuit:

$$\begin{aligned} Y &= \beta_0 U + S_1 \\ &= (\beta_0 U + \beta_1 dU) - \alpha_1 dY + dS_2 \\ \textbf{15–1} \quad &= (\beta_0 U + \beta_1 dU + \beta_2 d^2 U) - (\alpha_1 dY + \alpha_2 d^2 Y) + d^2 S_3 \\ &\;\ldots \\ &= (\beta_0 U + \beta_1 dU + \ldots + \beta_n d^n U) - (\alpha_1 dY + \alpha_2 d^2 Y + \ldots + \alpha_n d^n Y) \end{aligned}$$

Hence:

15–2
$$\mathfrak{Z} = \frac{Y}{U} = \frac{\beta_0 + \beta_1 d + \ldots + \beta_n d^n}{1 + \alpha_1 d + \ldots + \alpha_n d^n}$$

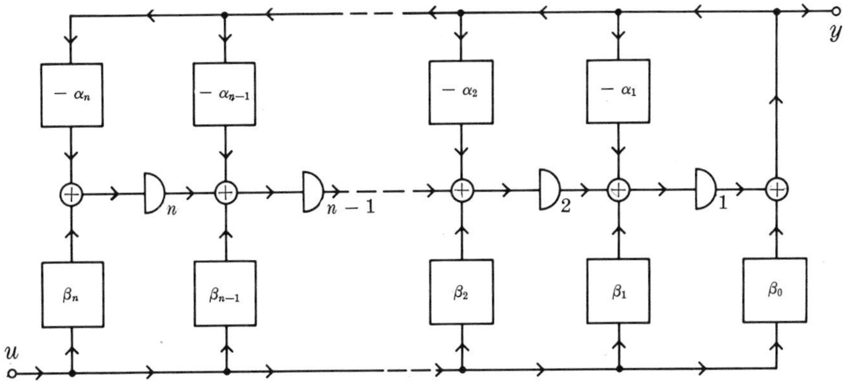

FIG. 4.5—Realization of $\mathfrak{Z} = (\beta_0 + \beta_1 d + \ldots + \beta_n d^n)/(1 + \alpha_1 d + \ldots + \alpha_n d^n)$

Thus, the QLSC of Fig. 4.5 can be used to realize any transfer function $\mathfrak{Z}$ as given in **15–2.**

An alternative realization of an arbitrary transfer function is shown in Fig. 4.6. Again, let $s_i(t)$ denote the output of delayer i. We have:

15–3 $$S_1 = d(-\alpha_1 S_1 - \alpha_2 S_2 - \ldots - \alpha_n S_n + U)$$

15–4 $$S_i = d^{i-1} S_1 \qquad (i = 1, 2, \ldots, n)$$

Hence:

15–5 $$S_1 = d(-\alpha_1 S_1 - \alpha_2 d S_1 - \ldots - \alpha_n d^{n-1} S_1 + U)$$

or

15–6 $$S_1 = \frac{d}{1 + \alpha_1 d + \alpha_2 d^2 + \ldots + \alpha_n d^n} U$$

Now,

15–7
$$Y = \beta_0 (U - \alpha_1 S_1 - \alpha_2 S_2 - \ldots - \alpha_n S_n) + \beta_1 S_1 + \beta_2 S_2 + \ldots + \beta_n S_n$$

Hence, by **15–4** and **15–6,**

15–8
$$\begin{aligned} Y &= \beta_0 \left(1 - \frac{\alpha_1 d + \alpha_2 d^2 + \ldots + \alpha_n d^n}{1 + \alpha_1 d + \alpha_2 d^2 + \ldots + \alpha_n d^n}\right) U \\ &\quad + \frac{\beta_1 d + \beta_2 d^2 + \ldots + \beta_n d^n}{1 + \alpha_1 d + \alpha_2 d^2 + \ldots + \alpha_n d^n} U \\ &= \frac{\beta_0 + \beta_1 d + \ldots + \beta_n d^n}{1 + \alpha_1 d + \ldots + \alpha_n d^n} U \end{aligned}$$

The transfer function of the QLSC, then, is $\mathfrak{Z}$ as given in **15–2.**

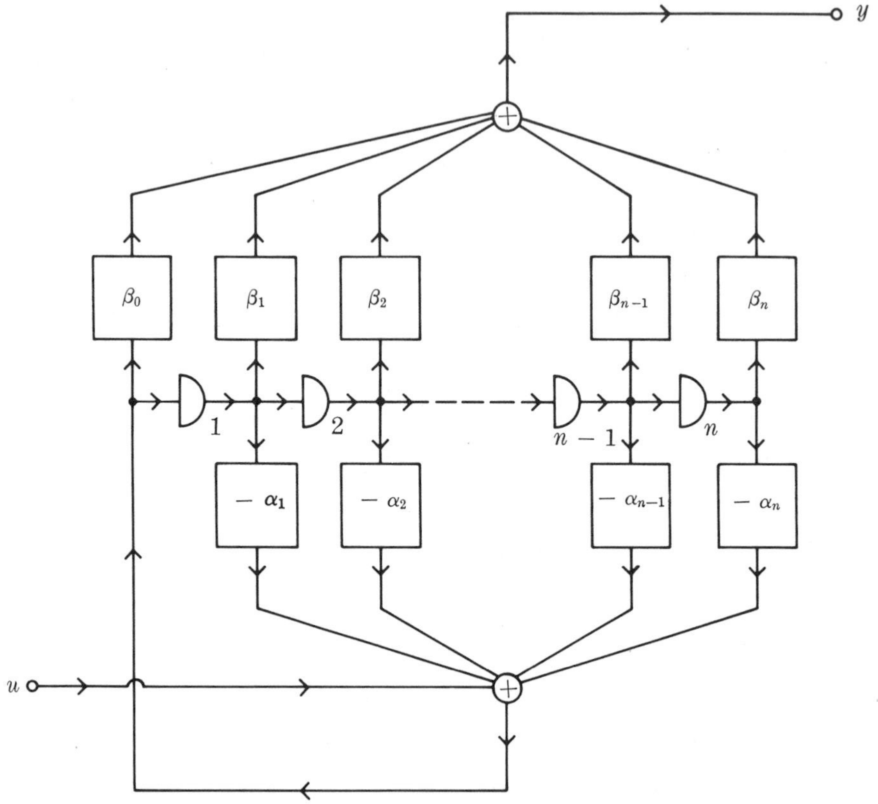

FIG. 4.6—Realization of $\mathfrak{I} = (\beta_0 + \beta_1 d + \ldots + \beta_n d^n)/(1 + \alpha_1 d + \ldots + \alpha_n d^n)$

Both of these realizations have the advantage of being constructible directly from the numerator and denominator of $\mathfrak{I}$, and of having an internal circuit in the form of a shift register (or a multi-adder shift-register). In further discussions, the first of these realizations (Fig. 4.5) will usually be employed, and referred to as a *shift-register QLSC.*

15–9 *Assertion:* Let $q(d)$ and $r(d)$ be relatively prime ($r(0) \neq 0$) and let

15–10 $$n = \max\,(\partial(q(d)),\ \partial(r(d)))$$

The realization of $\mathfrak{I} = q(d)/r(d)$ must be of dimension at least n.

Proof: Let $\mathcal{A}'$ be an n'-dimensional QLSC realizing $\mathfrak{I}$. Then we can write $\mathfrak{I} = q'(d)/r'(d)$, or $q(d)r'(d) = q'(d)r(d)$, where

15–11 $$n' = \max\,(\partial(q'(d)),\ \partial(r'(d)))$$

Since $q(d)$ and $r(d)$ are relatively prime, $q(d)$ must divide $q'(d)$, and $r(d)$ must divide $r'(d)$. Hence

15–12 $$\partial(q(d)) \leq \partial(q'(d)) \qquad \partial(r(d)) \leq \partial(r'(d))$$

which, by **15–10** and **15–11**, implies $n' \geq n$.

A *minimal realization* of $\mathfrak{I} = q(d)/r(d)$ is one whose dimension is exactly n (as defined in **15–10**.) It can always be achieved by eliminating all factors common to the numerator and denominator of $\mathfrak{I}$ (using the Euclidean algorithm 1.7–5) and constructing a shift-register QLSC based on the resulting ratio.

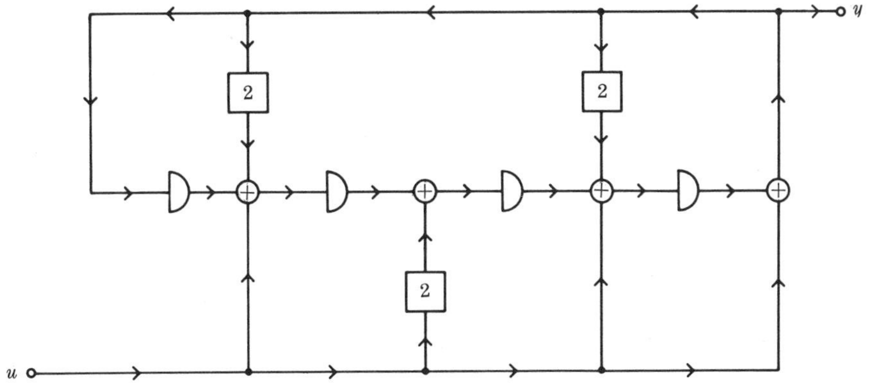

FIG. 4.7—Realization of QLSC over $GF(3)$

15–13 *Example:* Fig. 4.7 shows the shift-register realization of the following transfer function, over $GF(3)$:

15–14 $$\mathfrak{I} = \frac{1 + d + 2d^2 + d^3}{1 + d + d^3 + 2d^4}$$

16. Alternative Realizations of Transfer Functions

The flexibility available in expressing a transfer function offers a variety of alternative configurations in which a transfer function can be realized. For example, the form

16–1 $$\mathfrak{I} = \mathfrak{I}_1 + \mathfrak{I}_2 + \ldots + \mathfrak{I}_r$$

(such as the partial fraction expansion of $\mathfrak{I}$) implies that $\mathfrak{I}$ can be realized as a "parallel connection" of QLSCs (in particular, shift-register QLSCs) as shown in Fig. 4.8. The form

16–2 $$\mathfrak{I} = \mathfrak{I}_1 \mathfrak{I}_2 \ldots \mathfrak{I}_r$$

implies that $\mathfrak{I}$ can be realized as a "series connection" of QLSCs, as shown in Fig. 4.9.

If $\mathfrak{I} = q(d)/r(d)$ and n is the exponent of $r(x)$, we can always write $\mathfrak{I} = q'(d)/(1 - d^n)$ and hence realize $\mathfrak{I}$ as the QLSC of Fig. 4.5, with $-\alpha_1 = -\alpha_2 = \ldots = -\alpha_{n-1} = 0$ and $-\alpha_n = 1$ (the result is a "circulating shift register" such as shown in Fig. 3.7). While this realization is generally not a minimal realization of $\mathfrak{I}$, it has the advantage of requiring no scalers in the feedback links.

16–3 *Example:* $\mathfrak{I} = (d + d^2 + d^5)/(1 + d^6)$ is a transfer function over $GF(2)$. We can write (see **9–24**):

16–4 $$\mathfrak{I} = \frac{d + d^2 + d^5}{1 + d^6} = \frac{1}{(1 + d)^2} + \frac{d}{1 + d + d^2} + \frac{1}{(1 + d + d^2)^2}$$
$$= \left(\frac{1}{1 + d}\right)\left(\frac{1}{1 + d}\right) + \frac{1}{1 + d + d^2}\left(d + \frac{1}{1 + d + d^2}\right)$$

and hence realize $\mathfrak{I}$ as shown in Figure 4.10.

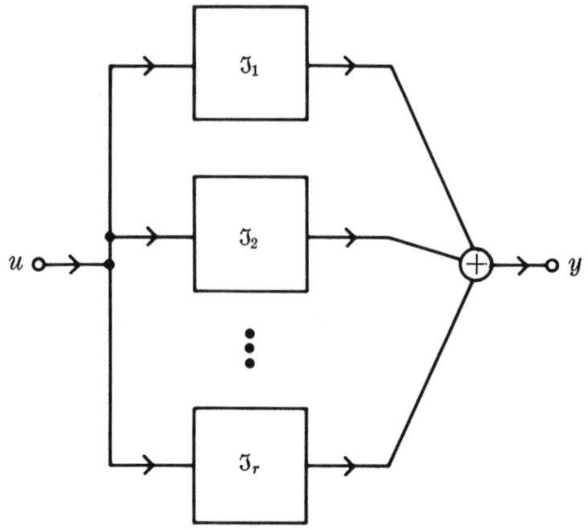

FIG. 4.8—Realization of $\mathfrak{J} = \mathfrak{J}_1 + \mathfrak{J}_2 + \ldots + \mathfrak{J}_r$

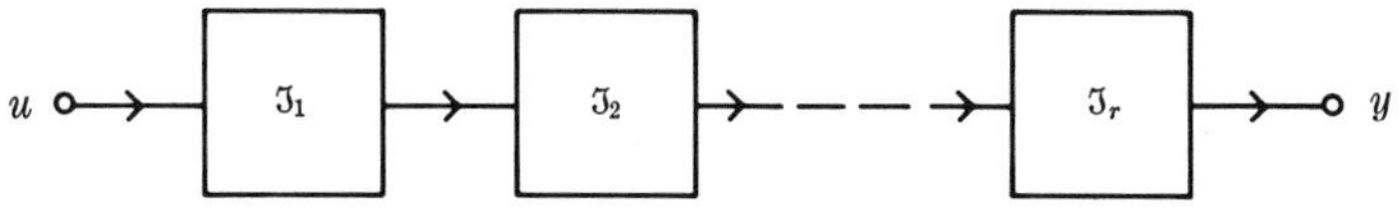

FIG. 4.9—Realization of $\mathfrak{J} = \mathfrak{J}_1 \mathfrak{J}_2 \ldots \mathfrak{J}_r$

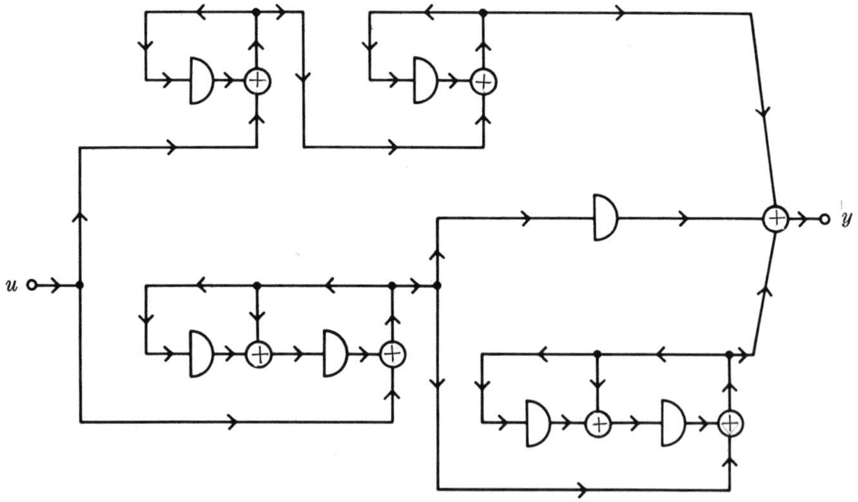

FIG. 4.10—Realization of QLSC of Example **16–3**

16–5 *Example:* $\mathfrak{I} = d/(1 + d + d^2)$ is a transfer function over $GF(2)$. The exponent of $1 + x + x^2$ is 3, and we can write:

16–6
$$\mathfrak{I} = \frac{d + d^2}{1 + d^3}$$

The corresponding realization (in the form of a circulating shift register) is shown in Fig. 4.11.

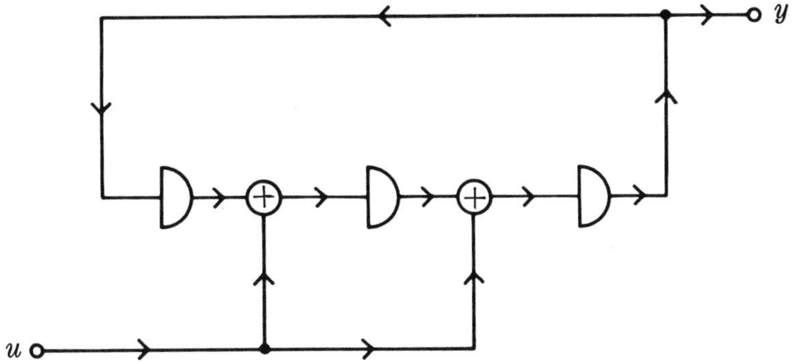

FIG. 4.11—Realization of QLSC of Example **16–5**

17. Realization with Primitive QLSCs

A QLSC $\mathfrak{A}_0$ is called a *primitive* QLSC, if every transfer function can be realized by means of adders, scalers and a finite number of $\mathfrak{A}_0$ circuits.

17–1 *Assertion:* A QLSC with a transfer function $F(d)$ is primitive if a function $G(x) = a(x)/b(x)$ exists such that $a(0) = 0$, $b(0) \neq 0$, and $G(F(d)) = d$.

Proof. Let $\mathfrak{I}(d)$ be an arbitrary transfer function, given by

17–2
$$\mathfrak{I}(d) = \frac{\beta_0 + \beta_1 d + \dots + \beta_n d^n}{1 + \alpha_1 d + \dots + \alpha_n d^n}$$

Now, consider the ratio

$$\mathfrak{I}'(d) = \mathfrak{I}(G(d)) = \frac{\beta_0 + \beta_1 G(d) + \dots + \beta_n (G(d))^n}{1 + \alpha_1 G(d) + \dots + \alpha_n (G(d))^n}$$

17–3
$$= \frac{\beta_0 + \beta_1 \dfrac{a(d)}{b(d)} + \dots + \beta_n \dfrac{(a(d))^n}{(b(d))^n}}{1 + \alpha_1 \dfrac{a(d)}{b(d)} + \dots + \alpha_n \dfrac{(a(d))^n}{(b(d))^n}}$$
$$= \frac{\beta_0 (b(d))^n + \beta_1 (b(d))^{n-1} a(d) + \dots + \beta_n (a(d))^n}{(b(d))^n + \alpha_1 (b(d))^{n-1} a(d) + \dots + \alpha_n (a(d))^n}$$

Since $a(0) = 0$ and $b(0) \neq 0$, $\mathfrak{I}'(d)$ is invertible, and hence is realizable by means of adders, scalers and delayers. In this realization, every delayer can be replaced with an $\mathfrak{A}_0$ circuit, to result in the new transfer function $\mathfrak{I}'(F(d)) = \mathfrak{I}(G(F(d))) = \mathfrak{I}(d)$, which is the desired one.

A QLSC whose transfer function is

17–4
$$F(d) = \frac{\beta_1 d}{1 + \alpha_1 d} \qquad (\beta_1 \neq 0)$$

is primitive, since

17–5
$$G(x) = \frac{-x}{-\beta_1 + \alpha_1 x}$$

is a ratio satisfying the conditions in **17–1:**

17–6
$$G(F(d)) = \left[-\frac{\beta_1 d}{1+\alpha_1 d}\right] \Big/ \left[-\beta_1 + \alpha_1\left(\frac{\beta_1 d}{1+\alpha_1 d}\right)\right]$$
$$= \frac{-\beta_1 d}{-\beta_1 - \beta_1\alpha_1 d + \alpha_1\beta_1 d} = d$$

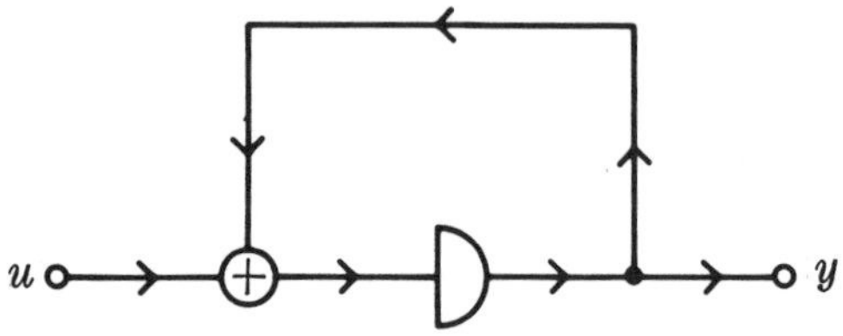

FIG. 4.12—Trigger flip-flop

17–7 *Example:* Consider a QLSC $\mathfrak{A}_0$ over $GF(2)$ whose transfer function is

17–8
$$F(d) = \frac{d}{1+d} = \Delta$$

(see Fig. 4.12). By **17–5,** $\mathfrak{A}_0$ is a primitive QLSC where

17–9
$$G(x) = \frac{x}{1+x} = F(x)$$

($\mathfrak{A}_0$ is commonly known as a "trigger flip-flop"; its output changes if and only if the input is 1). To illustrate how an arbitrary QLSC over $GF(2)$ can be realized by means of adders and trigger flip-flops only, consider the QLSC over $GF(2)$ with the transfer function

17–10
$$\mathfrak{Z}(d) = \frac{1+d^2}{1+d+d^2+d^3+d^4}$$

(whose shift-register realization is shown in Fig. 4.13a). In this case,

17–11
$$\mathfrak{Z}'(d) = \frac{1+\left(\frac{d}{1+d}\right)^2}{1+\frac{d}{1+d}+\left(\frac{d}{1+d}\right)^2+\left(\frac{d}{1+d}\right)^3+\left(\frac{d}{1+d}\right)^4} = \frac{1+d^2}{1+d+d^4}$$

Hence:

17–12
$$\mathfrak{Z}'(\Delta) = \frac{1+\Delta^2}{1+\Delta+\Delta^4}$$

The realization of $\mathfrak{Z}'(\Delta)$ [which is an alternative realization for $\mathfrak{Z}(d)$] is shown in Fig. 4.13b.

18. Accessible Periods

Let $\mathfrak{Z}$ be the transfer function of a two-terminal QLSC, given by

18–1
$$\mathfrak{Z} = \frac{q(d)}{r(d)} = \frac{q(d)}{[p_1(d)]^{e_1}[p_2(d)]^{e_2}\ldots[p_r(d)]^{e_r}}$$

where $q(d)$ and $r(d)$ are relatively prime and where the $[p_i(d)]^{e_i}$ are the prime factors of $r(d)$. Now, list the integers

18–2

$$\begin{array}{l} T_0^{(1)}, T_1^{(1)}, \ldots, T_{e1}^{(1)} \\ T_0^{(2)}, T_1^{(2)}, \ldots, T_{e2}^{(2)} \\ \cdot \\ \cdot \\ \cdot \\ T_0^{(r)}, T_1^{(r)}, \ldots, T_{er}^{(r)} \end{array}$$

where $T_0^{(i)} = 1$ $(i = 1, 2, \ldots, r)$ amd $T_j^{(i)}$ is the exponent of $[p_i(x)]^j$ $(i = 1, 2, \ldots, r; j = 1, 2, \ldots, e_i)$. Any integer expressible as

18–3 $$\text{lcm}\ (T_{j1}^{(1)}, T_{j2}^{(2)}, \ldots, T_{jr}^{(r)}) \qquad (0 \leq j_\nu \leq e_\nu)$$

is called an *accessible period* of the QLSC.

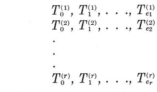

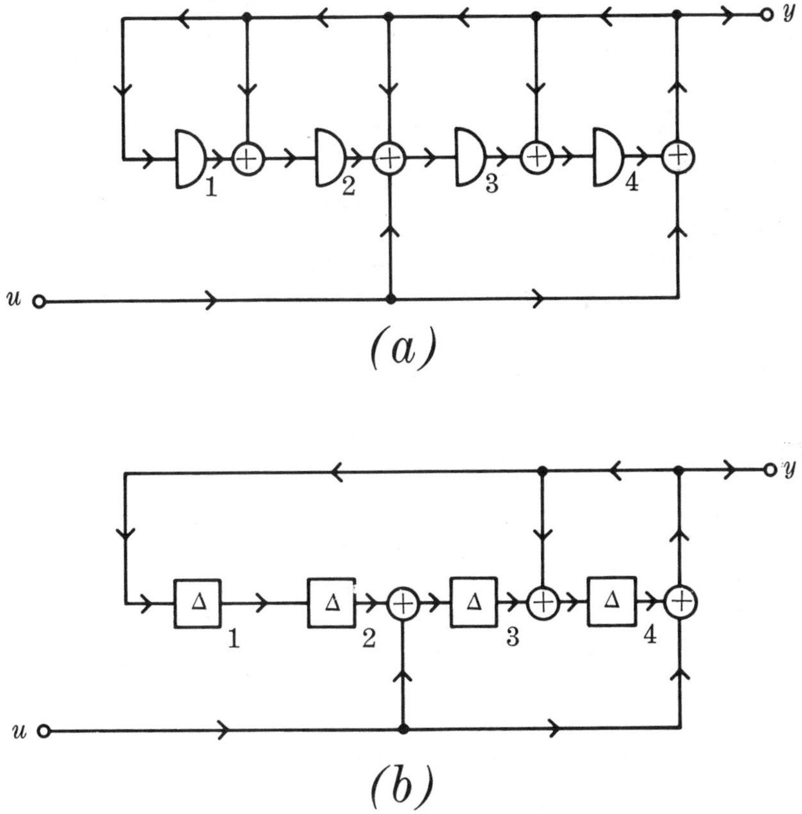

FIG. 4.13—Realization of QLSC of Example **17–7** with adders and (*a*) delayers, (*b*) trigger flip-flops

18–4 *Assertion:* Let $u(t)$ be an ultimately-zero sequence applied to a two-terminal QLSC $\mathcal{A}$, and $y(t)$ the corresponding output sequence of $\mathcal{A}$. Then $y(t)$ is a periodic function whose minimal period is an accessible period of $\mathcal{A}$. Moreover, given any accessible period T of $\mathcal{A}$, an ultimately-zero $u(t)$ exists such that $y(t)$ is periodic with minimal period T.

Proof: Let $\mathfrak{I}$ be as given in **18–1** and let $u(t)$ be an ultimately-zero input such that U is some polynomial $P(d)$. Then we can write:

18–5
$$Y = P(d)\mathfrak{I} = \frac{P(d)q(d)}{[p_1(d)]^{e_1}[p_2(d)]^{e_2} \ldots [p_r(d)]^{e_r}}$$
$$= \frac{q'(d)}{[p_1(d)]^{j_1}[p_2(d)]^{j_2} \ldots [p_r(d)]^{j_r}} = \frac{q'(d)}{r'(d)}$$

where $q'(d)$ and $r'(d)$ are relatively prime and $0 \leq j_\nu \leq e_\nu$. By **8–7**, $y(t)$ is a periodic function whose minimal period is the exponent of $r'(x)$. But, by **1.8–2**, this exponent is precisely the accessible period expressed in **18–3**. Now, let T be any accessible period, say the period expressed in **18–3**. Let $u(t)$ be an ultimately-zero sequence such that

18–6
$$U = [p_1(d)]^{e_1-j_1}[p_2(d)]^{e_2-j_2} \ldots [p_r(d)]^{e_r-j_r}$$

Hence,

18–7
$$Y = U\mathfrak{I} = \frac{q(d)}{[p_1(d)]^{j_1}[p_2(d)]^{j_2} \ldots [p_r(d)]^{j_r}} = \frac{q(d)}{r'(d)}$$

Since $q(d)$ and $r'(d)$ are relatively prime, $y(t)$—by **8–7** and **1.8–2**—is periodic with the minimal period T.

Thus, the set of accessible periods of a QLSC $\mathfrak{A}$ constitutes the set of periods realizable by the outputs of $\mathfrak{A}$ when $\mathfrak{A}$ is excited by ultimately-zero inputs. The manner in which any particular period can be realized is indicated in the preceding proof.

18–8 *Example:* Consider a two-terminal QLSC over $GF(2)$, with the transfer function

18–9
$$\mathfrak{I} = \frac{d + d^2 + d^5}{1 + d^6} = \frac{d + d^2 + d^5}{(1 + d)^2(1 + d + d^2)^2}$$

Letting $p_1(d) = 1 + d$ $(e_1 = 2)$ and $p_2(d) = 1 + d + d^2$ $(e_2 = 2)$, we have:

18–10
$$T_0^{(1)} = 1,\ T_1^{(1)} = 1,\ T_2^{(1)} = 2$$
$$T_0^{(2)} = 1,\ T_1^{(2)} = 3,\ T_2^{(2)} = 6$$

and hence the set of accessible periods is $\{1, 2, 3, 6\}$. To achieve minimal period 3, for example, we can write $3 = \text{lcm}\ (1, 3)$ and hence apply $u(t)$ such that

18–11
$$U = (1 + d)^2(1 + d + d^2) = 1 + d + d^3 + d^4$$

Hence:

18–12
$$u(t)\text{: } 11011000 \ldots$$

Correspondingly:

18–13
$$Y = U\mathfrak{I} = \frac{d + d^2 + d^5}{1 + d + d^2} = d^2 + d^3 + \frac{d + d^2}{1 + d^3}$$

or

18–14
$$y(t)\text{: } 0101.110{,}110, \ldots$$

19. Annihilating Sequences

Let $u(t)$ be an ultimately-zero sequence such that U is the polynomial $P(d)$. Let $\mathfrak{A}$ be a two-terminal QLSC with the transfer function $\mathfrak{I} = q(d)/r(d)$, where $q(d)$ and $r(d)$ are relatively prime. If $u(t)$ is applied to $\mathcal{A}$ at $t = 0$, the output $y(t)$ is the inverse transform of

19–1
$$Y = \frac{P(d)q(d)}{r(d)}$$

Let us now shift the origin of the time scale to $t = t_0 \geq 0$, and consider the d-transform of the sequence $y'(t)$, which is $y(t)$ observed starting at $t = t_0$. If $Q(d)$ is the sum of all terms involving d^i, $i = 0, 1, \ldots, t_0 - 1$, in the power series expansion of Y, then we can write

19–2
$$Y' = \frac{1}{d^{t_0}}\left[\frac{P(d)q(d)}{r(d)} - Q(d)\right] = \frac{q'(d)}{r(d)}$$

Now, let $u'(t)$ be an ultimately-zero sequence applied to the input terminal of $\mathcal{A}$ [or *added* to the input of $\mathcal{A}$, if $u(t)$ has not yet vanished] at $t = t_0$. If $U' = P'(d)$, the d-transform of the total output (with the time origin shifted to $t = t_0$) is given by

19–3
$$Y' + U'\mathfrak{I} = \frac{q'(d)}{r(d)} + \frac{P'(d)q(d)}{r(d)} = \frac{q'(d) + P'(d)q(d)}{r(d)}$$

Since $q(d)$ and $r(d)$ are relatively prime, we can write (see **1.7–8**):

19–4
$$1 = a_1(d)q(d) + a_2(d)r(d)$$

or, multiplying both sides of **19–4** by $q'(d)$,

19–5
$$q'(d) - [q'(d)a_1(d)]q(d) = [q'(d)a_2(d)]r(d)$$

Thus, if we choose

19–6
$$P'(d) = -\,q'(d)a_1(d)$$

we have

19–7
$$\begin{aligned} Y' + U'\mathfrak{I} &= \frac{q'(d) - [q'(d)a_1(d)]q(d)}{r(d)} \\ &= \frac{[q'(d)a_2(d)]r(d)}{r(d)} = q'(d)a_2(d) \end{aligned}$$

which is the d-transform of an ultimately-zero sequence. In conclusion, one can always find an ultimately-zero input sequence $u'(t)$ which, if applied to $\mathcal{A}$ at any specified time t_0, annihilates (after a finite delay) any output resulting from an earlier ultimately-zero input sequence $u(t)$. Insofar as the terminal behavior of the QLSC is concerned, the effect of the *annihilating sequence* $u'(t)$ is to return $\mathcal{A}$ back to the null state and hence to its initial status as a QLSC.

The question arises whether an input sequence $u''(t)$ exists which, when applied to $\mathcal{A}$ at $t = t_0$, reduces the output of $\mathcal{A}$ *instantaneously* to 0. If one exists, we have:

19–8
$$Y' + U''\mathfrak{I} = \frac{q'(d)}{r(d)} + U''\frac{q(d)}{r(d)} = 0$$

or

19–9
$$U'' = -\frac{Y''}{\mathfrak{I}} = -\frac{q'(d)}{q(d)}$$

Thus, $u''(t)$ exists whenever $q'(d)/q(d)$ is invertible [which is always the case when $q(d)$ is indivisible by d]. $u''(t)$ is not necessarily ultimately-zero, and hence does not always have the effect of restoring $\mathcal{A}$ to its null state.

19–10 *Example:* Let $\mathfrak{A}$ be a two-terminal QLSC over $GF(2)$, with the transfer function

19–11
$$\mathfrak{Z} = \frac{q(d)}{r(d)} = \frac{1 + d + d^2}{1 + d + d^2 + d^3}$$

We wish to find an ultimately-zero sequence $u'(t)$ which, when applied to $\mathfrak{A}$ at $t = 2$, annihilates the impulsive response of $\mathfrak{A}$. In this case:

19–12
$$Y = \frac{1 + d + d^2}{1 + d + d^2 + d^3} = 1 + d^2\left(\frac{d}{1 + d + d^2 + d^3}\right)$$

19–13
$$Y' = \frac{q'(d)}{r(d)} = \frac{d}{1 + d + d^2 + d^3}$$

Following **19–4**,

19–14
$$1 = a_1(d)(1 + d + d^2) + a_2(d)(1 + d + d^2 + d^3)$$
$$a_1(d) = d, \qquad a_2(d) = 1$$

Hence,

19–15
$$P'(d) = -\,q'(d)a_1(d) = d^2$$

and the desired sequence (starting at $t = 2$) is

19–16
$$u'(t)\colon 001000\ldots$$

For instantaneous annihilation at $t = 2$, we choose

19–17
$$U'' = -\frac{q'(d)}{q(d)} = \frac{d}{1 + d + d^2} = \frac{d + d^2}{1 + d^3}$$

and hence

19–18
$$u''(t)\colon 011, 011, 011, \ldots$$

20. Annihilating Sequences and Cyclic Spaces

Let $\mathfrak{A}'$ be a two-terminal QLSC with the transfer function

20–1
$$\mathfrak{Z} = q(d) = 1 + \alpha_{n-1}d + \alpha_{n-2}d^2 + \ldots + \alpha_0 d^n \qquad (\alpha_0 \neq 0)$$

Let the input $u(t) = u_t$ to $\mathfrak{A}'$ be arbitrary for $t = 0, 1, \ldots, n-1$; at $t = n$, $u(t)$ is required to become an annihilating sequence which causes the output $y'(t) = y'_t$ of $\mathfrak{A}'$ to become 0 instantaneously [i.e., $y'(t) = 0$ for all $t \geq n$]. Thus,

20–2
$$\begin{aligned} Y' &= \mathfrak{Z}U \\ &= (1 + \alpha_{n-1}d + \alpha_{n-2}d^2 + \ldots + \alpha_0 d^n)(u_0 + u_1 d + u_2 d^2 + \ldots) \end{aligned}$$

must be a polynomial of degree at most $n - 1$. Since the coefficients of d^{t+n} in Y' must be 0 for all $t \geq 0$, we have:

20–3
$$\alpha_0 u_t + \alpha_1 u_{t+1} + \ldots + \alpha_{n-1}u_{t+n-1} + u_{t+n} = 0$$

for all $t \geq 0$. $u(t)$, then, must satisfy the recurrence equation **3.4–4**. Thus, $u(t)$ is a sequence with the property defined above if and only if it can be generated by a simple ALSC $\mathfrak{A}$ whose feedback polynomial is

20–4
$$\phi(x) = \alpha_0 + \alpha_1 x + \ldots + \alpha_{n-1}x^{n-1} + x^n = [q(x)]^* \qquad (\alpha_0 \neq 0)$$

Writing

20–5
$$Y' = \mathfrak{Z}U = P(d) = y'_0 + y'_1 d + \ldots + y'_{n-1}d^{n-1}$$

we have:

20–6
$$\begin{aligned} y_0' &= u_0 \\ y_1' &= \alpha_{n-1}u_0 + u_1 \\ y_2' &= \alpha_{n-2}u_0 + \alpha_{n-1}u_1 + u_2 \\ &\cdot \\ &\cdot \\ &\cdot \\ y_{n-1}' &= \alpha_1 u_0 + \alpha_2 u_2 + \cdots + \alpha_{n-1}u_{n-2} + u_{n-1} \end{aligned}$$

and hence there is one-to-one correspondence between the input sequences $u(t)$ of the required property and the p^n possible output sequences $y'(t)$. Consequently, the set of p^n possible output sequences of the ALSC $\mathcal{A}$ is given by the power series expansion of the ratio

20–7
$$\frac{Y}{\mathcal{T}} = \frac{P(d)}{q(d)}$$

where $P(d)$ is any of the p^n possible polynomials of degree at most $n - 1$. We thus have an alternative characterization for the set of output sequences generated by a nonsingular ALSC:

20–8 *Assertion:* Let $\mathcal{A}$ be a simple ALSC with the feedback polynomial $\phi(x)$ (indivisible by x). Then the sequence

20–9
$$y(t)\colon\ y_0y_1y_2y_3 \ldots$$

is an output sequence of $\mathcal{A}$ if and only if, for some polynomial $P(d)$ of degree at most $n - 1$,

20–10
$$\frac{P(d)}{[\phi(d)]^*} = y_0 + y_1d + y_2d^2 + y_3d^3 + \cdots$$

21. Reciprocal QLSCs

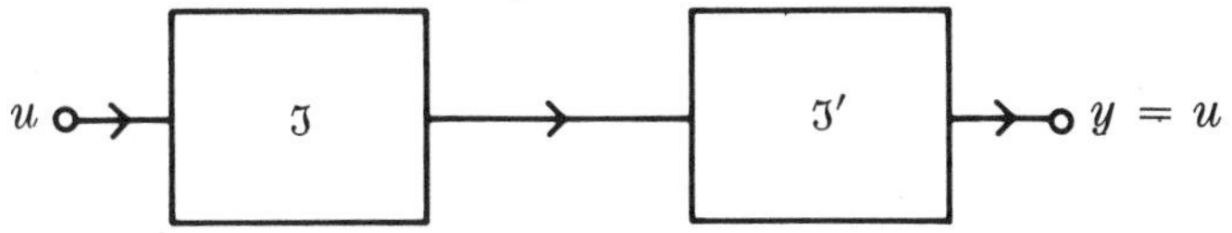

FIG. 4.14—Reciprocal QLSCs

Let $\mathcal{A}$ and $\mathcal{A}'$ be two-terminal QLSC's with the transfer functions $\mathcal{T}$ and $\mathcal{T}'$. respectively. $\mathcal{A}$ and $\mathcal{A}'$ are said to be *reciprocal* (to each other) if $\mathcal{T}\mathcal{T}' = \mathcal{T}'\mathcal{T} = 1$. Thus, if $\mathcal{A}$ and $\mathcal{A}'$ are connected in series (see Fig. 4.14), the input of the first can always be obtained by observing the output of the second (the second "unscrambles" the "scrambling" of the first). Let

21–1
$$\mathcal{T} = \frac{q(d)}{r(d)}$$

where $q(d)$ and $r(d)$ are relatively prime. Then $\mathcal{A}$ has a reciprocal if and only if $q(0) \neq 0$. When $q(0) \neq 0$, $\mathcal{T}'$ is given by

21–2
$$\mathcal{T}' = \frac{r(d)}{q(d)}$$

which is invertible and hence a realizable transfer function.

$\mathcal{A}$ and $\mathcal{A}'$ are said to be *quasi-reciprocal* if, for some $k > 0$, $\mathfrak{T}\mathfrak{T}' = \mathfrak{T}'\mathfrak{T} = d^k$. In this case the output of $\mathcal{A}'$ in the series connection of Fig. 4.14 equals the input of $\mathcal{A}$ *delayed k dits*. If

21–3 $$\mathfrak{T} = \frac{d^k q(d)}{r(d)}$$

where $q(0) \neq 0$ and $q(d)$ and $r(d)$ are relatively prime, then $\mathfrak{T}'$ is as given in **21–2.**

If $\mathcal{A}$ is a binary QLSC with an invertible transfer function ($\beta_0 = 1$, $-\alpha_i = \alpha_i$, $-\beta_i = \beta_i$ in **10–12**), $\mathcal{A}'$ can be obtained from $\mathcal{A}$ simply by reversing the roles of the input and output terminals (see Fig. 4.15).

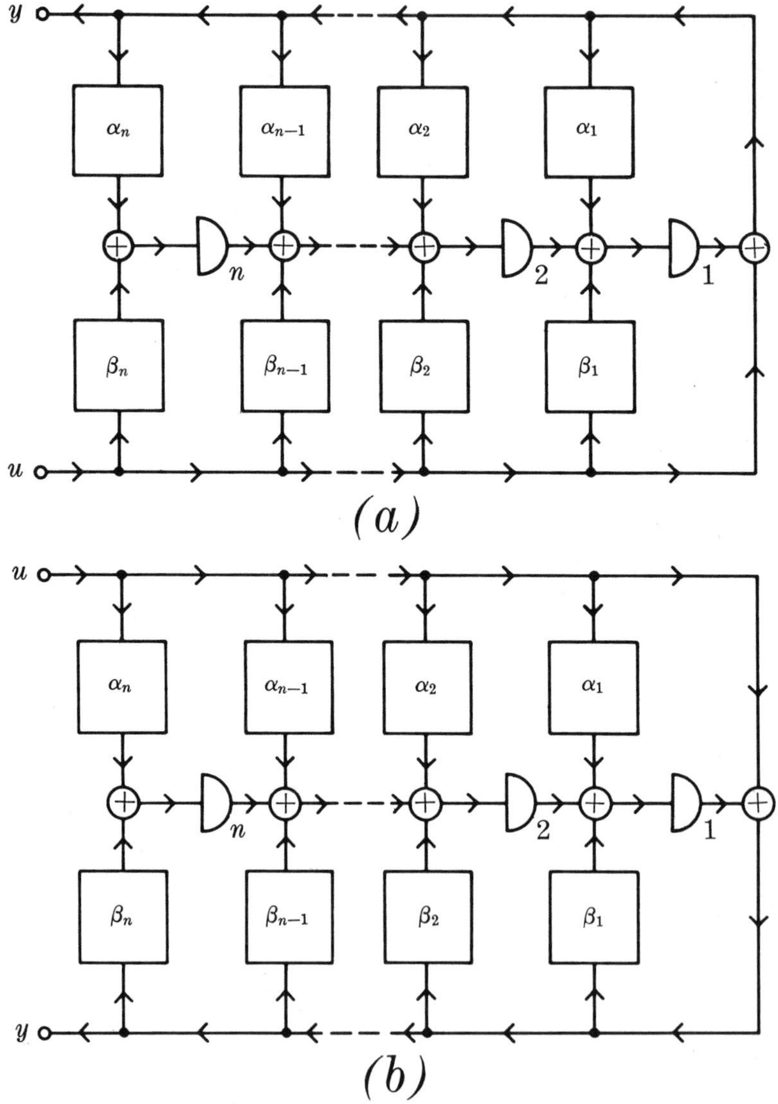

FIG. 4.15—(*a*) Binary QLSC; (*b*) its reciprocal

22. Decomposition of Periodic Sequences

A decomposition of periodic sequences of certain periods into "harmonic components" (somewhat analogously to Fourier decomposition of continuous periodic functions) is possible. However, since the components do not satisfy any orthogonality condition, this decomposition is of questionable value, and is presented here only as a curiosity.

The basis functions for the proposed decomposition of sequences over $GF(p)$ are chosen as

22-1 $$f_r(t) = \binom{r+t-1}{t}_p \qquad (r = 1, 2, 3, \ldots)$$

(where $\binom{k}{t}_p$ is as defined in Sec. **6**).

22-2 *Assertion:* $f_r(t)$ is a periodic sequence with period p^{j_r}, where $p^{j_r-1} < r \leq p^{j_r}$.

Proof: Using Pairs *10* and *6* of Table 4.1, we have:

22-3 $$\begin{aligned}\mathfrak{D}[f_r(t)] &= \mathfrak{D}\left[\binom{r+t-1}{t}_p\right] \\ &= \mathfrak{D}\left[(-1)^t(-1)^t\binom{r+t-1}{t}_p\right] = \frac{1}{(1-d)^r}\end{aligned}$$

The period of $f_r(t)$, then, is the exponent of $(1-d)^r$ which, by **1.8-2**, is p^{j_r}, where $p^{j_r-1} < r \leq p^{j_r}$.

22-4 *Assertion:* Every periodic function $f(t)$ of period $T = p^j$ can be expressed as a linear combination of $f_1(t), f_2(t), \ldots, f_T(t)$:

22-5 $$f(t) = \sum_{\nu=1}^{T} \eta_\nu f_\nu(t)$$

Proof: Since $f(t)$ is of period T, we can write:

22-6 $$F(d) = \frac{\epsilon_0 + \epsilon_1 d + \cdots + \epsilon_{T-1}d^{T-1}}{1-d^T}$$

By **1.8-5**, since T is a power of p,

22-7 $$F(d) = \frac{\epsilon_0 + \epsilon_1 d + \cdots + \epsilon_{T-1}d^{T-1}}{(1-d)^T}$$

As shown in Sec. **9**, the partial fraction expansion of $F(d)$ is of the form

22-8 $$F(d) = \frac{\eta_1}{1-d} + \frac{\eta_2}{(1-d)^2} + \cdots + \frac{\eta_T}{(1-d)^T}$$

By **22-3**, $1/(1-d)^i$ $(i = 1, 2, \ldots, T)$ is the d-transform of $f_i(t)$, and hence the inverse transform of $\eta_i/(1-d)^i$ can be identified with $\eta_i f_i(t)$ in **22-5**.

22-9 *Example:* For $p = 3$ we have:

$f_1(t)$: 1, . . .
$f_2(t)$: 120, . . .
$f_3(t)$: 100, . . .
$f_4(t)$: 111222000, . . .
22–10 $f_5(t)$: 120210000, . . .
$f_6(t)$: 100200000, . . .
$f_7(t)$: 111000000, . . .
$f_8(t)$: 120000000, . . .
$f_9(t)$: 100000000, . . .
. . .

22–11 *Example:* Consider the following sequence over $GF(3)$:

22–12 $f(t)$: 202112202, 202112202, . . .

(of period $9 = 3^2$). In this case:

22–13
$$F(d) = \frac{2 + 2d^2 + d^3 + d^4 + 2d^5 + 2d^6 + 2d^8}{1 - d^9}$$
$$= \frac{2}{1-d} + \frac{2}{(1-d)^2} + \frac{1}{(1-d)^3} + \frac{1}{(1-d)^5} + \frac{2}{(1-d)^8}$$

Hence:

22–14
$$f(t) = 2f_1(t) + 2f_2(t) + f_3(t) + f_5(t) + 2f_8(t)$$

Chapter 5
Internal Circuits

1 Introduction

In this chapter we shall consider internal circuits (abbreviated ICs) of linear sequential circuits. We shall thus concern outselves with LSCs where input and output connections are absent. An n-dimensional IC over $GF(p)$ is completely characterized by the $n \times n$ characteristic matrix $\mathbf{A}$ over $GF(p)$:

1–1 $$\mathbf{s}(t+1) = \mathbf{A}\mathbf{s}(t) \qquad \text{or} \qquad \mathbf{s}' = \mathbf{A}\mathbf{s}$$

The study of an IC, then, is essentially the study of the properties of a linear transformation expressed by its characteristic matrix.

In subsequent sections, ICs are studied primarily through the characteristics of their "state diagrams." It is shown in detail how state diagrams can be obtained from the algebraic description of an IC, and how an IC can be synthesized to satisfy given state-diagram specifications.

The material in this chapter is based in part on the work of Crowell,[26] Elspas,[32] Hotz,[57] and Tan (in Gill and Tan[47]).

2. State Diagrams

Let $\mathcal{A}$ be an n-dimensional IC over $GF(p)$, characterized by $\mathbf{A}$. The *state diagram* of $\mathcal{A}$, or of $\mathbf{A}$, is a directed graph consisting of p^n vertices labeled as the p^n states of $\mathcal{A}$. If $\mathbf{A}\mathbf{s}_1 = \mathbf{s}_2$, a branch is drawn between vertices $\mathbf{s}_1$ and $\mathbf{s}_2$, with an arrow sign pointing from $\mathbf{s}_1$ to $\mathbf{s}_2$. (Henceforth, the terms "vertices" and "states," as applied to state diagrams, will be used interchangeably.) State diagrams can be used to advantage to aid in the derivation of various properties of ICs, as well as to display all possible state transformations which an IC can undergo.

If $\mathbf{s}_2 = \mathbf{A}^\nu \mathbf{s}_1$, $\mathbf{s}_2$ is said to be the νth *successor* (or, when $\nu = 1$, simply the *successor*) of $\mathbf{s}_1$. In this case we say that $\mathbf{s}_1$ *reaches* $\mathbf{s}_2$ in ν dits or, in terms of the state diagram, *via a path* of *length* ν. Also, $\mathbf{s}_1$ is said to be a νth *predecessor* (or, when $\nu = 1$, simply a *predecessor*) of $\mathbf{s}_2$. Note that, while every state must have exactly one successor, the number of predecessors of any given state may vary from 0 to p^n.

Consider a path of length r in a state diagram, touching the states $\mathbf{s}_1, \mathbf{s}_2, \ldots, \mathbf{s}_{r+1}$. If $\mathbf{s}_1, \mathbf{s}_2, \ldots, \mathbf{s}_r$ are all distinct but $\mathbf{s}_{r+1} = \mathbf{s}_1$, the path is called a *cycle* (of length r). If none of the r states of the cycle have predecessors outside the cycle, it is called a *pure cycle* (see Fig. 5.1).

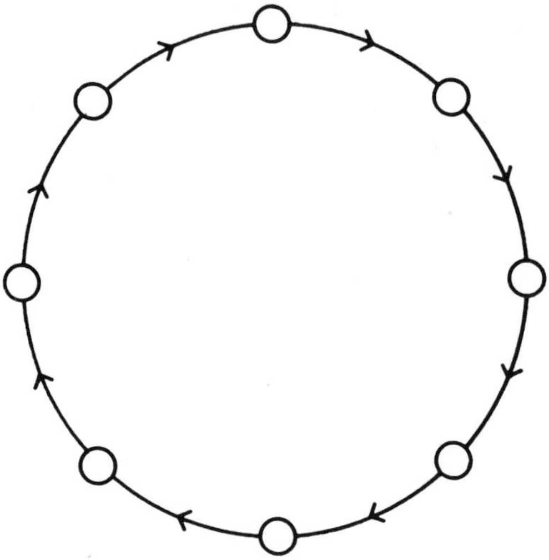

FIG. 5.1—A pure cycle of length 8

A *tree* is a subdiagram with the following properties: (a) A tree contains one state, called the *root* of the tree, which is reachable from all other tree states. (b) A tree contains no cycles. The tree states which reach the root in ν dits form the νth *level* of the tree (the root constitutes the 0th level). A tree whose highest level is the Lth is said to be a tree of *height* L (see Fig. 5.2).

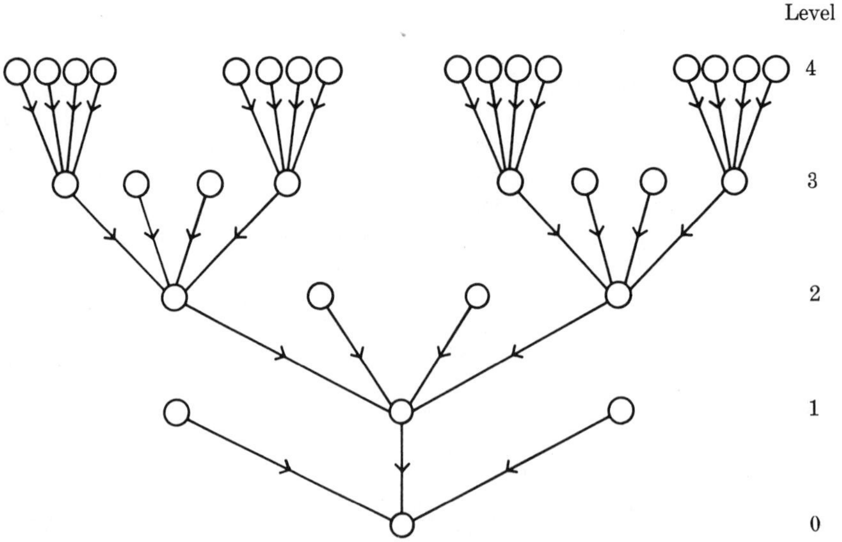

FIG. 5.2—A tree of height 4

3. Isomorphic ICs

Let $\mathcal{A}$ and $\bar{\mathcal{A}}$ be ICs characterized by $\mathbf{A}$ and $\bar{\mathbf{A}}$, respectively. $\mathcal{A}$ and $\bar{\mathcal{A}}$ are *isomorphic* if one-to-one relationship can be established between their state spaces in the following manner: If $\mathbf{s}$ of $\mathcal{A}$ corresponds to $\bar{\mathbf{s}}$ of $\bar{\mathcal{A}}$, then $\mathbf{As} = \mathbf{s}'$ of $\mathcal{A}$ corresponds to $\bar{\mathbf{A}}\bar{\mathbf{s}} = \bar{\mathbf{s}}'$ of $\bar{\mathcal{A}}$. Thus, the state diagrams of isomorphic ICs are identical except, possibly, for vertex labeling. Such state diagrams are likewise called *isomorphic.*

3–1 *Assertion:* The state diagrams of similar characteristic matrices are isomorphic.

Proof: Let $\mathbf{A}$ and $\bar{\mathbf{A}} = \mathbf{PAP}^{-1}$ be similar characteristic matrices. Establish the correspondence $\mathbf{s} \longleftrightarrow \bar{\mathbf{s}} = \mathbf{Ps}$. Since $\mathbf{P}$ is nonsingular, this correspondence is one to one. Moreover.

3–2
$$\bar{\mathbf{s}}' = \bar{\mathbf{A}}\bar{\mathbf{s}} = (\mathbf{PAP}^{-1})\mathbf{Ps} = \mathbf{P}(\mathbf{As}) = \mathbf{Ps}'$$

and hence $\mathbf{s}' \longleftrightarrow \bar{\mathbf{s}}'$.

Thus, if one is interested only in the structural features of the state diagram of $\mathbf{A}$, then $\mathbf{A}$ can be replaced by any matrix similar to $\mathbf{A}$. In particular, $\mathbf{A}$ can be replaced by its rational canonical form $\mathbf{A}^*$, as given in Sec. **1.17**.

4. Confluence Sets

The νth *confluence set* of a state $\mathbf{s}$ is the set of all νth predecessors of $\mathbf{s}$. This set will be denoted by $C_{\mathbf{s}}^{\nu}$; $\mathbf{s}$ will be referred to as the *focus* of $C_{\mathbf{s}}^{\nu}$.

4–1 *Assertion:* The νth confluence set of the null state $\mathbf{0}$ is a subspace of the state space S_n.

Proof: If $\mathbf{s}_1$ and $\mathbf{s}_2$ are in C_0^{ν}, then $\mathbf{A}^{\nu}\mathbf{s}_1 = \mathbf{A}^{\nu}\mathbf{s}_2 = \mathbf{0}$ and hence, for any α_1 and α_2 from $GF(p)$,

4–2
$$\mathbf{A}^{\nu}(\alpha_1\mathbf{s}_1 + \alpha_2\mathbf{s}_2) = \alpha_1(\mathbf{A}^{\nu}\mathbf{s}_1) + \alpha_2(\mathbf{A}^{\nu}\mathbf{s}_2) = \mathbf{0}$$

C_0^{ν}, being a subspace of S_n, is also a subgroup of the additive Abelian group S_n, and induces a coset partition on S_n.

4–3 *Assertion:* A subset of S_n is a coset in the coset partition induced by C_0^{ν} on S_n, if and only if it is a nonempty νth confluence set of some state in S_n.

Proof: $\mathbf{s}_1$ and $\mathbf{s}_2$ belong to the same coset if and only if $\mathbf{s}_1 - \mathbf{s}_2$ is in C_0^{ν}; hence if and only if $\mathbf{A}^{\nu}(\mathbf{s}_1 - \mathbf{s}_2) = \mathbf{0}$; hence if and only if $\mathbf{A}^{\nu}\mathbf{s}_1 = \mathbf{A}^{\nu}\mathbf{s}_2$; hence if and only if $\mathbf{s}_1$ and $\mathbf{s}_2$ are νth predecessors of the same state (namely the state $\mathbf{A}^{\nu}\mathbf{s}_1 = \mathbf{A}^{\nu}\mathbf{s}_2$).

The following is a direct corollary of **4–3**:

4–4 *Assertion:* All nonempty νth confluence sets have the same order, namely $|C_0^{\nu}|$.

Note that, if $\mathbf{s}$ is in the null space of $\mathbf{A}^{\nu}$, it is also in the null space of $\mathbf{A}^{\nu+1}$; consequently C_0^{ν} is always included in $C_0^{\nu+1}$.

5. Construction of State Diagram by Conflunce Sets

5–1 The results in Sec. **4**, when specialized for $\nu = 1$, suggest the following procedure for constructing the state diagram of $\mathbf{A}$:

(i) Determine C_0^1 by computing the null space of $\mathbf{A}$.

(ii) Determine the cosets induced by C_0^1 on S_n, say, $C_0^1, C_{\mathbf{s}_1}^1, \ldots C_{\mathbf{s}_{r-1}}^1$.

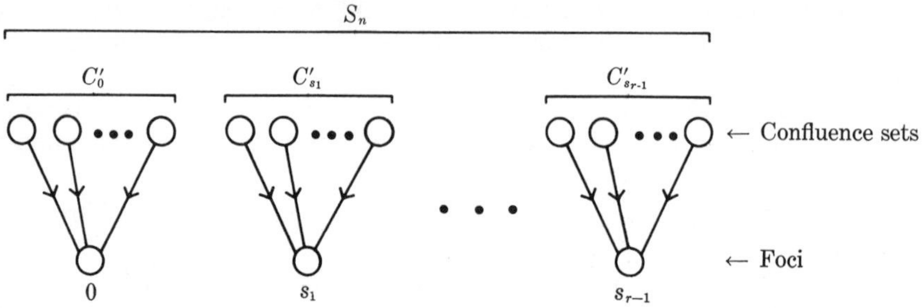

FIG. 5.3—Construction of state diagram by confluence sets

(iii) For each coset $C^1_{s_i}$ find the focus $\mathbf{s}_i$ by selecting an arbitrary element $\mathbf{s}$ from $C^1_{s_i}$ and computing $\mathbf{As} = \mathbf{s}_i$.

(iv) Knowing all 1st confluence sets and their foci, the state diagram can be constructed as indicated in Fig. 5.3.

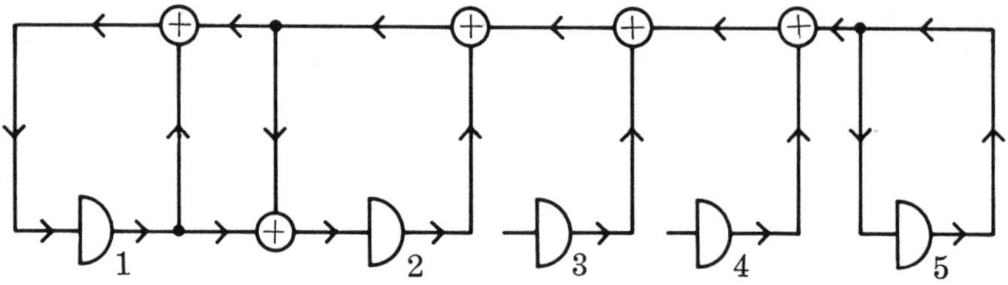

FIG. 5.4—IC over $GF(2)$

5-2 *Example:* Fig. 5.4 shows an IC over $GF(2)$, characterized by

5-3
$$\mathbf{A} = \begin{pmatrix} 1 & 1 & 1 & 1 & 1 \\ 1 & 1 & 1 & 1 & 1 \\ 0 & 0 & 0 & 0 & 0 \\ 0 & 0 & 0 & 0 & 0 \\ 0 & 0 & 0 & 0 & 1 \end{pmatrix}$$

C^1_0 is seen to consist of all column vectors with even number of 1s and a 0 in the 5th position. The remaining cosets can be compiled by inspection of C^1_0:

5-4
$$C^1_0 = \left\{ \begin{pmatrix}0\\0\\0\\0\\0\end{pmatrix}, \begin{pmatrix}0\\0\\1\\1\\0\end{pmatrix}, \begin{pmatrix}0\\1\\0\\1\\0\end{pmatrix}, \begin{pmatrix}0\\1\\1\\0\\0\end{pmatrix}, \begin{pmatrix}1\\0\\0\\1\\0\end{pmatrix}, \begin{pmatrix}1\\0\\1\\0\\0\end{pmatrix}, \begin{pmatrix}1\\1\\0\\0\\0\end{pmatrix}, \begin{pmatrix}1\\1\\1\\1\\0\end{pmatrix} \right\}$$

$$C^1_{s_1} = \left\{ \begin{pmatrix}0\\0\\0\\0\\1\end{pmatrix}, \begin{pmatrix}0\\0\\1\\1\\1\end{pmatrix}, \begin{pmatrix}0\\1\\0\\1\\1\end{pmatrix}, \begin{pmatrix}0\\1\\1\\0\\1\end{pmatrix}, \begin{pmatrix}1\\0\\0\\1\\1\end{pmatrix}, \begin{pmatrix}1\\0\\1\\0\\1\end{pmatrix}, \begin{pmatrix}1\\1\\0\\0\\1\end{pmatrix}, \begin{pmatrix}1\\1\\1\\1\\1\end{pmatrix} \right\}$$

$$C_{s2}^{1} = \left\{ \begin{pmatrix}0\\0\\0\\1\\0\end{pmatrix} \begin{pmatrix}0\\0\\1\\0\\0\end{pmatrix} \begin{pmatrix}0\\1\\0\\0\\0\end{pmatrix} \begin{pmatrix}0\\1\\1\\1\\0\end{pmatrix} \begin{pmatrix}1\\0\\0\\0\\0\end{pmatrix} \begin{pmatrix}1\\0\\1\\1\\0\end{pmatrix} \begin{pmatrix}1\\1\\0\\1\\0\end{pmatrix} \begin{pmatrix}1\\1\\1\\0\\0\end{pmatrix} \right\}$$

5–4 (Cont'd)

$$C_{s3}^{1} = \left\{ \begin{pmatrix}0\\0\\0\\1\\1\end{pmatrix}, \begin{pmatrix}0\\0\\1\\0\\1\end{pmatrix}, \begin{pmatrix}0\\1\\0\\0\\1\end{pmatrix}, \begin{pmatrix}0\\1\\1\\1\\1\end{pmatrix}, \begin{pmatrix}1\\0\\0\\0\\1\end{pmatrix}, \begin{pmatrix}1\\0\\1\\1\\1\end{pmatrix}, \begin{pmatrix}1\\1\\0\\1\\1\end{pmatrix}, \begin{pmatrix}1\\1\\1\\0\\1\end{pmatrix} \right\}$$

Picking, say, the first element in each set and multiplying it by **A**, we obtain the four foci:

5–5 $$\mathbf{0} = \begin{pmatrix}0\\0\\0\\0\\0\end{pmatrix}, \ \mathbf{s}_1 = \begin{pmatrix}1\\1\\0\\0\\1\end{pmatrix}, \ \mathbf{s}_2 = \begin{pmatrix}1\\1\\0\\0\\0\end{pmatrix}, \ \mathbf{s}_3 = \begin{pmatrix}0\\0\\0\\0\\1\end{pmatrix}$$

The state diagram of **A** can now be constructed as shown in Fig. 5.5 (where, for convenience, $\mathbf{s} = (\alpha_0, \alpha_1, \ldots, \alpha_{n-1})^{TR}$ is denoted by the decimal integer $\sum_{\nu=0}^{n-1} \alpha_\nu 2^\nu$).

In cases where $|C_0^1| = 1$ the above procedure amounts to an exhaustive enumeration of **As** for all **s** in S_n. However, in cases where $|C_0^1| >> 1$, this procedure results in considerable computational saving. (Note that $|C_0^1| = 1$ if and only if the nullity of **A** is 0, and hence if and only if **A** is nonsingular).

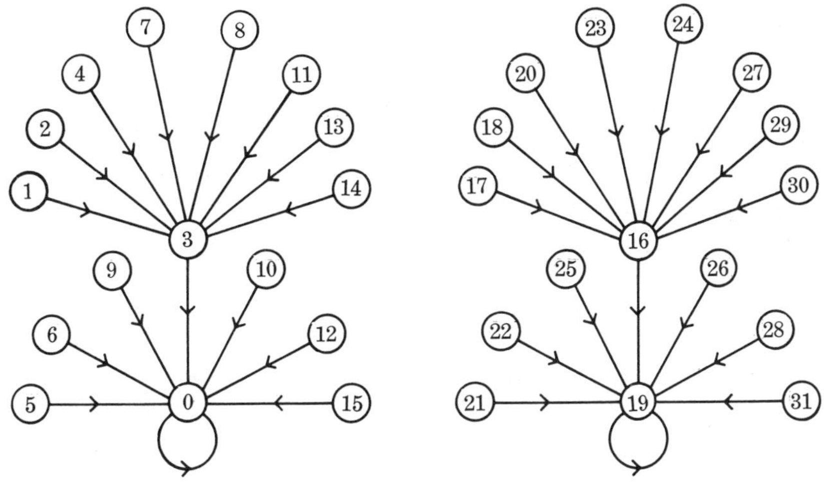

FIG. 5.5—State diagram of IC of Fig. 5.4

6. Nonsingular ICs

An IC is *nonsingular* if its characteristic matrix **A** is nonsingular. In this case none of the elementary divisors of **A** are divisible by x, and every elementary block in the rational canonical form $\mathbf{A}^*$ is nonsingular.

6–1 *Assertion:* The state diagram of a nonsingular IC consists of pure cycles only.

Proof: Since **A** is nonsingular, every state **s** has exactly one predecessor, namely $\mathbf{A}^{-1}\mathbf{s}$. Since **s** necessarily has exactly one successor, namely **As**, **6–1** follows.

In Secs. **7** through **15**, our discussion will be confined entirely to nonsingular ICs. In this discussion the term "cycle" will be understood to mean "pure cycle."

7. State Period

The *period* of a given state **s** is the least integer T such that $\mathbf{A}^T\mathbf{s} = \mathbf{s}$. Thus, the period of **s** is the length of the cycle which includes **s**. (The cycle containing **0** is always of length 1.)

7–1 *Assertion:* Let $\mathcal{A}$ be an n-dimensional IC with the characteristic matrix

7–2
$$\mathbf{A} = \begin{pmatrix} \mathbf{A}_1 & \\ & \mathbf{A}_2 \end{pmatrix}$$

(where $\mathbf{A}_1$ and $\mathbf{A}_2$ are square), and let $\begin{pmatrix} \mathbf{s}_1 \\ \mathbf{0} \end{pmatrix}$ and $\begin{pmatrix} \mathbf{0} \\ \mathbf{s}_2 \end{pmatrix}$ be n-dimensional vectors, where $\mathbf{s}_1$ and $\mathbf{s}_2$ occupy the same rows as $\mathbf{A}_1$ and $\mathbf{A}_2$, respectively, occupy in **A**. If $\begin{pmatrix} \mathbf{s}_1 \\ \mathbf{0} \end{pmatrix}$ has period T_1 and $\begin{pmatrix} \mathbf{0} \\ \mathbf{s}_2 \end{pmatrix}$ period T_2, then the period of $\begin{pmatrix} \mathbf{s}_1 \\ \mathbf{s}_2 \end{pmatrix}$ is lcm (T_1, T_2).

Proof: The period T of $\begin{pmatrix} \mathbf{s}_1 \\ \mathbf{s}_2 \end{pmatrix}$ is the least integer such that

7–3
$$\mathbf{A}^T \begin{pmatrix} \mathbf{s}_1 \\ \\ \mathbf{s}_2 \end{pmatrix} = \begin{pmatrix} \mathbf{s}_1 \\ \\ \mathbf{s}_2 \end{pmatrix}$$

or

7–4
$$\begin{pmatrix} \mathbf{A}_1^T\mathbf{s}_1 \\ \\ \mathbf{A}_2^T\mathbf{s}_2 \end{pmatrix} = \begin{pmatrix} \mathbf{s}_1 \\ \\ \mathbf{s}_2 \end{pmatrix}$$

Hence, T must be a multiple of T_1 and T_2. Since **7–3** holds when T = lcm (T_1, T_2), **7–1** follows.

8. Cycle Sets

Let $\mathcal{A}$ be an IC with the characteristic matrix **A**. Suppose the state diagram of $\mathcal{A}$ consists of N_1 cycles of length T_1, N_2 cycles of length T_2, . . . , N_q cycles of length T_q. The diagram can be specified uniquely, up to isomorphism, by the expression

8–1
$$\Sigma = \{N_1[T_1] + N_2[T_2] + \cdots + N_q[T_q]\}$$

Σ is called the *cycle set* of $\mathcal{A}$, or of **A**. Each term $N_i[T_i]$ in Σ is called a *cycle term*. Clearly,

8–2
$$N_i[T_i] + N_j[T_i] = (N_i + N_j)[T_i]$$

Now, let **A** be given as in **7–2**. Also, suppose the cycle set of $\mathbf{A}_1$ has a cycle term $N_1[T_1]$ and that of $\mathbf{A}_2$ a cycle term $N_2[T_2]$. Hence, there are N_1T_1 states of the form $\begin{pmatrix} \mathbf{s}_1 \\ \mathbf{0} \end{pmatrix}$ and period T_1, and N_2T_2 states of the form $\begin{pmatrix} \mathbf{0} \\ \mathbf{s}_2 \end{pmatrix}$ and period T_2. By **7–1**, then, the state diagram of **A** must contain $(N_1T_1)(N_2T_2)$ states of period lcm (T_1, T_2), and hence

8–3 $$\frac{N_1N_2T_1T_2}{\text{lcm }(T_1, T_2)} = N_1N_2 \text{ gcd } (T_1, T_2)$$

cycles of length lcm (T_1, T_2).

We shall now define the *product* of two cycle terms as a cycle term obtained by the following formula

8–4 $$N_i[T_i]N_j[T_j] = N_iN_j \text{ gcd } (T_i, T_j)[\text{lcm } (T_i, T_j)]$$

If $\Sigma_1 = \{a_1 + a_2 + \ . \ . \ . \ + a_r\}$ and $\Sigma_2 = \{b_1 + b_2 + \ . \ . \ . \ + b_s\}$, where the a_i and b_j are cycle terms, then the *cycle set product* $\Sigma_1\Sigma_2$ is defined as the cycle set whose cycle terms are all possible products a_ib_j, computed as per **8–4**. Thus, cycle set multiplication is seen to be commutative and associative. In view of this definition and the remarks in the preceding paragraph, we can now state the following

8–5 *Assertion:* Let

8–6 $$\mathbf{A} = \begin{pmatrix} \mathbf{A}_1 & \\ & \mathbf{A}_2 \end{pmatrix}$$

If the cycle sets of $\mathbf{A}_1$ and $\mathbf{A}_2$ are Σ_1 and Σ_2, respectively, then the cycle set of **A** is $\Sigma_1\Sigma_2$.

8–7 *Example:* Given:

8–8 $$\begin{aligned} \Sigma_1 &= \{2[1] + 3[2] + 7[8]\} \\ \Sigma_2 &= \{4[1] + 2[6]\} \end{aligned}$$

we have:

8–9 $$\begin{aligned} \Sigma_1\Sigma_2 &= \{2[1] + 3[2] + 7[8]\}\{4[1] + 2[6]\} \\ &= \{2[1]4[1] + 2[1]2[6] + 3[2]4[1] + 3[2]2[6] + 7[8]4[1] + 7[8]2[6]\} \\ &= \{8[1] + 4[6] + 12[2] + 12[6] + 28[8] + 28[24]\} \\ &= \{8[1] + 12[2] + 16[6] + 28[8] + 28[24]\} \end{aligned}$$

9. Cycle Set Computation

For the purpose of computing its cycle set, the characteristic matrix **A** can be replaced with its rational canonical form

9–1 $$\mathbf{A}^* = \begin{pmatrix} \mathbf{M}_{d_1(x)} & & & & \\ & \mathbf{M}_{d_2(x)} & & & \\ & & \cdot & & \\ & & & \cdot & \\ & & & & \cdot \\ & & & & & \mathbf{M}_{d_w(x)} \end{pmatrix}$$

From **8–5**, by induction, we have

9–2 *Assertion:* Let $d_1(x), d_2(x), \ . \ . \ . \ , d_w(x)$ be the elementary divisors of **A**, and let Σ_i denote the cycle set of $\mathbf{M}_{d_i(x)}$. Then the cycle set of **A** is given by

9–3 $$\Sigma = \Sigma_1\Sigma_2 \ldots \Sigma_w$$

What remains to be worked out is the formulation of a procedure for determining the cycle set of a typical elementary block $\mathbf{M}_{d_i(x)}$. Once the cycle set is determined for each such block in $\mathbf{A}^*$, the cycle set of $\mathbf{A}$ can be computed directly by **9–3**.

10. Elementary Cycle Sets

Consider an n-dimensional IC $\mathfrak{M}$ over $GF(p)$, with the characteristic matrix $\mathbf{M}_{d(x)}^{\mathrm{TR}}$, where

10–1 $$d(x) = \alpha_0 + \alpha_1 x + \ldots + \alpha_{n-1}x^{n-1} + x^n = [p(x)]^e \qquad (\alpha_0 \neq 0)$$

where $p(x)$ is an irreducible monic polynomial of degree h. We shall represent a state

10–2 $$\mathbf{s} = \begin{pmatrix} \sigma_0 \\ \sigma_1 \\ \cdot \\ \cdot \\ \cdot \\ \sigma_{n-1} \end{pmatrix}$$

of $\mathfrak{M}$ by an element $s(\xi)$ in $R_{d(\xi)}$ [the ring of polynomials over $GF(p)$ modulo $d(x)$] in the following manner:

10–3 $$s(\xi) = \sigma_0 + \sigma_1\xi + \ldots + \sigma_{n-1}\xi^{n-1}$$

10–4 *Assertion:* If $\mathbf{s}$ is represented by $s(\xi)$ (in $R_{d(\xi)}$), then the νth successor of $\mathbf{s}$ is represented by $\xi^\nu s(\xi)$.

Proof: The successor of $\mathbf{s}$ is given by

10–5 $$\mathbf{s}' = \mathbf{M}_{d(x)}^{\mathrm{TR}}\,\mathbf{s} = \begin{pmatrix} & & & & -\alpha_0 \\ 1 & & & & -\alpha_1 \\ & 1 & & & -\alpha_2 \\ & & \cdot & & \cdot \\ & & & \cdot & \cdot \\ & & & \cdot & \cdot \\ & & & 1 & -\alpha_{n-1} \end{pmatrix} \begin{pmatrix} \sigma_0 \\ \sigma_1 \\ \sigma_2 \\ \cdot \\ \cdot \\ \cdot \\ \sigma_{n-1} \end{pmatrix} = \begin{pmatrix} -\alpha_0\sigma_{n-1} \\ \sigma_0 - \alpha_1\sigma_{n-1} \\ \sigma_1 - \alpha_2\sigma_{n-1} \\ \cdot \\ \cdot \\ \cdot \\ \sigma_{n-2} - \alpha_{n-1}\sigma_{n-1} \end{pmatrix}$$

In $R_{d(\xi)}$, $\mathbf{s}'$ is represented by

10–6 $$\begin{aligned} s'(\xi) &= -\alpha_0\sigma_{n-1} + (\sigma_0 - \alpha_1\sigma_{n-1})\xi + (\sigma_1 - \alpha_2\sigma_{n-1})\xi^2 + \ldots \\ &\quad + (\sigma_{n-2} - \alpha_{n-1}\sigma_{n-1})\xi^{n-1} \\ &= \sigma_0\xi + \sigma_1\xi^2 + \ldots + \sigma_{n-2}\xi^{n-1} + \sigma_{n-1}\xi^n \\ &\quad - \sigma_{n-1}(\alpha_0 + \alpha_1\xi + \ldots + \alpha_{n-1}\xi^{n-1} + \xi^n) \\ &= \xi s(\xi) - \sigma_{n-1}d(\xi) = \xi s(\xi) \end{aligned}$$

10–4 follows by induction.

In view of **10–4**, the period of any state $\mathbf{s}$ of $\mathfrak{M}$ is the least integer T such that $\xi^T s(\xi) = s(\xi)$, or such that

10–7 $$(1 - \xi^T)s(\xi) = 0$$

Hence, T is the least integer such that, for some $a(x)$,

10–8 $$(1 - x^T)s(x) = a(x)[p(x)]^e$$

In what follows, T_i will denote the exponent of $[p(x)]^i$.

10–9 *Assertion:* If $s(x)$ is divisible by $[p(x)]^{e-i}$ but not by $[p(x)]^{e-i+1}$, then the period of **s** is T_i.

Proof: By **10–8**, $[p(x)]^i$ must divide $1 - x^T$. Hence T is the least integer such that $[p(x)]^i$ divides $1 - x^T$. By definition, then, $T = T_i$.

10–10 *Assertion:* $\mathfrak{M}$ has $p^{ih} - p^{(i-1)h}$ distinct states **s** such that $s(x)$ is divisible by $[p(x)]^{e-i}$ but not by $[p(x)]^{e-i+1}$.

Proof: If $s(x)$ is divisible by $[p(x)]^{e-i}$, it has the form $s(x) = b(x)[p(x)]^{e-i}$ with some $b(x)$ of degree at most $n - h(e - i) = ih$. Since there are p^{ih} distinct polynomials $b(x)$, the number of distinct **s** such that $s(x)$ is divisible by $[p(x)]^{e-i}$ is p^{ih}. Similarly, the number of distinct **s** such that $s(x)$ is divisible by $[p(x)]^{e-i+1}$ is $p^{(i-1)h}$.

Combining **10–9** and **10–10**, we have

10–11 *Assertion:* $\mathfrak{M}$ has $p^{ih} - p^{(i-1)h}$ states of period T_i $(i = 1, 2, \ldots, e)$.

10–12 *Assertion:* The cycle set of $\mathfrak{M}$ is given by

10–13
$$\left\{1[1] + \frac{p^h - 1}{T_1}[T_1] + \frac{p^{2h} - p^h}{T_2}[T_2] + \frac{p^{3h} - p^{2h}}{T_3}[T_3] + \cdots + \frac{p^{eh} - p^{(e-1)h}}{T_e}[T_e]\right\}$$

Proof: By **10–11**, the cycle set must include all cycle terms listed after 1[1]. The number of states accounted for in these terms is

10–14
$$\sum_{i=1}^{e}(p^{ih} - p^{(i-1)h}) = p^{eh} - 1 = p^n - 1$$

The only state unaccounted for is **0**, as 0 is the only polynomial divisible by both $[p(x)]^{e-i}$ and $[p(x)]^{e-i+1}$ for every i. Since the period of **0** is 1, 1[1] can be added to the other cycle terms to account for all p^n states of $\mathfrak{M}$.

The cycle set **10–13** is the cycle set of $\mathbf{M}_{d(x)}^{\mathrm{TR}}$, and hence (since $\mathbf{M}_{d(x)}^{\mathrm{TR}}$ is similar to $\mathbf{M}_{d(x)}$) the cycle set of an elementary block in a rational canonical matrix. Such a cycle set—i.e., a cycle set of the companion matrix of a power of an irreducible polynomial—will be called an *elementary cycle set.*

11. Properties of Elementary Cycle Sets

The period T_1 in the elementary cycle set **10–13** is called the *basic period* of the cycle set. It equals the exponent of $p(x)$, as well as the length of the shortest cycle (other than the cycle of length 1 containing **0**) in the cycle set.

11–1 *Assertion:* A basic period and p are relatively prime.

Proof: Let T_1 be a basic period. By **1.8–1**, T_1 must divide $p^h - 1$. If T_1 were a multiple of p, we could write

11–2
$$kp = p^h - 1$$

with some integer k. Since **11–2** is false modulo p, it is false over the ring of integers. Hence T_1 cannot be a multiple of p. Since p is prime, **11–1** follows.

By **1.8–2**, if T_i is as defined in Sec. **10**, then $T_i = p^{r_i}T_1$, where p^{r_i} is the least integer such that $p^{r_i} \geq i$. Thus, $T_2, T_3, \ldots, T_e$ in **10–13** are all multiples of p (and, in particular, $T_2 = pT_1$).

11–3 *Assertion:* If the $n \times n$ matrices $\mathbf{M}_{[p_1(x)]^{e_1}}$ and $\mathbf{M}_{[p_2(x)]^{e_2}}$ have cycle sets with identical basic periods, then $p_1(x)$ and $p_2(x)$ have the same degree (and $e_1 = e_2$).

Proof: Let $p_1(x)$ be of degree h_1 and exponent T_1, and $p_2(x)$ of degree h_2 and exponent T_2. By **1.8–1**, h_1 (or h_2) is the least integer ν such that T_1 (or T_2) divides $p^\nu - 1$. Hence, if $T_1 = T_2$, $h_1 = h_2$ (and hence $e_1 = e_2$).

11–4 *Assertion:* An elementary cycle set cannot be expressed as the product of two or more elementary cycle sets.

Proof: Let $\Sigma = \Sigma_1\Sigma_2 \ldots \Sigma_r$ $(r > 1)$, where $\Sigma, \Sigma_1, \Sigma_2, \ldots, \Sigma_r$ are all elementary cycle sets:

11–5
$$\begin{aligned}
\Sigma &= \left\{1[1] + \frac{p^h - 1}{T_1}[T_1] + N_2[T_2] + \cdots + N_e[T_e]\right\} \\
\Sigma_1 &= \left\{1[1] + \frac{p^{h_1} - 1}{T_{11}}[T_{11}] + N_{21}[T_{21}] + \cdots + N_{e1}[T_{e1}]\right\} \\
\Sigma_2 &= \left\{1[1] + \frac{p^{h_2} - 1}{T_{12}}[T_{12}] + N_{22}[T_{22}] + \cdots + N_{e2}[T_{e2}]\right\} \\
&\ \ \vdots \\
\Sigma_r &= \left\{1[1] + \frac{p^{h_r} - 1}{T_{1r}}[T_{1r}] + N_{2r}[T_{2r}] + \cdots + N_{er}[T_{er}]\right\}
\end{aligned}$$

For all $i > 1$, T_i must be a multiple of pT_1, and T_{ij} a multiple of pT_{1j}. Suppose the Σ_j are arranged so that

11–6 $T_{11} = T_{12} = \cdots = T_{1k} < T_{1(k+1)} \leq T_{1(k+2)} \leq \cdots \leq T_{1r}$ $(1 \leq k \leq r)$

By the rules of cycle set multiplication, we must have $T_{11} = T_{12} = \cdots = T_{1k} = T_1$, and (equating terms in Σ and $\Sigma_1\Sigma_2 \ldots \Sigma_r$):

11–7 $1 + (p^h - 1) = [1 + (p^{h_1} - 1)][1 + (p^{h_2} - 1)] \ldots [1 + (p^{h_k} - 1)]$

or

11–8
$$p^h = p^{h_1 + h_2 + \cdots + h_k}$$

and hence

11–9
$$h = h_1 + h_2 + \cdots + h_k$$

But, by **1.8–1**, the integers $h, h_1, h_2, \ldots, h_k$ all equal the least integer ν such that T_1 divides $p^\nu - 1$. Hence $h = h_1 = h_2 = \cdots = h_k$ which, by **11–9**, implies $k = 1$ and, by **11–6**, implies $T_{11} < T_{12}$. Since $h = h_1$ and $T_1 = T_{11}$,

11–10
$$T_{i1} = T_i,\ N_{i1} = N_i \qquad (i = 2, 3, \ldots, e_1)$$

Hence $T_{12} = T_{e_1+1}$. But this is impossible, since T_{e_1+1} is a multiple of p while—by **11–1**—T_{12} is not a multiple of p. The assumption $r > 1$, therefore, is false.

12. Cycle Set Computation—Summary

12–1 On the basis of the results in Sec. **10**, we can now summarize a procedure for obtaining the cycle set of an arbitrary nonsingular IC over $GF(p)$ with the characteristic matrix **A**:

(i) Find the elementary divisors of **A**, say, $d_1(x), d_2(x), \ldots, d_w(x)$.

(ii) Let $d_j(x) = [p_j(x)]^{e_j}$, where $p_j(x)$ is of degree h_j. Find the exponent T_{1j} of $p_j(x)$ (from Table A4 of the Appendix, or by trial and error, exploiting the fact that T_{1j} divides $p^{h_j} - 1$). Find the periods $T_{ij} = p^{r_i}T_{1j}$, where p^{r_i} is the least integer such that $p^{r_i} \geq i$. (Repeat for $j = 1, 2, \ldots, w$; $i = 1, 2, \ldots, e_j$.)

(iii) The cycle set of $\mathbf{M}_{d_j(x)}$ is

12–2 $$\Sigma_j = \left\{1[1] + \frac{p^{h_j} - 1}{T_{1j}}[T_{1j}] + \frac{p^{2h_j} - p^{h_j}}{T_{2j}}[T_{2j}] + \frac{p^{3h_j} - p^{2h_j}}{T_{3j}}[T_{3j}] + \cdots + \frac{p^{e_jh_j} - p^{(e_j-1)h_j}}{T_{e_jj}}[T_{e_jj}]\right\}$$

(iv) The cycle set of $\mathbf{A}$ is

12–3 $$\Sigma = \Sigma_1\Sigma_2 \ldots \Sigma_w$$

12–4 *Example:* Consider the following characteristic matrix over $GF(2)$:

12–5 $$\mathbf{A} = \mathbf{A}^* = \begin{pmatrix} 0 & 1 & 0 & & \\ 0 & 0 & 1 & & \\ 1 & 1 & 1 & & \\ & & & 0 & 1 \\ & & & 1 & 1 \end{pmatrix}$$

In this case:

12–6 $$\begin{aligned} d_1(x) &= 1 + x + x^2 + x^3 = (1 + x)^3,\ d_2(x) = 1 + x + x^2 \\ p_1(x) &= 1 + x\ (h_1 = 1,\ e_1 = 3),\ p_2(x) = 1 + x + x^2\ (h_2 = 2,\ e_2 = 1) \\ T_{11} &= 1,\ T_{21} = 2,\ T_{31} = 4,\ T_{12} = 3 \end{aligned}$$

Hence:

12–7 $$\begin{aligned} \Sigma_1 &= \left\{1[1] + \frac{2 - 1}{1}[1] + \frac{2^2 - 2}{2}[2] + \frac{2^3 - 2^2}{4}[4]\right\} \\ &= \{1[1] + 1[1] + 1[2] + 1[4]\} \\ &= \{2[1] + 1[2] + 1[4]\} \end{aligned}$$

12–8 $$\Sigma_2 = \left\{1[1] + \frac{2^2 - 1}{3}[3]\right\} = \{1[1] + 1[3]\}$$

12–9 $$\begin{aligned} \Sigma = \Sigma_1\Sigma_2 &= \{2[1] + 1[2] + 1[4]\}\{1[1] + 1[3]\} \\ &= \{2[1] + 1[2] + 2[3] + 1[4] + 1[6] + 1[12]\} \end{aligned}$$

The state diagram of $\mathbf{A}$ is shown in Fig. 5.6.

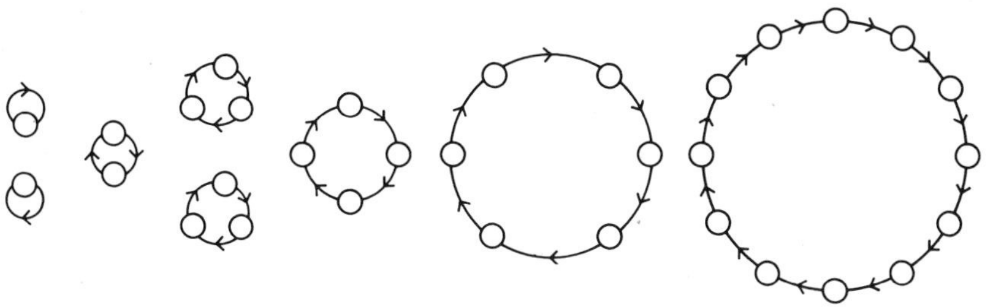

FIG. 5.6—State diagram of IC of Example **12–4**

13. Natural Periods

Let us list the periods associated with each Σ_j, as given in **12–2** (with $T_{0j} = 1$ for all j):

13–1

$$\begin{array}{l} T_{01}, T_{11}, T_{21}, \ldots, T_{e_1 1} \\ T_{02}, T_{12}, T_{22}, \ldots, T_{e_2 2} \\ \cdot \\ \cdot \\ \cdot \\ T_{0w}, T_{1w}, T_{2w}, \ldots, T_{e_w w} \end{array}$$

From the rules of cycle set multiplication it follows that the cycle lengths associated with Σ are all the integers of the form

13–2 $$\text{lcm}\,(T_{i1}, T_{i2}, \ldots, T_{i_w w}) \qquad (0 \le i_j \le e_j)$$

An integer of the form **13–2** is called a *natural period* of the IC. Thus, a state diagram of an IC contains a cycle of length T if and only if T is a natural period of the IC.

If the elementary divisor $d_{j1}(x)$ divides the elementary divisor $d_{j2}(x)$, Σ_{j1} is completely included in Σ_{j2}; moreover, the lcm of a period in Σ_{j1} and a period in Σ_{j2} is some period in Σ_{j2}. Hence, for purpose of compiling a list of natural periods, only cycle sets associated with *leading* elementary divisors need to be considered.

13–3 *Example:* Let **A** be the characteristic matrix of an IC $\mathcal{A}$ over $GF(2)$, and suppose the minimum polynomial of **A** is given by

13–4 $$m_{\mathbf{A}}(x) = (1 + x)^5(1 + x + x^3)^3$$

The cycle sets of $\mathbf{M}_{(1+x)^5}$ and $\mathbf{M}_{(1+x+x^3)^3}$ contain, respectively, the following periods:

13–5

$$\begin{array}{l} 1,\ 1,\ 2,\ 4,\ 4,\ 8 \\ 1,\ 7,\ 14,\ 28 \end{array}$$

Hence, the natural periods of $\mathcal{A}$ are

13–6 $$1,\ 2,\ 4,\ 7,\ 8,\ 14,\ 28,\ 56$$

14. Computation of State Period

14–1 On the basis of **10–9** and **7–1**, we can now formulate a procedure for determining the period of any state **s** in the nonsingular IC whose characteristic matrix is **A** (notation as in Sec. **12**):

(i) Find the transposed rational canonical form $(\mathbf{A}^*)^{TR} = \mathbf{PAP}^{-1}$ of **A**.
(ii) Compute

14–2 $$\mathbf{s}^* = \mathbf{Ps} = \begin{bmatrix} \mathbf{s}_1 \\ \mathbf{s}_2 \\ \cdot \\ \cdot \\ \cdot \\ \mathbf{s}_w \end{bmatrix}$$

where $\mathbf{s}_j$ occupies the same rows as $\mathbf{M}_{d_j(x)}^{TR}$ does in $(\mathbf{A}^*)^{TR}$. Let $s_j(\xi)$ be the representation of $\mathbf{s}_j$ in $R_{d_j(\xi)}$ (see **10–3**).

(iii) Let $d_j(x) = [p_j(x)]^{e_j}$. For every nonzero $\mathbf{s}_j$ find the highest power of $p_j(x)$ which divides $s_j(x)$. If this power is k_j, the period of $\mathbf{s}_j$ is $T_{(e_j-k_j)j}$ (i.e., the exponent of $[p_j(x)]^{e_j-k_j}$). If $\mathbf{s}_j = \mathbf{0}$, its period is 1.

(iv) If T_j denotes the period of $\mathbf{s}_j$, then the period of $\mathbf{s}$ is lcm $(T_1, T_2, \ldots, T_w)$.

14–3 *Example:* Consider the IC whose characteristic matrix is the transpose of $\mathbf{A}$ as given in **12–5**. Let

14–4
$$\mathbf{s} = \mathbf{s}^* = \begin{pmatrix} 0 \\ 1 \\ 1 \\ 0 \\ 1 \end{pmatrix} \begin{matrix} \left.\begin{matrix} \\ \\ \\ \end{matrix}\right\} \mathbf{s}_1 \\ \left.\begin{matrix} \\ \\ \end{matrix}\right\} \mathbf{s}_2 \end{matrix}$$

In this case:

14–5
$$\begin{aligned} d_1(x) &= (1+x)^3, & d_2(x) &= 1 + x + x^2 \\ s_1(x) &= x + x^2 = x(1+x), & s_2(x) &= x \\ k_1 &= 1,\ T_{(3-1)1} = T_{21} = 2, & k_2 &= 0,\ T_{(1-0)2} = T_{12} = 3 \end{aligned}$$

Hence, the period of $\mathbf{s}$ is lcm $(2, 3) = 6$.

15. Initiation of a Specified Cycle

15–1 One can also formulate a procedure for finding a state $\mathbf{s}$ in an IC, which initiates a cycle of specified length T, where T is a natural period of the IC (notation as in Sec. **12**):

(i) Find the transposed rational canonical form $(\mathbf{A}^*)^{\mathrm{TR}} = \mathbf{PAP}^{-1}$ of $\mathbf{A}$.

(ii) Find any set of periods $T_{i_1 1}, T_{i_2 2}, \ldots, T_{i_w w} (0 \le i_j \le e_j)$, such that

15–2
$$T = \operatorname{lcm}(T_{i_1 1}, T_{i_2 2}, \ldots, T_{i_w w})$$

(iii) For each $T_{i_j j}$ select a polynomial $s_j(x)$ in the following manner: If $T_{i_j j} = 1$, choose $s_j(x) = 0$; otherwise, choose $s_j(x) = [p_j(x)]^{e_j - i_j}$.

(iv) Construct the vector

15–3
$$\mathbf{s}^* = \begin{pmatrix} \mathbf{s}_1 \\ \mathbf{s}_2 \\ \cdot \\ \cdot \\ \cdot \\ \mathbf{s}_w \end{pmatrix}$$

where $\mathbf{s}_j$ occupies the same rows as $\mathbf{M}^{\mathrm{TR}}_{d_j(x)}$ does in $(\mathbf{A}^*)^{\mathrm{TR}}$, and where $\mathbf{s}_j$ is the state represented by $s_j(\xi)$ in $R_{d_j(\xi)}$ (see **10–3**).

(v) A state which initiates a cycle of length T is $\mathbf{s} = \mathbf{P}^{-1}\mathbf{s}^*$.

15–4 *Example:* Consider an IC over $GF(2)$ with the characteristic matrix

15–5
$$\mathbf{A} = (\mathbf{A}^*)^{\mathrm{TR}} = \begin{pmatrix} \mathbf{M}^{\mathrm{TR}}_{(1+x)^3} & & \\ & \mathbf{M}^{\mathrm{TR}}_{1+x+x^2} & \\ & & \mathbf{M}^{\mathrm{TR}}_{(1+x+x^3)^3} \end{pmatrix}$$

In this case, the polynomials and periods of interest can be summarized as follows:

15–6

j	$d_j(x)$	$p_j(x)$	e_j	$T_{ij} (i = 0, 1, \ldots, e_j)$
1	$(1+x)^3$	$1+x$	3	1, 1, 2, 4
2	$1+x+x^2$	$1+x+x^2$	1	1, 3
3	$(1+x+x^3)^3$	$1+x+x^3$	3	1, 7, 14, 28

The natural periods are:

15–7 $$1,\ 2,\ 3,\ 4,\ 6,\ 7,\ 12,\ 14,\ 21,\ 28,\ 42,\ 84$$

Suppose we wish to initiate a cycle of length $T = 42$. We can write:

15–8 $$42 = \text{lcm}\ (2, 3, 7) = \text{lcm}\ (T_{21}, T_{12}, T_{13})$$

Hence,

15–9 $$\begin{aligned} s_1(x) &= (1 + x)^{3-2} = 1 + x \\ s_2(x) &= (1 + x + x^2)^{1-1} = 1 \\ s_3(x) &= (1 + x + x^3)^{3-1} = 1 + x^2 + x^6 \end{aligned}$$

A state satisfying the requirement is given by

15–10 $$\mathbf{s} = \mathbf{s}^* = \begin{pmatrix} \mathbf{s}_1 \\ \mathbf{s}_2 \\ \mathbf{s}_3 \end{pmatrix}$$

where

15–11 $$\mathbf{s}_1 = \begin{pmatrix} 1 \\ 1 \\ 0 \end{pmatrix} \quad \mathbf{s}_2 = \begin{pmatrix} 1 \\ 0 \end{pmatrix} \quad \mathbf{s}_3 = \begin{pmatrix} 1 \\ 0 \\ 1 \\ 0 \\ 0 \\ 0 \\ 1 \\ 0 \\ 0 \end{pmatrix}$$

16. Nilpotent ICs

An IC is *nilpotent* if its characteristic matrix **A** is nilpotent (i.e., if for some finite r, $\mathbf{A}^r = \mathbf{0}$). By **1.16–3** and **1.16–4**, **A** is nilpotent if and only if its characteristic polynomial is of the form x^r, and hence if and only if its rational canonical form is given by

16–1 $$\mathbf{A}^* = \begin{pmatrix} \mathbf{M}_{x^{r_1}} & & & & \\ & \mathbf{M}_{x^{r_2}} & & & \\ & & \cdot & & \\ & & & \cdot & \\ & & & & \cdot \\ & & & & & \mathbf{M}_{x^{r_w}} \end{pmatrix}$$

In this case each elementary block has the form

16–2 $$\mathbf{M}_{x^{r_i}} = \begin{pmatrix} & 1 & & & & \\ & & 1 & & & \\ & & & \cdot & & \\ & & & & \cdot & \\ & & & & & \cdot \\ & & & & & 1 \\ 0 & 0 & 0 & \cdots & & 0 \end{pmatrix}$$

The matrix **16–2** will be referred to as an $r_i \times r_i$ *nilpotent block*. Up to similarity, **A** can be specified by the vector

16–3 $$\mathbf{m} = \begin{pmatrix} m_1 \\ m_2 \\ \cdot \\ \cdot \\ \cdot \\ m_L \end{pmatrix}$$

where m_i is the number of $i \times i$ nilpotent blocks in $\mathbf{A}^*$, and where L is the dimension of the largest nilpotent block. If n is the dimension of $\mathbf{A}$ and w the number of elementary divisors, we have the identities

16–4 $$m_1 + m_2 + \cdots + m_L = w$$

16–5 $$m_1 + 2m_2 + 3m_3 + \cdots + Lm_L = n$$

17. Properties of State Diagram of Nilpotent IC

17–1 *Assertion:* The state diagram of a nilpotent IC $\mathcal{A}$ consists of a tree and a cycle of length 1 touching the root of this tree. The root is the null state of $\mathcal{A}$.

Proof: Since $\mathbf{M}_{x^{r_i}}$ is 0 below the principal diagonal, so is $\mathbf{M}_{x^{r_i}}^t$ for any $t \geq 0$. Hence $(\mathbf{A}^*)^t - \mathbf{I}$, for any $t \geq 0$, is a triangular matrix with nonzero elements on the principal diagonal. This implies that $(\mathbf{A}^*)^t - \mathbf{I}$ is nonsingular, and hence that the only state such that $[(\mathbf{A}^*)^t - \mathbf{I}]\mathbf{s} = \mathbf{0}$, or such that $(\mathbf{A}^*)^t\mathbf{s} = \mathbf{s}$, is the state $\mathbf{0}$. Thus, the state diagram has no loops except the cycle of length 1 touching $\mathbf{0}$; moreover, since $\mathbf{A}$ is nilpotent, every state reaches $\mathbf{0}$ in a finite number of dits.

The tree in the state diagram of $\mathcal{A}$ will be referred to as the *tree of* $\mathcal{A}$. Properties of the tree of $\mathcal{A}$ can be readily deduced from a typical state sequence pursued by an IC whose characteristic matrix is $\mathbf{M}_{x^r}$. If $\mathbf{s}^0$ is an arbitrary r-dimensional vector, and $\mathbf{s}^t = \mathbf{M}_{x^r}^t\mathbf{s}^0$ $(t \geq 0)$, we have:

17–2 $$\mathbf{s}^0 = \begin{pmatrix} \alpha_1 \\ \alpha_2 \\ \cdot \\ \cdot \\ \cdot \\ \alpha_{r-2} \\ \alpha_{r-1} \\ \alpha_r \end{pmatrix}, \mathbf{s}^1 = \begin{pmatrix} \alpha_2 \\ \alpha_3 \\ \cdot \\ \cdot \\ \cdot \\ \alpha_{r-1} \\ \alpha_r \\ 0 \end{pmatrix}, \mathbf{s}^2 = \begin{pmatrix} \alpha_3 \\ \alpha_2 \\ \cdot \\ \cdot \\ \cdot \\ \alpha_r \\ 0 \\ 0 \end{pmatrix}, \ldots \mathbf{s}^{r-1} = \begin{pmatrix} \alpha_r \\ 0 \\ \cdot \\ \cdot \\ \cdot \\ 0 \\ 0 \\ 0 \end{pmatrix}, \mathbf{s}^r = \begin{pmatrix} 0 \\ 0 \\ \cdot \\ \cdot \\ \cdot \\ 0 \\ 0 \\ 0 \end{pmatrix}$$

Clearly, $\mathbf{s}^t = \mathbf{0}$ for all $t \geq r$. In view of **17–2**, we have immediately:

17–3 *Assertion:* Let $\mathcal{A}$ be a nilpotent IC whose characteristic matrix has the rational canonical form $\mathbf{A}^*$. The height of the tree of $\mathcal{A}$ equals the dimension L of the largest nilpotent block in $\mathbf{A}^*$.

The *tree set* τ of the nilpotent IC $\mathcal{A}$ is a set of integers $\{N_1, N_2, \ldots, N_L\}$, where N_i is the number of states in the ith level of the tree of $\mathcal{A}$ (N_0 is always 0). Given the vector $\mathbf{m}$, τ can readily be computed recursively, as follows:

17–4 *Assertion:*

$$N_i = p^{m_1+2m_2+3m_3+\cdots+(i-1)m_{i-1}+i(m_i+m_{i+1}+\cdots+m_L)} - (N_0 + N_1 + N_2 + \cdots + N_{i-1}) \qquad (i = 1, 2, \ldots, L)$$

Proof: Let $\mathcal{A}^*$ be the IC whose characteristic matrix is $\mathbf{A}^*$ of **16–1**, and consider an arbitrary state

17–5 $$\mathbf{s}^* = \begin{pmatrix} \mathbf{s}_1 \\ \mathbf{s}_2 \\ \cdot \\ \cdot \\ \cdot \\ \mathbf{s}_w \end{pmatrix}$$

of $\mathcal{A}^*$, where $\mathbf{s}_j$ occupies the same rows as $\mathbf{M}_{x^{r_i}}$ does in $\mathbf{A}^*$. The number of states of $\mathcal{A}^*$ reaching $\mathbf{0}$ in i dits *or less* equals the number of distinct vectors $\mathbf{s}^*$ such that every $\mathbf{s}_\nu$ of dimension $i + 1$ or greater has zeros below the ith element (see **17–2**). Hence

17–6
$$N_0 + N_1 + \cdots + N_i = p^{m_1+2m_2+\cdots+im_i+im_{i+1}+\cdots+im_L}$$

which yields **17–4.**

The following is a direct corollary of **4–4**:

17–7 *Assertion:* The number of ith predecessors of any given state in the tree of $\mathcal{A}$ is either 0 or $N_0 + N_1 + \cdots + N_i$.

17–8 *Example:* An IC over $GF(2)$ is characterized by

17–9
$$\mathbf{A} = \mathbf{A}^* = \begin{pmatrix} & 1 & & & & & \\ & & 1 & & & & \\ & & & 1 & & & \\ 0 & 0 & 0 & 0 & & & \\ & & & & & 1 & \\ & & & & 0 & 0 & \\ & & & & & & 0 \end{pmatrix}$$

In this case:

17–10
$$m_1 = 1,\ m_2 = 1,\ m_3 = 0,\ m_4 = 1;\ L = 4$$

17–11
$$\begin{aligned} N_1 &= 2^{1(1+1+1)} - 1 = 7 \\ N_2 &= 2^{1+2(1+1)} - (1 + 7) = 24 \\ N_3 &= 2^{1+2+3(1)} - (1 + 7 + 24) = 32 \\ N_4 &= 2^{1+2+4(1)} - (1 + 7 + 24 + 32) = 64 \end{aligned}$$

By **17–7**, the number of 1st predecessors of any state is either 0 or 8; the number of 2nd predecessors either 0 or 32; the number of 3rd predecessors either 0 or 64; the number of 4th predecessors either 0 or 128.

18. Construction of State Diagram of Nilpotent IC

In the notation of Secs. **16** and **17**, $\mathbf{A}$ determines $\mathbf{A}^*$, $\mathbf{A}^*$ determines $\mathbf{m}$, and $\mathbf{m}$ determines τ. We now wish to show that τ uniquely determines the structure of the tree of $\mathcal{A}$. This will be done by showing how the tree can be constructed recursively, proceeding from the root towards the highest level.

18–1 Trivially, level 0 has a single state, namely $\mathbf{0}$. Level 1 consists of N_1 states leading to $\mathbf{0}$. Now, suppose the first i levels of the tree have been constructed. Level $i + 1$ consists of a set of N_{i+1} states. Partition this set into "primary subsets" of order $N_0 + N_1 + \cdots + N_i$, such that each subset is the ith confluence set of a state in level 1. Each primary subset, in turn, is to be partitioned into "secondary subsets" of order $N_0 + N_1 + \cdots + N_{i-1}$, such that each subset is the $(i - 1)$st confluence set of a state in level 2. Each secondary subset is to be partitioned into "ternary subsets" of order $N_0 + N_1 + \cdots + N_{i-2}$, such that each subset is the $(i - 2)$nd confluence set of a state in level 3. The process is continued until subsets are obtained of order $N_0 + N_1$, which constitute the 1st confluence sets of states in level i. At this point, each state in level $i + 1$ can be assigned a successor in level i—this successor being unique up to isomorphism.

18–2 *Example:* Fig. 5.7 shows the tree for the IC of Example **17–8**. To illustrate the procedure described in **18–1**, consider the construction of level 4 (assuming all previous levels have been constructed). By **17–11**, $N_4 = 64$. Partition the set of 64 states into "primary subsets" of order $N_0 + N_1 + N_2 + N_3 = 64$ (one subset only, in this case), each subset leading to a different state in level 1. Partition each primary subset into "secondary subsets" of order $N_0 + N_1 + N_2 = 32$ (two secondary subsets per primary subset), each of which leads to a different state in level 2. Partition each secondary subset into "ternary subsets" of order $N_0 + N_1 = 8$ (four ternary subsets per secondary subset), each of which leads to a different state in level 3.

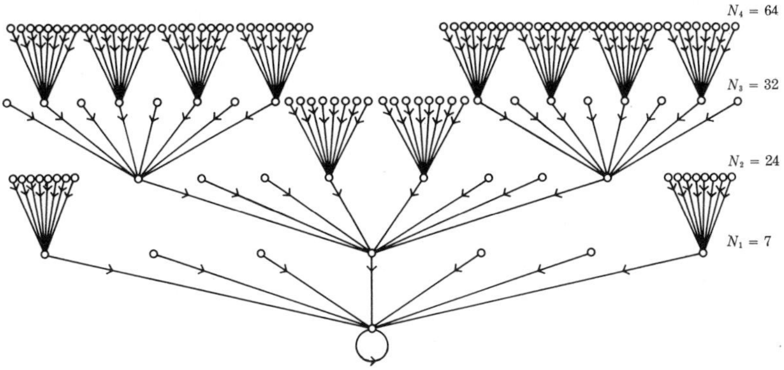

FIG. 5.7—Tree of IC of Example **17–8**

19. State Diagrams of Arbitrary ICs

Let $\mathfrak{A}$ be an arbitrary IC with the characteristic matrix **A**. Every elementary divisor $d_i(x)$ of **A** is of the form $[p_i(x)]^{e_i}$. If $p_i(0) \neq 0$, $M_{d_i(x)}$ is nonsingular; if $p_i(0) = 0$, $[p_i(x)]^{e_i} = x^{e_i}$ and $M_{d_i(x)}$ is nilpotent. Thus, the rational canonical form $\mathbf{A}^*$ of **A** can be written in the form

19–1 $$\mathbf{A}^* = \begin{pmatrix} \mathbf{A}_1 & \\ & \mathbf{A}_0 \end{pmatrix}$$

where $\mathbf{A}_1$ consists of all the nonsingular elementary blocks, and $\mathbf{A}_0$ of all nilpotent elementary blocks. Hence $\mathbf{A}_1$ and $\mathbf{A}_0$ are nonsingular and nilpotent, respectively.

Let $\mathfrak{A}^*$ denote the IC whose characteristic matrix is $\mathbf{A}^*$. Clearly, all states of $\mathfrak{A}^*$ expressible as $\begin{pmatrix} \mathbf{s}_1 \\ \mathbf{0} \end{pmatrix}$ (where $\mathbf{s}_1$ occupies the same rows as $\mathbf{A}_1$ does in $\mathbf{A}^*$) form cycles in the state diagram of $\mathfrak{A}^*$. These cycles constitute precisely the state diagram of $\mathbf{A}_1$. Each such state will be called a *cycle state*. Also, all states expressible as $\begin{pmatrix} \mathbf{0} \\ \mathbf{s}_0 \end{pmatrix}$ (where $\mathbf{s}_0$ occupies the same rows as $\mathbf{A}_0$ does in $\mathbf{A}^*$) form a tree in the state diagram of $\mathfrak{A}^*$. This tree, together with the cycle of length 1 at the root, constitute precisely the state diagram of $\mathbf{A}_0$. Each such state will be called a *tree state*.

Let $\begin{pmatrix} \Theta \\ \mathbf{0} \end{pmatrix}$ be any (fixed) cycle state and $\begin{pmatrix} \mathbf{0} \\ \mathbf{s}_0 \end{pmatrix}$ ($\mathbf{s}_0 \neq \mathbf{0}$) a tree state reaching **0** in t dits. Now, establish the following correspondence:

19–2 $$\mathbf{s} = \begin{pmatrix} \mathbf{0} \\ \mathbf{s}_0 \end{pmatrix} \longleftrightarrow \bar{\mathbf{s}} = \begin{pmatrix} (\mathbf{A}_1^{-1})^t \Theta \\ \mathbf{s}_0 \end{pmatrix}$$

which is, clearly, one to one. When $\mathbf{s} = \mathbf{0}$, $t = 0$ and we have the correspondence

19–3
$$\mathbf{0} \longleftrightarrow \begin{pmatrix} \Theta \\ \mathbf{0} \end{pmatrix}$$

Suppose $\mathbf{s}$ reaches $\mathbf{0}$ in t dits, where $t > 0$. Then

19–4
$$\mathbf{s}' = \mathbf{A}^*\mathbf{s} = \begin{pmatrix} \mathbf{A}_1 & \\ & \mathbf{A}_0 \end{pmatrix} \begin{pmatrix} \mathbf{0} \\ \mathbf{s}_0 \end{pmatrix} = \begin{pmatrix} \mathbf{0} \\ \mathbf{A}_0\mathbf{s}_0 \end{pmatrix}$$

19–5
$$\bar{\mathbf{s}}' = \mathbf{A}^*\bar{\mathbf{s}} = \begin{pmatrix} \mathbf{A}_1 & \\ & \mathbf{A}_0 \end{pmatrix} \begin{pmatrix} (\mathbf{A}_1^{-1})^t\Theta \\ \mathbf{s}_0 \end{pmatrix} = \begin{pmatrix} (\mathbf{A}_1^{-1})^{t-1}\Theta \\ \mathbf{A}_0\mathbf{s}_0 \end{pmatrix}$$

Since $\mathbf{s}'$ is a tree state reaching $\mathbf{0}$ in $t - 1$ dits, $\bar{\mathbf{s}}'$ is precisely the state which corresponds to $\mathbf{s}'$ under the correspondence **19–2.** Thus, the set of all states of the form $\bar{\mathbf{s}}$ constitute a subdiagram which is isomorphic to the subdiagram consisting of all states of the form $\mathbf{s}$ as defined in **19–2**. In other words, the set of all tree states which converge on Θ (where Θ is any fixed cycle state) form a tree which is structurally identical to the tree of $\mathbf{A}_0$.

19–6 In summary, we can now formulate the following procedure for determining the state diagram of $\mathcal{A}$:

(i) Find $\mathbf{A}^*$, partitioned as in **19–1.**

(ii) Construct the cycles of $\mathbf{A}_1$ (using cycle set methods) and the tree of $\mathbf{A}_0$ (using tree set methods).

(iii) The state diagram of $\mathcal{A}$ consists of the cycles of $\mathbf{A}_1$, with each state in each cycle serving as the root of a tree; all these trees are identical to the tree of $\mathbf{A}_0$.

19–7 *Example:* Consider the IC over $GF(2)$, characterized by

19–8
$$\mathbf{A} = \mathbf{A}^* = \begin{pmatrix} & 1 & & & & \\ & & 1 & & & \\ 1 & 1 & 1 & & & \\ & & & 0 & & \\ & & & & & 1 \\ & & & & 0 & 0 \end{pmatrix}$$

In this case:

19–9
$$\mathbf{A}_1 = \begin{pmatrix} & 1 & \\ & & 1 \\ 1 & 1 & 1 \end{pmatrix} \qquad \mathbf{A}_0 = \begin{pmatrix} 0 & & \\ & & 1 \\ & 0 & 0 \end{pmatrix}$$

The state diagram of $\mathbf{A}_1$ consists of cycles, specified by the cycle set $\Sigma = \{2[1] + 1[2] + 1[4]\}$. The state diagram of $\mathbf{A}_0$ consists of a tree, specified by $\tau = \{3, 4\}$, with a cycle of length 1 attached to the root. The complete diagram is shown in Fig. 5.8.

20. Realization of Characteristic Matrix

An IC $\mathcal{A}$ will be said to *realize* a characteristic matrix $\mathbf{A}$ *up to isomorphism*, if the state diagram of $\mathcal{A}$ is isomorphic to that of $\mathbf{A}$. Thus, the realization of $\mathbf{A}$ up to isomorphism can be the realization of $\mathbf{A}^*$, the rational canonical form of $\mathbf{A}$. More specifically, if the elementary divisors of $\mathbf{A}$ are $d_1(x), d_2(x), \ldots, d_w(x)$, then a realization of $\mathbf{A}$ up to isomorphism can be the union of the realizations of $\mathbf{M}_{d_1(x)}, \mathbf{M}_{d_2(x)}, \ldots, \mathbf{M}_{d_w(x)}$, each of which assumes the configuration of a shift register. The realization of any $\mathbf{M}_{d_i(x)}$ can be replaced with the

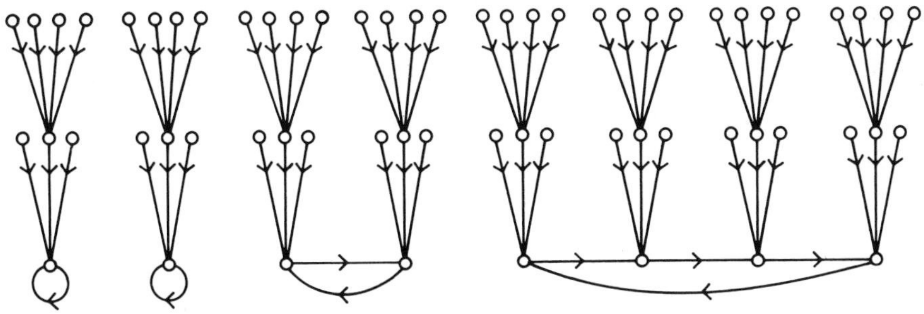

FIG. 5.8—State diagram of IC of Example **19–7**

realization of $\mathbf{M}^{\mathrm{TR}}_{d_i(x)}$, to result in a multi-adder shift register. Alternatively, $\mathbf{M}_{d_i(x)}$ can be replaced with the hypercompanion matrix $\mathbf{H}_{d_i(x)}$ (see **1.17–7**); if $d_i(x) = [p_i(x)]^{e_i}$, this results in e_i identical shift registers (each realizing $\mathbf{M}_{p_i(x)}$) connected in series. The latter substitution might be advantageous when the $d_i(x)$ consist of different powers of the same irreducible polynomial.

20–1 *Example:* Consider the following characteristic matrix over $GF(2)$:

20–2
$$\mathbf{A} = \begin{pmatrix} 0 & 0 & 1 & 1 & 1 & 1 & 1 & 1 \\ 0 & 1 & 0 & 0 & 0 & 0 & 0 & 0 \\ 0 & 1 & 1 & 1 & 1 & 1 & 1 & 1 \\ 0 & 0 & 0 & 0 & 1 & 1 & 1 & 1 \\ 0 & 0 & 0 & 0 & 1 & 0 & 0 & 0 \\ 0 & 0 & 0 & 0 & 0 & 1 & 0 & 1 \\ 0 & 0 & 0 & 0 & 0 & 0 & 1 & 1 \\ 0 & 0 & 0 & 0 & 0 & 0 & 1 & 0 \end{pmatrix}$$

As computed in **1.15–7**, the elementary divisors of **A** are

20–3
$$1 + x,\ 1 + x,\ (1 + x)^2,\ 1 + x + x^2,\ x,\ x$$

Up to isomorphism, then, the realization of **A** is the union of the realizations of $\mathbf{M}_{1+x}$, $\mathbf{M}_{1+x}$, $\mathbf{M}_{1+x^2}$, $\mathbf{M}_{1+x+x^2}$, $\mathbf{M}_x$, $\mathbf{M}_x$ (see Fig. 5.9).

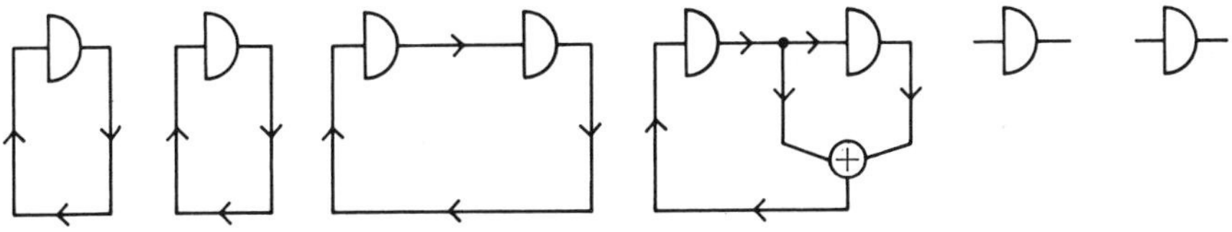

FIG. 5.9—Realization (up to isomorphism) of characteristic matrix **20–2**

20–4 *Example:* **A** is a characteristic matrix over $GF(2)$, with the elementary divisors

20–5
$$(1 + x + x^2)^3,\ (1 + x + x^2)^2,\ 1 + x + x^2$$

Hence, **A** is similar to

$$\mathbf{A}' = \begin{pmatrix} \mathbf{H}_{(1+x+x^2)^3} & \mathbf{J} & \\ & \mathbf{H}_{(1+x+x^2)^2} & \mathbf{J} \\ & & \mathbf{H}_{1+x+x^2} \end{pmatrix}$$

20–6

$$= \begin{pmatrix} 0 & 1 & & & & & & & & & & \\ 1 & 1 & 1 & & & & & & & & & \\ & & 0 & 1 & & & & & & & & \\ & & 1 & 1 & 1 & & & & & & & \\ & & & & 0 & 1 & & & & & & \\ & & & & 1 & 1 & & & & & & \\ & & & & & & 0 & 1 & & & & \\ & & & & & & 1 & 1 & 1 & & & \\ & & & & & & & & 0 & 1 & & \\ & & & & & & & & 1 & 1 & & \\ & & & & & & & & & & 0 & 1 \\ & & & & & & & & & & 1 & 1 \end{pmatrix}$$

The realization of **A**′, which is that of **A** up to isomorphism, is shown in Fig. 5.10.

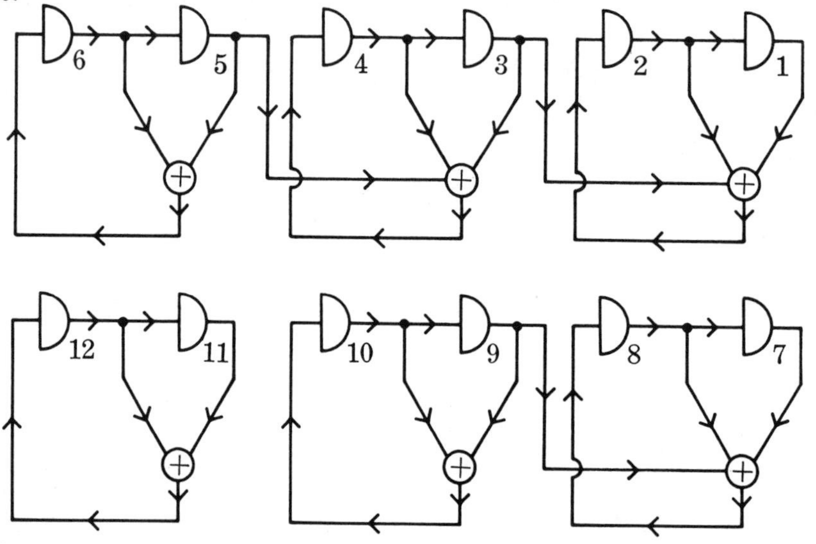

FIG. 5.10—Realization (up to isomorphism) of characteristic matrix **20–6**

21. Alternative Realizations of Characteristic Matrix

21–1 *Assertion:* Let

21–2

$$\mathbf{A} = \begin{pmatrix} \mathbf{M}_{f_1(x)} & & & \\ & \mathbf{M}_{f_2(x)} & & \\ & & \ddots & \\ & & & \mathbf{M}_{f_r(x)} \end{pmatrix}$$

where every $f_i(x)$ and $f_j(x)$ $(j \neq i)$ are relatively prime. Then, up to isomorphism, the realization of **A** is that of

21–3

$$\mathbf{A}' = \mathbf{M}_{f_1(x)f_2(x)\cdots f_r(x)}$$

Proof: The minimum polynomial of each $\mathbf{M}_{f_i(x)}$ is $f_i(x)$. Since the $f_i(x)$ are relatively prime, the elementary divisors of **A** are precisely the prime factors of $f_1(x)f_2(x) \ldots f_r(x)$. On the other hand, the minimum polynomial of $\mathbf{A}'$ is $f_1(x)f_2(x) \ldots f_r(x)$, and hence the elementary divisors of $\mathbf{A}'$ are the prime factors of $f_1(x)f_2(x) \ldots f_r(x)$. Thus, **A** and $\mathbf{A}'$ are similar, which implies **21–1.**

The following is a direct corollary of **21–1**:

21–4 *Assertion:* Let $d_1(x), d_2(x), \ldots, d_w(x)$ be the elementary divisors of **A**, and let $d_i(x)$ and $d_j(x)$ be relatively prime for every i and $j \neq i$. Then, up to isomorphism, **A** can be realized by a single shift register (namely, that which realizes $\mathbf{M}_{\phi_{\mathbf{A}}(x)}$).

21–5 *Assertion:* Let

21–6
$$\mathbf{A} = \begin{pmatrix} \mathbf{M}_{f_1(x)} & \\ & \mathbf{M}_{f_2(x)} \end{pmatrix}$$

where $f_1(x)$ and $f_2(x)$ are relatively prime. Then, up to isomorphism, the realization of **A** is that of

21–7
$$\mathbf{A}' = \begin{pmatrix} \mathbf{M}_{f_1(x)} & \mathbf{L} \\ & \mathbf{M}_{f_2(x)} \end{pmatrix}$$

where **L** is arbitrary.

Proof: By a series of row and column operations as defined in **1.15–1**, **L** in $\mathbf{A}'$ can be replaced with **0**, and hence $\mathbf{A}'$ can be converted to **A**. Thus **A** and $\mathbf{A}'$ have the same elementary divisors, which implies **21–5.**

In terms of the realization of **A**, it follows from **21–5** that the shift register realizing $\mathbf{M}_{f_1(x)}$ can accept arbitrary inputs from the shift register realizing $\mathbf{M}_{f_2(x)}$, (or conversely), with no effect on the structure of the state diagram.

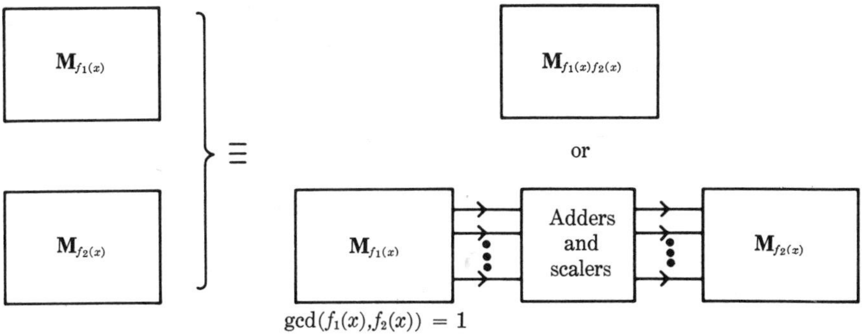

FIG. 5.11—Alternative realizations of characteristic matrix

21–1 and **21–5** are summarized in Fig. 5.11, where a box labeled $\mathbf{M}_{f(x)}$ stands for a realization of $\mathbf{M}_{f(x)}$.

21–8 *Example:* Let **A** be a characteristic matrix over $GF(2)$, with the elementary divisors

21–9
$$1 + x,\ (1 + x)^2,\ 1 + x + x^2,\ 1 + x + x^2$$

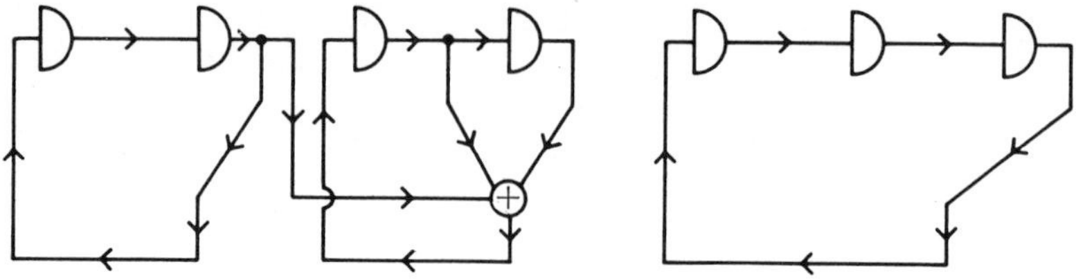

FIG. 5.12—IC for Example **21–8**

Fig. 5.12 shows a realization of **A** (up to isomorphism) with shift registers realizing (left to right) $\mathbf{M}_{(1+x)^2} = \mathbf{M}_{1+x^2}$, $\mathbf{M}_{1+x+x^2}$ and $\mathbf{M}_{(1+x)(1+x+x^2)} = \mathbf{M}_{1+x^3}$. The connection of the first shift register to the second is permitted by virtue of **21–5** (although no particular advantage is gained by this connection). The third shift register replaces, by **21–1**, the shift registers realizing $\mathbf{M}_{1+x}$ and $\mathbf{M}_{1+x+x^2}$ (this substitution results in the saving of one adder).

22. Realization of Cycle Sets

An IC $\mathcal{A}$ having a specified state diagram will be referred to as the *realization* of this state diagram. In particular, one may speak of $\mathcal{A}$ as the realization of a specified cycle set, of a specified tree set, or of both.

22–1 *Assertion:* A cycle set Σ is realizable by an IC if and only if it is factorable into elementary cycle sets.

Proof: Let $\mathcal{A}$ be a realization of Σ. Let **A** be the characteristic matrix of $\mathcal{A}$, and $d_1(x), d_2(x), \ldots, d_w(x)$ the elementary divisors of **A**. Then, by Sec. **12**, $\Sigma = \Sigma_1\Sigma_2 \ldots \Sigma_w$ where Σ_j is the cycle set of $\mathbf{M}_{d_j(x)}$ and hence an elementary cycle set. Conversely, suppose $\Sigma = \Sigma_1\Sigma_2 \ldots \Sigma_w$, where each Σ_j is an elementary cycle set. By definition, Σ_j must be the cycle set of some companion matrix $\mathbf{M}_{d_j(x)}$. Σ, therefore, is realized by the IC whose characteristic matrix is

22–2
$$\mathbf{A} = \begin{pmatrix} \mathbf{M}_{d_1(x)} & & & & \\ & \mathbf{M}_{d_2(x)} & & & \\ & & \cdot & & \\ & & & \cdot & \\ & & & & \mathbf{M}_{d_w(x)} \end{pmatrix}$$

The determination of $d_j(x)$ from Σ_j can be carried out as follows: Let

22–3
$$\Sigma_j = \{1[1] + N_1[T_1] + \ldots + N_r[T_r]\}$$

where $1 \le T_1 < T_2 < \ldots < T_r$. Comparing with **12–2**, we have $T_1 = T_{1j}$ and

22–4
$$N_1 = \frac{p^{h_j} - 1}{T_1}$$

or

22–5
$$h_j = \log_p(1 + N_1T_1)$$

(also, h_j is the least integer ν such that T_1 divides $p^\nu - 1$, which can be found with the aid of Table A2 in the Appendix). From Table A4 in the Appendix one can select an irreducible polynomial over $GF(p)$ of degree h_j and exponent T_1, say $p_j(x)$. Equating the number of states in Σ_j and in the cycle set of $\mathbf{M}_{d_j(x)}$ as given in **12–2**, we have

22–6 $$p^{e_j h_j} = 1 + N_1T_1 + \ldots + N_rT_r$$

or

22–7 $$e_j = \frac{1}{h_j}\log_p(1 + N_1T_1 + \ldots + N_rT_r)$$

The desired polynomial is $d_j(x) = [p_j(x)]^{e_j}$.

23. Cycle Set Division

Consider the realizable cycle set

23–1 $$\Sigma = \{N_1[T_1] + N_2[T_2] + \ldots + N_r[T_r]\}$$

where $1 \leq T_1 < T_2 < \ldots < T_r$. Suppose $\Sigma = \Sigma'\Sigma''$, where Σ' and Σ'' are realizable. In this case we say that Σ'' *divides* Σ, and write $\Sigma'' = \Sigma/\Sigma'$. By the rules of cycle set multiplication, every period appearing in Σ' and Σ'' must appear in Σ (but not necessarily conversely). Hence, Σ' and Σ'' can be written in the form

23–2 $$\Sigma' = \{\eta_1[T_1] + \eta_2[T_2] + \ldots + \eta_r[T_r]\}$$

23–3 $$\Sigma'' = \{x_1[T_1] + x_2[T_2] + \ldots + x_r[T_r]\}$$

where the η_k and x_j are non-negative integers—possibly zero. A typical term in the product $\Sigma'\Sigma''$ is

23–4 $$\eta_k[T_k]x_j[T_j] = \eta_k x_j \gcd(T_k,T_j)\ [\operatorname{lcm}(T_k,T_j)]$$

lcm (T_k, T_j) must be some period in Σ, say, T_i. For any fixed i and j, let

23–5 $$f_{ij} = \sum_{k(i,j)} \eta_k \gcd(T_k, T_j)$$

where the summation extends over all integers k such that lcm $(T_k, T_j) = T_i$. Comparing terms in Σ and $\Sigma'\Sigma''$, we thus have:

23–6 $$N_i = f_{i1}x_1 + f_{i2}x_2 + \ldots + f_{ir}x_r$$

(with summation over the field of real numbers). Defining

23–7 $$\mathbf{N} = \begin{pmatrix} N_1 \\ N_2 \\ \cdot \\ \cdot \\ \cdot \\ N_r \end{pmatrix} \qquad \mathbf{F} = [f_{ij}]_{r\times r} \qquad \mathbf{x} = \begin{pmatrix} x_1 \\ x_2 \\ \cdot \\ \cdot \\ \cdot \\ x_r \end{pmatrix}$$

we thus have:

23–8 $$\mathbf{N} = \mathbf{Fx}$$

(where all operations are over the field of real numbers).

Since $T_i = \operatorname{lcm}(T_k, T_j)$, we must have $T_i \geq T_j$ and hence, for all $j > i$, $f_{ij} = 0$. Also, for every i, f_{ii} as expressed in **23–5** must contain the term

23–9 $$\eta_1 \gcd(T_1, T_i) = \eta_1 \gcd(1, T_i) = \eta_1$$

Sinec Σ' is realizable, $\eta_1 \neq 0$ and hence $f_{ii} \neq 0$. Thus, **F** is a triangular matrix with nonzero elements on the principal diagonal, and hence a nonsingular matrix. We can thus write

23–10 $$\mathbf{x} = \mathbf{F}^{-1}\mathbf{N}$$

The preceding shows that, if Σ is divisible by Σ' (where both Σ and Σ' are realizable) such that $\Sigma'' = \Sigma/\Sigma'$ is realizable, then Σ'' is unique (this, however, does not imply that if Σ' divides Σ, then Σ/Σ' is realizable). The division of Σ by Σ' can be performed by solving **23–8** (which is especially simple, since **F** is triangular).

23–11 *Example:* Consider the division of $\Sigma = \{4[1] + 6[2] + 4[4]\}$ by $\Sigma' = \{2[1] + 1[2] + 1[4]\}$. Assuming $\Sigma/\Sigma' = \{x_1[1] + x_2[2] + x_3[4]\}$, we can write:

23–12
$$\begin{aligned}\{4[1] + 6[2] + 4[4]\} &= \{2[1] + 1[2] + 1[4]\}\{x_1[1] + x_2[2] + x_3[4]\} \\ &= \{2x_1[1] + 2x_2[2] + 2x_3[4] \\ &\quad + x_1[2] + 2x_2[2] + 2x_3[4] \\ &\quad + x_1[4] + 2x_2[4] + 4x_3[4]\} \\ &= \{2x_1[1] + (x_1 + 4x_2)[2] + (x_1 + 2x_2 + 8x_3)[4]\}\end{aligned}$$

In this case, **23–8** has the form

23–13
$$\begin{pmatrix}4\\6\\4\end{pmatrix} = \begin{pmatrix}2 & & \\ 1 & 4 & \\ 1 & 2 & 8\end{pmatrix}\begin{pmatrix}x_1\\x_2\\x_3\end{pmatrix}$$

which yields $x_1 = 2$, $x_2 = 1$, $x_3 = 0$, or

23–14 $$\Sigma/\Sigma' = \{2[1] + 1[2]\}$$

24. Cycle Set Factorization

While factorization of a given cycle set into elementary cycle sets (or the discovery that such factorization is impossible) is necessarily a finite process, it can rarely be accomplished without trial and error. Thus, there is no simple, direct procedure for realizing a specified cycle set (or of discovering its unrealizability when this is the case).

The specialized form of elementary cycle sets and the rules of cycle set multiplication imply a number of necessary realizability conditions which are helpful in the search for acceptable factors:

24–1 *Assertion:* Let $\Sigma = \Sigma_1\Sigma_2 \ldots \Sigma_w$ be a realizable cycle set (where the Σ_i are elementary cycle sets). Then every period in every Σ_i must be a period in Σ.

24–2 *Assertion:* Let $\Sigma = \Sigma_1\Sigma_2 \ldots \Sigma_w$ be defined as in **24–1**, and let $\{T_1, T_2, \ldots, T_r\}$ be the set of periods (ignoring 1[1]) in Σ such that no T_i is a multiple of any $T_j (j \neq i)$ in Σ. Then each T_i is a basic period of some Σ_i.

24–3 *Assertion:* The largest period in a realizable cycle set must be the lcm of all other periods.

The search for acceptable factors is also simplified by the division procedure described in Sec. **23**.

It should be remarked that the factorization of a realizable cycle set into elementary cycle sets is not necessarily unique. For example, it can be readily verified that the product of $\{2[1] + 1[2]\}$ [the cycle set of $\mathbf{M}_{(1+x)^2}$, over $GF(2)$]

and $\{2[1] + 1[2] + 3[4]\}$ [the cycle set of $\mathbf{M}_{(1+x)^4}$] equals the product of $\{2[1] + 1[2] + 1[4]\}$ [the cycle set of $\mathbf{M}_{(1+x)^3}$] by itself.

24–4 *Example:* Consider the realization of

24–5 $$\Sigma = \{2[1] + 2[3] + 2[7] + 8[14] + 2[21] + 8[42]\}$$

by an IC over $GF(2)$ (the dimension of the IC is $\log_2 512 = 9$). Trying the elementary cycle set $\Sigma_1 = \{1[1] + 1[3]\}$ (of $\mathbf{M}_{1+x+x^2}$) as a factor of Σ, yields

24–6 $$\Sigma' = \Sigma/\Sigma_1 = \{2[1] + 2[7] + 8[14]\}$$

Trying the elementary cycle set $\Sigma'' = \{1[1] + 1[7]\}$ [of $\mathbf{M}_{1+x+x^3}$] as a factor of Σ', yields

24–7 $$\Sigma'' = \Sigma'/\Sigma_2 = \{2[1] + 1[14]\}$$

which is not realizable, since 14 cannot be a basic period (see **24–2** and **11–1**). Trying the elementary cycle set $\Sigma_3 = \{1[1] + 1[7] + 4[14]\}$ [of $\mathbf{M}_{(1+x+x^3)^2}$] as a factor of Σ', yields

24–8 $$\Sigma''' = \Sigma'/\Sigma_3 = \{2[1]\}$$

which is an elementary cycle set (of $\mathbf{M}_{1+x}$). Hence, a factorization of Σ into elementary cycle sets is given by

24–9 $$\Sigma = \{1[1] + 1[3]\}\{1[1] + 1[7] + 4[14]\}\{2[1]\}$$

Thus, Σ can be realized by the union of the shift registers realizing $\mathbf{M}_{1+x+x^2}$, $\mathbf{M}_{(1+x+x^3)^2}$ and $\mathbf{M}_{1+x}$.

25. Realization of Specified Periods

An IC is said to *realize* the period T if its cycle set contains this period (and perhaps some other periods).

If T is 1 or a prime integer other than p, by Fermat's theorem (see **1.5–8**) $p^{T-1} - 1$ is a multiple of T, and hence there is at least one positive integer i (namely $T - 1$) such that T divides $p^i - 1$. Let the least such integer (which must divide $T - 1$) be h, and let $p(x)$ be any irreducible polynomial of degree h and exponent T over $GF(p)$. Then the IC which realizes $\mathbf{M}_{p(x)}$ is also an IC which realizes T. In fact, it is the least-dimensional IC which realizes T (see **1.8–1**).

Let T be expressible as p^kT', where T' is relatively prime to p. Let h' be the least integer such that T' divides $p^{h'} - 1$, and $p(x)$ any irreducible polynomial of degree h' and period T' over $GF(p)$. If $e = p^k$, then the period T can be realized by the IC which realizes $\mathbf{M}_{[p(x)]^e}$. (In this case, however, there is no guarantee that the realization is of least dimension.)

In general we can write $T = p^kT_1T_2 \ldots T_r$, where the T_i are relatively prime to each other and to p. ICs realizing $p^kT_1, T_2, \ldots, T_r$ can be constructed as shown above. Let $\mathcal{A}$ be the IC consisting of the union of these r ICs. The cycle set of $\mathcal{A}$ has at least one period given by

25–1 $$\text{lcm}\,(p^kT_1, T_2, \ldots, T_r) = p^kT_1T_2 \ldots T_r = T$$

and hence $\mathcal{A}$ realizes T.

25–2 *Example:* Consider the realization of $T = 90$ by an IC over $GF(2)$. We can write $90 = 2 \cdot 3^2 \cdot 5$. The least integers h such that 9 and 5 divide $2^h - 1$

are 6 and 4, respectively (see Table A2 in the Appendix). $1 + x^3 + x^6$ and $1 + x + x^4$ are irreducible polynomials of exponents 9 and 5, respectively (see Table A4 in the Appendix). Hence, an IC realizing $T = 90$ consists of the union of the shift registers realizing $\mathbf{M}_{(1+x+x^4)^2}$ and $\mathbf{M}_{1+x^3+x^6}$.

26. Realization of Some Special Sets of Periods

Fig. 5.13 shows an n-dimensional IC (a *circulating shift register*) which, clearly, realizes a period T if and only if T divides n. Thus, a circulating shift register realizes all periods which divide its dimension.

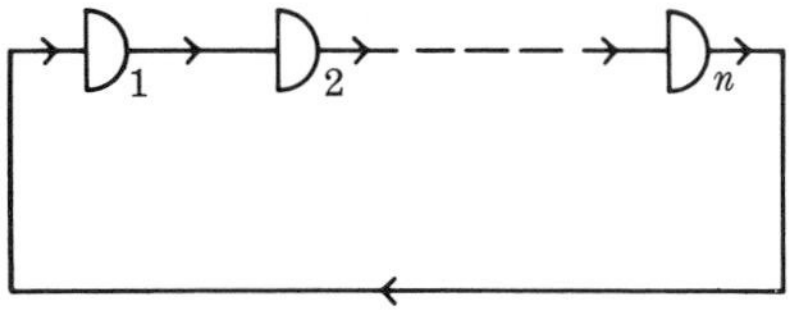

FIG. 5.13—Circulating shift register

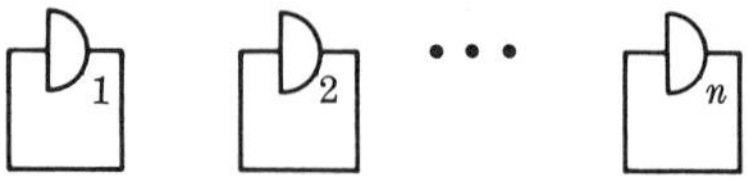

FIG. 5.14—Realization of $\mathbf{M}_{(x-1)^n}$

Fig. 5.14 shows the IC realizing $\mathbf{M}_{(x-1)^n}$. Since the exponent of $x - 1$ is 1, the cycle set of this IC is given by

26–1 $$\left\{p[1] + \frac{p^2 - p}{p^{i_2}}[p^{i_2}] + \frac{p^3 - p^2}{p^{i_3}}[p^{i_3}] + \ldots + \frac{p^n - p^{n-1}}{p^{i_n}}[p^{i_n}]\right\}$$

where p^{i_ν} is the least integer such that $p^{i_\nu} \geq \nu$. Thus, this IC realizes the periods $1, p, p^2, \ldots, p^r$, where p^r is the least integer such that $p^r \geq n$.

27. Realization of Tree Sets

As shown in Secs. **17** and **18**, the state diagram of a nilpotent IC conssists of a tree with a cycle of length 1 attached to the root. The structure of the tree is uniquely defined by the tree set $\tau = \{N_1, N_2, \ldots, N_L\}$, where N_i is the number of states in the ith tree level ($N_0 = 1$) and L is the height of the tree. Let

27–1 $$k_i = \log_p(1 + N_1 + N_2 + \ldots + N_i) \qquad (i = 1, 2, \ldots, L)$$

Then, by **17–4**,

27–2 $$k_i = m_1 + 2m_2 + 3m_3 + \ldots + (i-1)m_{i-1} + i(m_i + m_{i+1} + \ldots + m_L)$$

(where m_i is the number of $i \times i$ nilpotent blocks in $\mathbf{A}^*$). Thus, if we define

27–3

$$\mathbf{k} = \begin{pmatrix} k_1 \\ k_2 \\ k_3 \\ \cdot \\ \cdot \\ \cdot \\ k_{L-1} \\ k_L \end{pmatrix} \qquad \mathbf{E} = \begin{pmatrix} 1 & 1 & 1 & 1 & \ldots & 1 & 1 & 1 \\ 1 & 2 & 2 & 2 & & 2 & 2 & 2 \\ 1 & 2 & 3 & 3 & & 3 & 3 & 3 \\ \cdot & & & & & & & \\ \cdot & & & & & & & \\ \cdot & & & & & & & \\ 1 & 2 & 3 & 4 & & L-2 & L-1 & L-1 \\ 1 & 2 & 3 & 4 & & L-2 & L-1 & L \end{pmatrix} \qquad \mathbf{m} = \begin{pmatrix} m_1 \\ m_2 \\ m_3 \\ \cdot \\ \cdot \\ \cdot \\ m_{L-1} \\ m_L \end{pmatrix}$$

we have

27–4 $$\mathbf{k} = \mathbf{E}\mathbf{m}$$

where all operations are over the field of real numbers. **E** is nonsingular and has the inverse

27–5
$$\mathbf{E}^{-1} = \begin{pmatrix} 2 & -1 & 0 & 0 & \cdots & 0 & 0 & 0 \\ -1 & 2 & -1 & 0 & & 0 & 0 & 0 \\ 0 & -1 & 2 & -1 & & 0 & 0 & 0 \\ 0 & 0 & -1 & 2 & & 0 & 0 & 0 \\ \cdot & & & & & & & \\ \cdot & & & & & & & \\ \cdot & & & & & & & \\ 0 & 0 & 0 & 0 & & 2 & -1 & 0 \\ 0 & 0 & 0 & 0 & & -1 & 2 & -1 \\ 0 & 0 & 0 & 0 & & 0 & -1 & 1 \end{pmatrix}$$

(as can be readily verified). By **27–4**, then, we can write

27–6 $$\mathbf{m} = \mathbf{E}^{-1}\mathbf{k}$$

which enables us to compute the integers m_i (and hence the form of $\mathbf{A}^*$) from the integers k_i (and hence from the numbers N_i).

27–2 implies a number of *necessary* conditions which the k_i must satisfy if the m_i are to be non-negative integers:

27–7 k_i is a non-negative integer ($i = 1, 2, \ldots, L$)

For $i = 2, 3, \ldots, L - 1$, **27–2** implies:

27–8
$$\begin{aligned} k_{i-1} + k_{i+1} &= m_1 + 2m_2 + \ldots + (i-2)m_{i-2} \\ &\quad + (i-1)(m_{i-1} + m_i + \ldots + m_L) \\ &\quad + m_1 + 2m_2 + \ldots + im_i \\ &\quad + (i+1)(m_{i+1} + m_{i+2} + \ldots + m_L) \\ &= 2m_1 + 2m_2 + \ldots + 2(i-1)m_{i-1} \\ &\quad + 2i(m_i + m_{i+1} + \ldots + m_L) - m_i \\ &= 2k_i - m_i \end{aligned}$$

and hence

27–9 $$k_{i+1} \leq 2k_i - k_{i-1} \qquad (i = 2, 3, \ldots, L - 1)$$

Also:

27–10
$$\begin{aligned} k_2 - k_1 &= m_1 + 2(m_2 + m_3 + \ldots + m_L) - (m_1 + m_2 + \ldots + m_L) \\ &= (m_1 + m_2 + \ldots + m_L) - m_1 = k_1 - m_1 \end{aligned}$$

and hence

27–11 $$k_2 \leq 2k_1$$

Clearly, we must also have (see **27–1**):

27–12 $$k_i \geq k_{i-1} \qquad (i = 2, 3, \ldots, L)$$

Thus, the k_i must satisfy the following system of inequalities:

27–13
$$\begin{aligned} &k_1 \leq k_2 \leq 2k_1 \\ &k_2 \leq k_3 \leq 2k_2 - k_1 \\ &k_3 \leq k_4 \leq 2k_3 - k_2 \\ &\cdot \\ &\cdot \\ &\cdot \\ &k_{L-2} \leq k_{L-1} \leq 2k_{L-2} - k_{L-3} \\ &k_{L-1} \leq k_L \leq 2k_{L-1} - k_{L-2} \end{aligned}$$

These inequalities are consistent, since $k_i \geq k_{i-1}$ guarantees the inequality $2k_i - k_{i-1} \geq k_i$.

27–5 and **27–6** provide *sufficient* conditions which the k_i must satisfy if the m_i are to be non-negative integers:

27–14 k_i is a non-negative integer $(i = 1, 2, \ldots, L)$

27–15 $$2k_1 - k_2 \geq 0$$

27–16 $$-k_{i-1} + 2k_i - k_{i+1} \geq 0 \qquad (i = 2, 3, \ldots, L-1)$$

27–17 $$-k_{L-1} + k_L \geq 0$$

But these are already included in the necessary conditions **27–7**, **27–11**, **27–9** and **27–12**, respectively. Hence, **27–7** and **27–13** constitute necessary and sufficient conditions for **k** to yield an **m** with non-negative integers as elements, and hence for a given tree set to correspond to a nilpotent IC which realizes it. When these conditions are satisfied, **m** can be computed via **27–6** and **27–5** to yield the numbers m_i of $i \times i$ nilpotent matrices in $\mathbf{A}^*$. The realization of $\mathbf{A}^*$, and hence the realization of the specified tree set, consists of m_i feedback-free shift registers of i delayers each $(i = 1, 2, \ldots, L)$.

27–18 *Example:* Consider the tree set

27–19 $$\tau = \{15, 16, 32, 64, 128\}$$

to be realized by an IC over $GF(2)$. In this case $k_1 = 4$, $k_2 = 5$, $k_3 = 6$, $k_4 = 7$ and $k_5 = 8$, and conditions **27–7** and **27–13** are satisfied. Following **27–5** and **27–6**:

27–20 $$\mathbf{m} = \mathbf{E}^{-1}\mathbf{k} = \begin{pmatrix} 2 & -1 & 0 & 0 & 0 \\ -1 & 2 & -1 & 0 & 0 \\ 0 & -1 & 2 & -1 & 0 \\ 0 & 0 & -1 & 2 & -1 \\ 0 & 0 & 0 & -1 & 1 \end{pmatrix} \begin{pmatrix} 4 \\ 5 \\ 6 \\ 7 \\ 8 \end{pmatrix} = \begin{pmatrix} 3 \\ 0 \\ 0 \\ 0 \\ 1 \end{pmatrix}$$

$\mathbf{A}^*$, then, consists of three 1×1 nilpotent blocks and one 5×5 nilpotent block. The realization of τ is shown in Fig. 5.15.

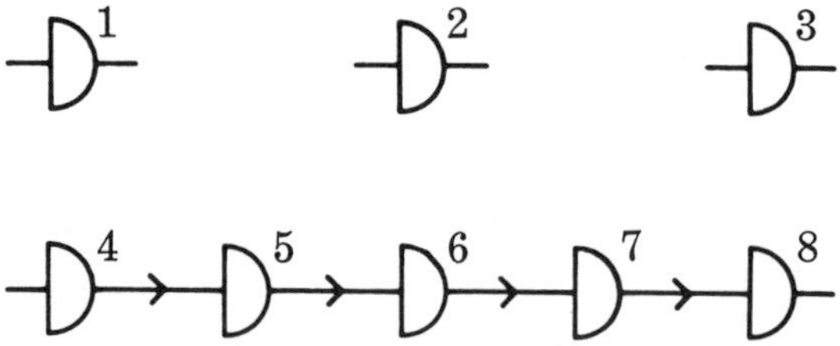

FIG. 5.15—Realization of tree set of Example **27–18**

28. Realization of Arbitrary State Diagrams

From **19–6** it follows that every realizable state diagram can be specified uniquely (up to isomorphism) by a cycle set and a tree set. One can realize the cycle set and the tree set separately as shown in the preceding sections, and then take the union of these realizations to constitute the realization of the entire state diagram. The realization of the cycle set would consist of a number of shift registers with feedback, which can be looked upon as the subcircuit responsible for the "steady state" behavior of the IC. The realization of the tree set would consist of a number of feedback-free shift registers, which can be looked upon as the subcircuit responsible for the "transient" behavior of the IC.

29. State Diagram for Specified Input

Let $\mathcal{A}$ be an n-dimensional LSC over $GF(p)$, characterized by **A**, **B**, **C** and **D**. The *state diagram for input* $\mathbf{u}^i$ of $\mathcal{A}$ is a directed graph consisting of p^n vertices labeled as the p^n states of $\mathcal{A}$. If $\mathbf{As}_1 + \mathbf{Bu}^i = \mathbf{s}_2$, a branch is drawn between $\mathbf{s}_1$ and $\mathbf{s}_2$, with an arrow sign pointing from $\mathbf{s}_1$ to $\mathbf{s}_2$. Thus, the state diagram for $\mathbf{u}^i$ describes the state behavior of the LSC when the input is restricted to $\mathbf{u}^i$. (The state diagram for input **0** is simply the state diagram of **A**, or of $\mathcal{A}$, as defined in Sec. **2**.)

29–1 *Assertion:* The state diagram for input $\mathbf{u}^i$ of $\mathcal{A}$ is isomorphic to the state diagram of **A** if and only if the equation

29–2 $$(\mathbf{I} - \mathbf{A})\mathbf{s} = \mathbf{Bu}^i$$

is solvable for **s**.

Proof: Suppose the diagrams are isomorphic, and let state **0** in the diagram of **A** correspond to $\mathbf{s}^i$ in the diagram for $\mathbf{u}^i$. Since $\mathbf{A0} = \mathbf{0}$, we must have

29–3 $$\mathbf{As}^i + \mathbf{Bu}^i = \mathbf{s}^i$$

or

29–4 $$(\mathbf{I} - \mathbf{A})\mathbf{s}^i = \mathbf{Bu}^i$$

and hence **29–2** must be solvable. If **29–4** holds, let every state **s** in the diagram of **A** correspond to $\mathbf{s} + \mathbf{s}^i$ in the diagram for $\mathbf{u}^i$. Clearly, this is a one-to-one correspondence. The successor of **s** is $\mathbf{s}' = \mathbf{As}$, while the successor of $\mathbf{s} + \mathbf{s}^i$ is

29–5 $$\mathbf{A}(\mathbf{s} + \mathbf{s}^i) + \mathbf{Bu}^i = \mathbf{A}(\mathbf{s} + \mathbf{s}^i) + (\mathbf{I} - \mathbf{A})\mathbf{s}^i = \mathbf{As} + \mathbf{s}^i = \mathbf{s}' + \mathbf{s}^i$$

Hence, the same correspondence holds among the successors, which implies the isomorphism.

29–6 *Assertion:* If the characteristic polynomial of **A** is indivisible by $1 - x$, then the state diagram for *any* input of $\mathcal{A}$ is isomorphic to the state diagram of **A**.

Proof: If $\phi_{\mathbf{A}}(x) = |\mathbf{A} - x\mathbf{I}|$ is indivisible by $1 - x$, then $|\mathbf{A} - \mathbf{I}| \neq 0$, which implies that $\mathbf{I} - \mathbf{A}$ is nonsingular. Hence, for any $\mathbf{u}^i$ we can compute

29–7 $$\mathbf{s}^i = (\mathbf{I} - \mathbf{A})^{-1}\mathbf{Bu}^i$$

29–8 *Example:* Consider an LSC over $GF(3)$, where

29–9 $$\mathbf{A} = \begin{pmatrix} 1 & 2 \\ 2 & 1 \end{pmatrix} \qquad \mathbf{B} = \begin{pmatrix} 1 \\ 1 \end{pmatrix}$$

In this case:

29–10 $$\mathbf{I} - \mathbf{A} = \begin{pmatrix} 0 & 1 \\ 1 & 0 \end{pmatrix} = (\mathbf{I} - \mathbf{A})^{-1}$$

For $\mathbf{u}^1 = 1$, we have

29–11 $$\mathbf{s}^1 = (\mathbf{I} - \mathbf{A})^{-1}\mathbf{Bu}^1 = \begin{pmatrix} 1 \\ 1 \end{pmatrix}$$

For $\mathbf{u}^2 = 2$, we have

29–12 $$\mathbf{s}^2 = (\mathbf{I} - \mathbf{A})^{-1}\mathbf{B}\mathbf{u}^2 = \begin{pmatrix} 2 \\ 2 \end{pmatrix}$$

Thus, the state diagrams for inputs 1 and 2 can be obtained from the state diagram of $\mathbf{A}$ simply by adding $\mathbf{s}^1$ and $\mathbf{s}^2$, respectively, to every vertex label in the diagram of $\mathbf{A}$ (see Fig. 5.16).

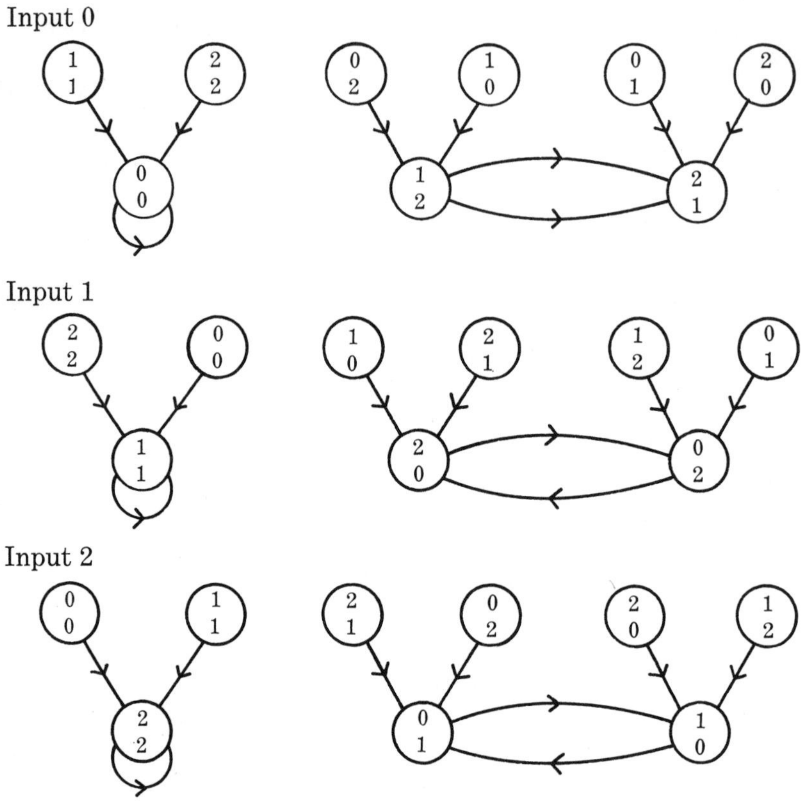

FIG. 5.16—State diagrams for LSC of Example **29–8**

Chapter 6

Applications of Linear Sequential Circuits

1. Introduction

As demonstrated in the preceding chapters, many excellent techniques are available for both the analysis and synthesis of LSCs. This, plus the fact that the shift register has an especially appealing hardware realization, resulted in the application of LSCs in numerous tasks associated with digital computation, communication and simulation.

In this chapter we exemplify the usefulness of LSCs by showing, in detail, how they can be employed in the multiplication and division of polynomials, in computation over Galois fields, in counting, and in error detection and correction. In the latter area, only the simplest coding schemes have been treated. For more complete coverage of the coding applications, the reader is referred to

W. W. Peterson, "Error-Correcting Codes," The M. I. T. Press, Cambridge, Mass., 1961.

(which is the source for most of the material in parts I, II, and IV of this chapter). Some miscellaneous applications are described briefly at the end of the chapter.

2. Input, Output, and Internal Polynominals

In many of the applications discussed in subsequent sections, LSCs are employed to transform one "polynomial" into another. Specifically, if the inputs applied to an LSC $\mathcal{A}$ at times $0, 1, \ldots, k$ (where k is fixed for a given application) are $\eta_0, \eta_1, \ldots, \eta_k$, respectively (and 0 thereafter), then the *input polynomial* to $\mathcal{A}$ is defined as

2–1 $$a(x) = \eta_k + \eta_{k-1}x + \ldots + \eta_1 x^{k-1} + \eta_0 x^k$$

(where the leading or any other coefficient may be 0). If the outputs of $\mathcal{A}$ at times $0, 1, \ldots, r$ (where r is fixed for a given application) are $\gamma_0, \gamma_1, \ldots, \gamma_r$, respectively, then the *output polynomial* of $\mathcal{A}$ is defined as

2–2 $$b(x) = \gamma_r + \gamma_{r-1}x + \ldots + \gamma_1 x^{r-1} + \gamma_0 x^r$$

(where the leading or any other coefficient may be 0). In each case, the first symbol is the coefficient (possibly 0) associated with the highest permissible power (k or r) of x.

The n delayers of $\mathcal{A}$ are numbered $1, 2, \ldots, n$. If ρ_i is the output of delayer i at time t, the *internal polynomial* of $\mathcal{A}$ at that time is defined as

2–3 $$w(x) = \rho_1 + \rho_2 x + \ldots + \rho_{n-1}x^{n-2} + \rho_n x^{n-1}$$

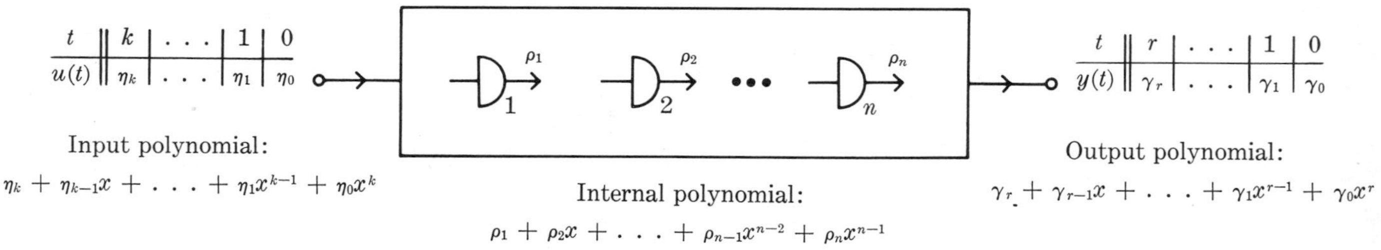

FIG. 6.1—Input, output, and internal polynomials

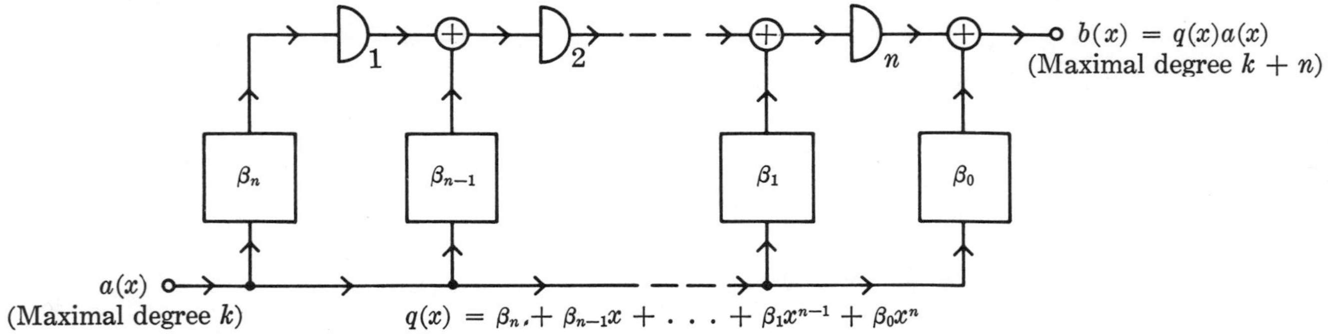

FIG. 6.2—Polynomial multiplication

Fig. 6.1 illustrates the above notation.

Finally, we should point out that the input, output, and internal polynomial of an LSC need not be polynomials in x, but may be polynomials in any other indeterminate (such as ξ).

I. MULTIPLICATION AND DIVISION OF POLYNOMINALS

3. Polynominal Multiplication

Consider a shift-register QLSC $\mathcal{A}$, with the transfer function

3–1 $$\mathfrak{T} = \beta_0 + \beta_1 d + \ldots + \beta_n d^n$$

(see Fig. 6.2). Let the input to $\mathcal{A}$ be

3–2 $$u(t)\colon\ \eta_0\eta_1 \ldots \eta_k 000 \ldots$$

The d-transform of the output is given by

3–3 $$\begin{aligned} Y = U\mathfrak{T} &= (\eta_0 + \eta_1 d + \ldots + \eta_k d^k)(\beta_0 + \beta_1 d + \ldots + \beta_n d^n) \\ &= \gamma_0 + \gamma_1 d + \ldots + \gamma_{n+k} d^{n+k} \end{aligned}$$

where

3–4 $$\gamma_i = \sum_{\mu+\nu=i} \eta_\mu \beta_\nu$$

Now, consider the product

3–5 $$\begin{aligned} f(x) &= (\eta_k + \eta_{k-1}x + \ldots + \eta_0 x^k)(\beta_n + \beta_{n-1}x + \ldots + \beta_0 x^n) \\ &= \gamma'_{n+k} + \gamma'_{n+k-1}x + \ldots + \gamma'_0 x^{n+k} \end{aligned}$$

where

3–6 $$\gamma'_{n+k-j} = \sum_{\mu+\nu=n+k-j} \eta_\mu \beta_\nu$$

or

3–7 $$\gamma'_i = \sum_{\mu+\nu=i} \eta_\mu \beta_\nu = \gamma_i$$

and hence

3–8 $$f(x) = \gamma_0 x^{n+k} + \gamma_1 x^{n+k-1} + \ldots + \gamma_{n+k-1}x + \gamma_{n+k}$$

Thus, the output of $\mathcal{A}$ at $t = i$ is precisely the ith coefficient (starting with that of x^{n+k}) of $f(x)$.

In conclusion, if $a(x)$ (of maximal degree k) is the input polynomial to $\mathcal{A}$, then the output polynomial is given by $b(x) = q(x)a(x)$, where

3–9 $$q(x) = \beta_n + \beta_{n-1}x + \ldots + \beta_1 x^{n-1} + \beta_0 x^n$$

$\mathcal{A}$, then, can be used to multiply arbitrary polynomials by a fixed polynomial $q(x)$.

Using the superposition property of QLSCs, a circuit such as shown in Fig. 6.3 can be constructed to compute

3–10 $$b(x) = q_1(x)a_1(x) + q_2(x)a_2(x) + \ldots + q_v(x)a_v(x)$$

where the $a_i(x)$ are input polynomials of maximal degree k and the $q_i(x)$ are fixed polynomials of maximal degree n.

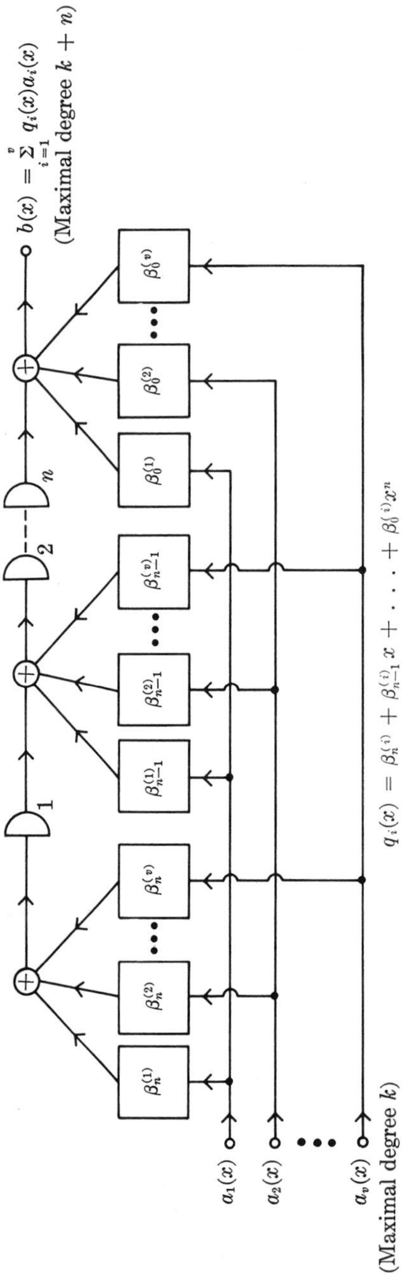

$$q_i(x) = \beta_n^{(i)} + \beta_{n-1}^{(i)}x + \cdots + \beta_0^{(i)}x^n$$
$$(i = 1, 2, \ldots, v)$$

FIG. 6.3—Summation of polynomial multiples

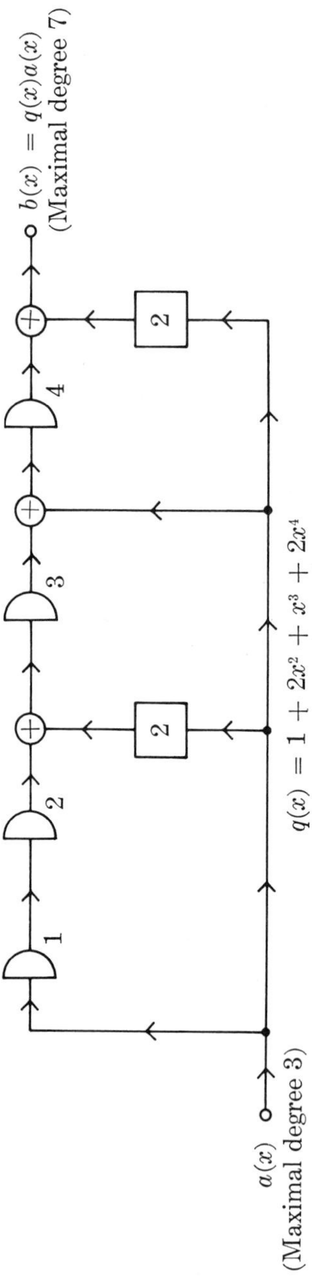

$$q(x) = 1 + 2x^2 + x^3 + 2x^4$$

FIG. 6.4—Polynomial multiplier by $1 + 2x^2 + x^3 + 2x^4$

3–11 *Example:* Fig. 6.4 shows a QLSC over $GF(3)$ with the transfer function

3–12 $$\mathfrak{T} = 2 + d + 2d^2 + d^4$$

It can be used to multiply polynomials over $GF(3)$, say of degree 3 or less, by

3–13 $$q(x) = 1 + 2x^2 + x^3 + 2x^4$$

For example, suppose the input polynomial is $a(x) = x^2 + 1$. In this case ($n = 4$, $k = 3$):

3–14 $$u(t)\colon\ 0101.000\ \ldots$$

3–15 $$U = d + d^3$$

3–16 $$Y = U\mathfrak{T} = (d + d^3)(2 + d + 2d^2 + d^4) = 2d + d^2 + d^3 + d^4 + d^7$$

3–17 $$y(t)\colon\ 02111001.000\ \ldots$$

Hence, the output polynomial, as expected, is

3–18 $$b(x) = 2x^6 + x^5 + x^4 + x^3 + 1 = q(x)a(x)$$

4. Polynomial Division

Consider a shift-register QLSC $\mathcal{A}$, with the transfer function

4–1 $$\mathfrak{T} = \frac{d^n}{1 + \alpha_1 d + \ldots + \alpha_n d^n}$$

(see Fig. 6.5). Let the input to $\mathcal{A}$ be

4–2 $$u(t)\colon\ \eta_0\eta_1\ \ldots\ \eta_k 000\ \ldots$$

The d-transform of the output is given by

4–3 $$Y = U\mathfrak{T} = \frac{\eta_0 d^n + \eta_1 d^{n+1} + \ldots + \eta_k d^{n+k}}{1 + \alpha_1 d + \ldots + \alpha_n d^n}$$

which can be expanded in power series by long division. **4–4** below shows the first $k - n + 1$ steps of this division. In the notation of **4–4**, the first $k + 1$ outputs of $\mathcal{A}$ are given by

4–5 $$\underbrace{00\ \ldots\ 0}_{n}\eta_0\eta_1^{(1)}\eta_2^{(2)}\ \ldots\ \eta_{k-n}^{(k-n)}$$

Now, consider the ratio

4–6 $$f(x) = \frac{\eta_0 x^k + \eta_1 x^{k-1} + \ldots + \eta_k}{x^n + \alpha_1 x^{n-1} + \ldots + \alpha_n} = \langle f(x) \rangle + \frac{f_1(x)}{x^n + \alpha_1 x^{n-1} + \ldots + \alpha_n}$$

where $< f(x) >$ denotes the *principal part* of $f(x)$, i.e., the polynomial obtained by dividing the numerator of $f(x)$ by the denominator (both arranged in descending powers of x), as shown in **4–7** below:

4–8 $$< f(x) > = \eta_0 x^{k-n} + \eta_1^{(1)} x^{k-n-1} + \eta_2^{(2)} x^{k-n-2} + \ldots + \eta_{k-n}^{(k-n)}$$

4–4
$$\begin{array}{r|l}
 & \eta_0 d^n + \eta_1^{(1)} d^{n+1} + \eta_2^{(2)} d^{n+2} + \ldots + \eta_{k-n}^{(k-n)} d^k \\
\hline
1 + \alpha_1 d + \ldots + \alpha_n d^n & \eta_0 d^n + \eta_1 d^{n+1} + \eta_2 d^{n+2} + \ldots + \eta_k d^{n+k} \\
 & \eta_0 d^n + \eta_0\alpha_1 d^{n+1} + \eta_0\alpha_2 d^{n+2} + \ldots + \eta_0\alpha_n d^{2n} \\
\cline{2-2}
 & \eta_1^{(1)} d^{n+1} + \eta_2^{(1)} d^{n+2} + \ldots + \eta_k^{(1)} d^{n+k} \\
 & \eta_1^{(1)} d^{n+1} + \eta_1^{(1)}\alpha_1 d^{n+2} + \ldots + \eta_1^{(1)}\alpha_n d^{2n+1} \\
\cline{2-2}
 & \eta_2^{(2)} d^{n+2} + \ldots + \eta_k^{(2)} d^{n+k} \\
 & \eta_2^{(2)} d^{n+2} + \ldots + \eta_2^{(2)}\alpha_n d^{2n+2} \\
\cline{2-2}
 & \vdots \\
\cline{2-2}
 & \eta_{k-n}^{(k-n)} d^k + \ldots + \eta_k^{(k-n)} d^{n+k} \\
 & \eta_{k-n}^{(k-n)} d^k + \ldots + \eta_{k-n}^{(k-n)} d^{n+k} \\
 & \rho_n d^{1+k} + \ldots + \rho_1 d^{n+k}
\end{array}$$

4–7
$$\begin{array}{r|l}
 & \eta_0 x^{k-n} + \eta_1^{(1)} x^{k-n-1} + \eta_2^{(2)} x^{k-n-2} + \ldots + \eta_{k-n}^{(k-n)} \\
\hline
x^n + \alpha_1 x^{n-1} + \ldots + \alpha_n & \eta_0 x^k + \eta_1 x^{k-1} + \eta_2 x^{k-2} + \ldots + \eta_k \\
 & \eta_0 x^k + \eta_0\alpha_1 x^{k-1} + \eta_0\alpha_2 x^{k-2} + \ldots + \eta_0\alpha_n x^{k-n} \\
\cline{2-2}
 & \eta_1^{(1)} x^{k-1} + \eta_2^{(1)} x^{k-2} + \ldots + \eta_k^{(1)} \\
 & \eta_1^{(1)} x^{k-1} + \eta_1^{(1)}\alpha_1 x^{k-2} + \ldots + \eta_1^{(1)}\alpha_n x^{k-n-1} \\
\cline{2-2}
 & \eta_2^{(2)} x^{k-2} + \ldots + \eta_k^{(2)} \\
 & \eta_2^{(2)} x^{k-2} + \ldots + \eta_2^{(2)}\alpha_n x^{k-n-2} \\
\cline{2-2}
 & \vdots \\
\cline{2-2}
 & \eta_{k-n}^{(k-n)} x^n + \ldots + \eta_k^{(k-n)} \\
 & \eta_{k-n}^{(k-n)} x^n + \ldots + \eta_{k-n}^{(k-n)}\alpha_n \\
 & \rho_n x^{n-1} + \ldots + \rho_1
\end{array}$$

From **4–5**, then, it follows that the output polynomial (of maximal degree k) of $\mathcal{a}$ is precisely $< f(x) >$.

If $s_j(t)$ denotes the output of delayer j at time t, for any $1 \leq i \leq k - n + 1$ we have:

4–9

j	If $s_j(n + i - 1) =$	then $s_j(n + i) =$
n	$\eta_{i-1}^{(i-1)}$	$\eta_i^{(i-1)} - \eta_{i-1}^{(i-1)}\alpha_1 = \eta_i^{(i)}$
$n - 1$	$\eta_i^{(i-1)}$	$\eta_{i+1}^{(i-1)} - \eta_{i-1}^{(i-1)}\alpha_2 = \eta_{i+i}^{(i)}$
$\vdots$		
2	$\eta_{i+n-3}^{(i-1)}$	$\eta_{i+n-2}^{(i-1)} - \eta_{i-1}^{(i-1)}\alpha_{n-1} = \eta_{i+n-2}^{(i)}$
1	$\eta_{i+n-2}^{(i-1)}$	$\eta_{i+n-1} - \eta_{i-1}^{(i-1)}\alpha_n = \eta_{i+n-1}^{(i)}$

By induction it follows that, at $t = n + i - 1$, the outputs of the n delayers (observed right to left in Fig. 6.5) are the coefficients (starting with the leading one) of the remainder polynomial obtained in the ith step of the division **4–7**.

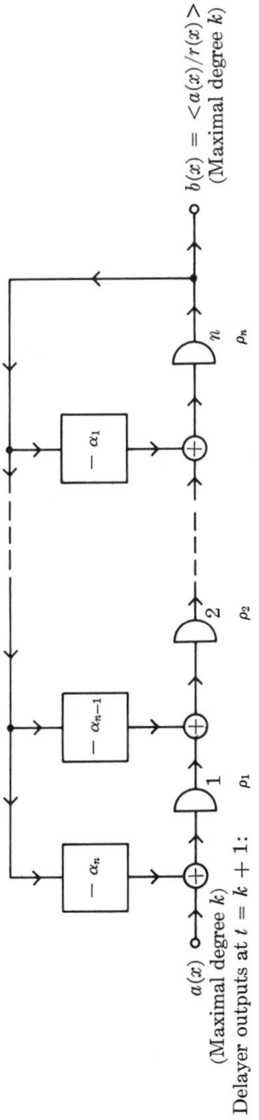

$$r(x) = \alpha_n + \alpha_{n-1}x + \cdots + \alpha_1 x^{n-1} + x^n$$
$$w(x) = \rho_1 + \rho_2 x + \cdots + \rho_{n-1}x^{n-2} + \rho_n x^{n-1}$$
$$\frac{a(x)}{r(x)} = b(x) + \frac{w(x)}{r(x)}$$

FIG. 6.5—Polynomial division

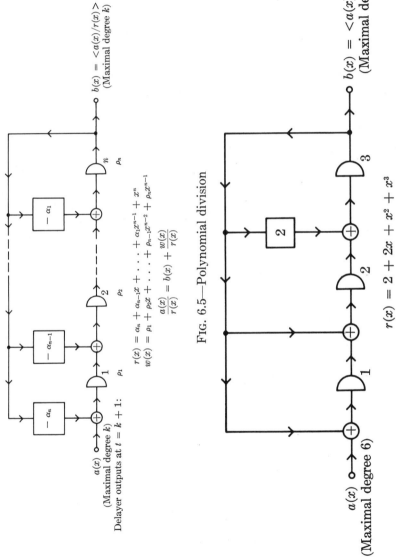

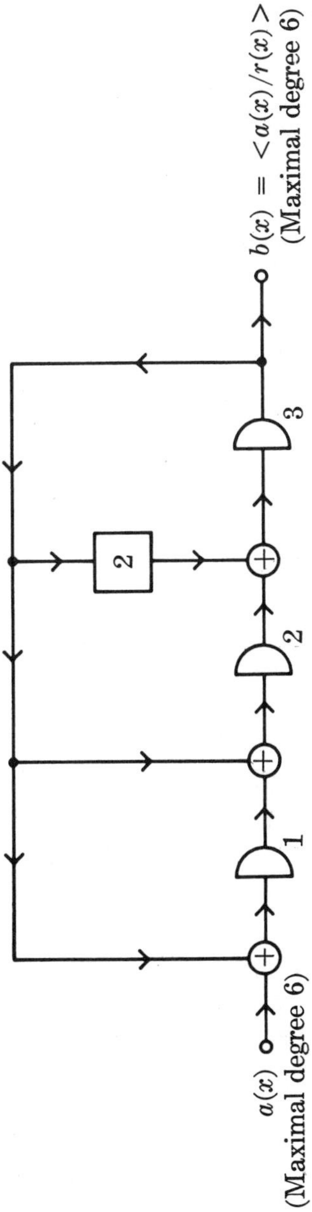

$$r(x) = 2 + 2x + x^2 + x^3$$

FIG. 6.6—Polynomial divider by $2 + 2x + x^2 + x^3$

In particular, at $t = k + 1$, these outputs are the coefficient of the final remainder $f_1(x)$.

In conclusion, if $a(x)$ (of maximal degree k) is the input polynomial to $\mathfrak{A}$, then the output polynomial is the principal part of $a(x)/r(x)$, where

4–10 $$r(x) = \alpha_n + \alpha_{n-1}x + \ldots + \alpha_1 x^{n-1} + x^n$$

At $t = k + 1$, the internal polynomial of $\mathfrak{A}$ is the remainder of $a(x)/r(x)$.

4–11 *Example:* Fig. 6.6 shows a QLSC over $GF(3)$ with the transfer function

4–12 $$\mathfrak{T} = \frac{d^3}{1 + d + 2d^2 + 2d^3}$$

It can be used to divide polynomials over $GF(3)$, say of degree 6 or less, by

4–13 $$r(x) = 2 + 2x + x^2 + x^3$$

For example, suppose the input polynomial is $a(x) = x^2 + x^4 + x^5$. In this case ($n = 3$, $k = 6$):

4–14 $$u(t)\colon 0110100.000 \ldots$$

4–15 $$U = d + d^2 + d^4$$

4–16 $$Y = U\mathfrak{T} = \frac{d^4 + d^5 + d^7}{1 + d + 2d^2 + 2d^3} = d^4 + d^6 + \ldots$$

4–17 $$y(t)\colon 0000101 \ldots$$

where the expansion of Y shown in **4–16** is carried out in **4–18** below (in **4–16** and **4–17**, only the first 7 terms are relevant). Hence, as expected in view of **4–20** below, the output polynomial is

4–19 $$b(x) = 1 + x^2 = < \frac{x^5 + x^4 + x^2}{x^3 + x^2 + 2x + 2} >$$

Table 6.1 For Example **4–11**

t	$u(t)$	Output of delayer 1	2	3	$y(t)$
0	0	0	0	0	0
1	1	0	0	0	0
2	1	1	0	0	0
3	0	1	1	0	0
4	1	0	1	1	1
5	0	2	1	0	0
6	0	0	2	1	1
7	0	1	1	1	1

(Rows $t = 0$ to 6 of the $u(t)$ column form $a(x)$; rows $t = 0$ to 6 of the $y(t)$ column form $b(x)$; the delayer outputs 1, 2, 3 at $t = 7$ form $w(x)$.)

Table 6.1 indicates the internal polynomials of the circuit at $t = 0, 1, \ldots, 7$. The internal polynomial at $t = k + 1 = 7$ is seen to be the remainder $1 + x + x^2$ obtained in **4–20**.

4–18

$$
\begin{array}{r|l}
 & 0 + d^4 + 0 + d^6 \\
\hline
1 + d + 2d^2 + 2d^3 & 0 + d^4 + d^5 + 0 + d^7 + 0 + 0 \\
 & 0 + 0 + 0 + 0 \\
\cline{2-2}
 & d^4 + d^5 + 0 + d^7 \\
 & d^4 + d^5 + 2d^6 + 2d^7 \\
\cline{2-2}
 & 0 + d^6 + 2d^7 + 0 \\
 & 0 + 0 + 0 + 0 \\
\cline{2-2}
 & d^6 + 2d^7 + 0 + 0 \\
 & d^6 + d^7 + 2d^8 + 2d^9 \\
\cline{2-2}
 & d^7 + d^8 + d^9
\end{array}
$$

4–20

$$
\begin{array}{r|l}
 & 0 + x^2 + 0 + 1 \\
\hline
x^3 + x^2 + 2x + 2 & 0 + x^5 + x^4 + 0 + x^2 + 0 + 0 \\
 & 0 + 0 + 0 + 0 \\
\cline{2-2}
 & x^5 + x^4 + 0 + x^2 \\
 & x^5 + x^4 + 2x^3 + 2x^2 \\
\cline{2-2}
 & 0 + x^3 + 2x^2 + 0 \\
 & 0 + 0 + 0 + 0 \\
\cline{2-2}
 & x^3 + 2x^2 + 0 + 0 \\
 & x^3 + x^2 + 2x + 2 \\
\cline{2-2}
 & x^2 + x + 1
\end{array}
$$

5. Polynomial Multiplication and Division

Let us multiply the dividend $\eta_0 x^k + \eta_1 x^{k-1} + \ldots + \eta_k$ in **4–7** by βx^h where β is from $GF(p)$ and $0 \leq h \leq n$. The coefficients of the quotient in **4–7** are then the same as those obtained in the quotient of **4–4** when the dividend $\eta_0 d^n + \eta_1 d^{n+1} + \ldots + \eta_k d^{n+k}$ is multiplied by βd^{-h}. In particular, the coefficient of $x^{k-n+h-\nu}$ in the first quotient now matches the coefficient of $d^{n-h+\nu}$ in the second. As compared with the original situation, the sequence whose d-transform is the quotient of **4–4** is advanced h dits and multiplied by β. Thus, if the input polynomial $a(x)$ (of maximal degree k) is applied to a shift-register QLSC whose transfer function is

5–1
$$\frac{\beta d^{n-h}}{1 + \alpha_1 d + \ldots + \alpha_n d^n}$$

then the output polynomial (of maximal degree k) is

5–2
$$\left\langle \frac{\beta x^h a(x)}{x^n + \alpha_1 x^{n-1} + \ldots + \alpha_n} \right\rangle$$

More generally, the shift-register QLSC whose transfer function is

5–3
$$\mathfrak{T} = \frac{\beta_0 + \beta_1 d + \ldots + \beta_n d^n}{1 + \alpha_1 d + \ldots + \alpha_n d^n}$$

can be used to compute

5–4
$$\left\langle a(x) \frac{\beta_0 x^n + \beta_1 x^{n-1} + \ldots + \beta_n}{x^n + \alpha_1 x^{n-1} + \ldots + \alpha_n} \right\rangle$$

where $a(x)$ is an arbitrary polynomial of maximal degree k (see Fig. 6.7). The corresponding remainder is the internal polynomial of the QLSC at $t = k + 1$.

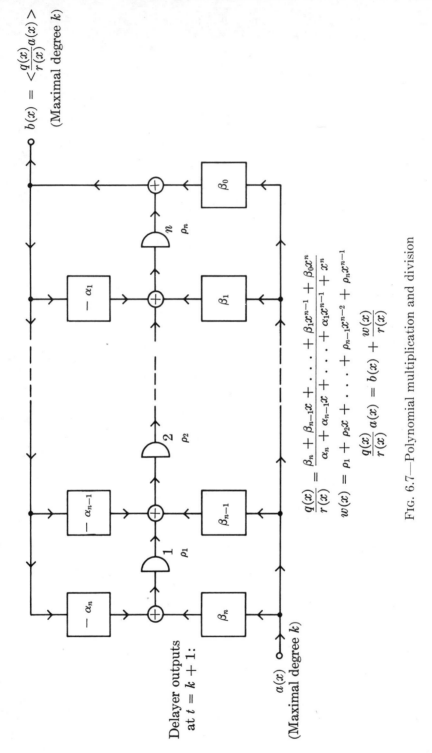

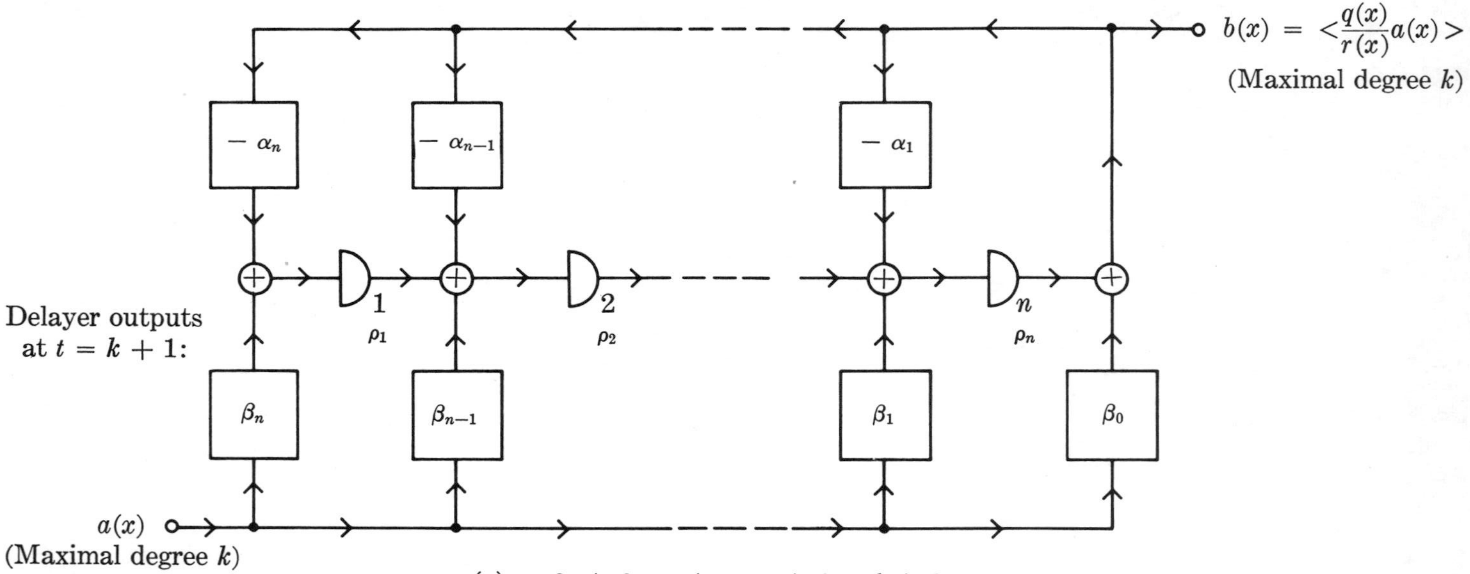

$$\frac{q(x)}{r(x)} = \frac{\beta_n + \beta_{n-1}x + \ . \ . \ . + \beta_1 x^{n-1} + \beta_0 x^n}{\alpha_n + \alpha_{n-1}x + \ . \ . \ . + \alpha_1 x^{n-1} + x^n}$$

$$w(x) = \rho_1 + \rho_2 x + \ . \ . \ . + \rho_{n-1}x^{n-2} + \rho_n x^{n-1}$$

$$\frac{q(x)}{r(x)}\,a(x) = b(x) + \frac{w(x)}{r(x)}$$

FIG. 6.7—Polynomial multiplication and division

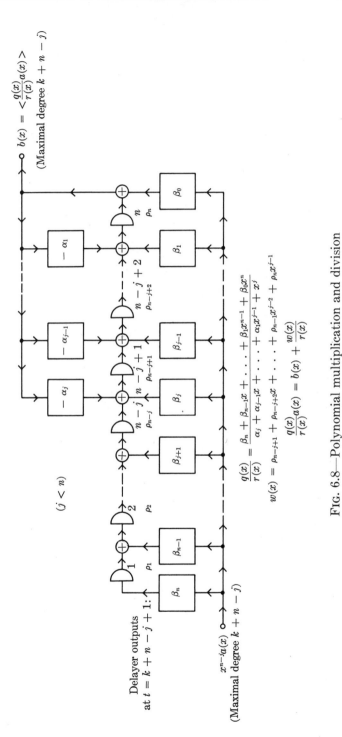

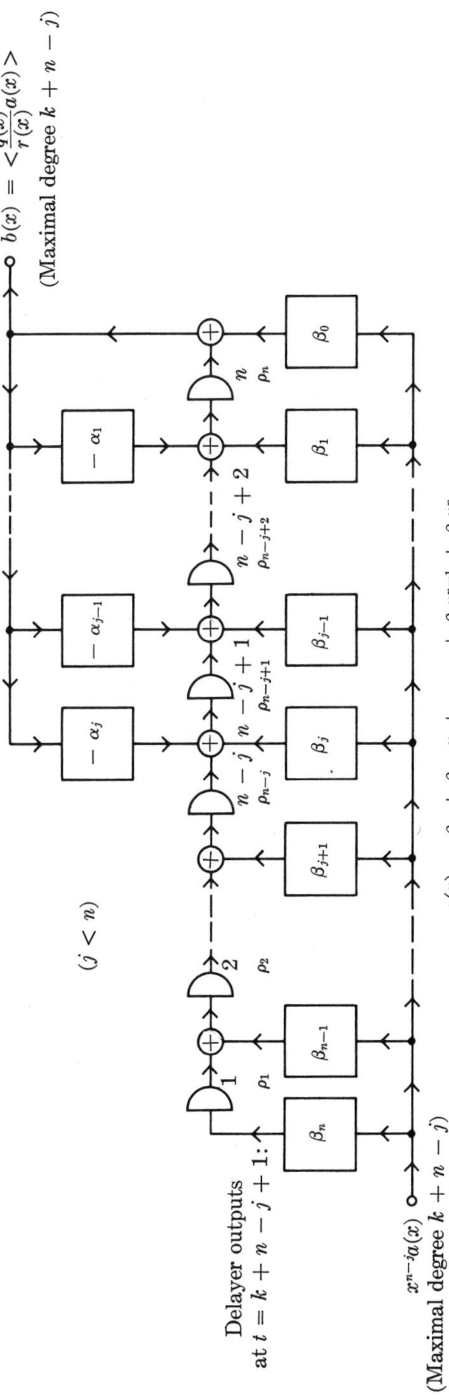

$$\frac{q(x)}{r(x)} = \frac{\beta_n + \beta_{n-1}x + \cdots + \beta_1 x^{n-1} + \beta_0 x^n}{\alpha_j + \alpha_{j-1}x + \cdots + \alpha_1 x^{j-1} + x^j}$$

$$w(x) = \rho_{n-j+1} + \rho_{n-j+2}x + \cdots + \rho_{n-1}x^{j-2} + \rho_n x^{j-1}$$

$$\frac{q(x)}{r(x)} a(x) = b(x) + \frac{w(x)}{r(x)}$$

FIG. 6.8—Polynomial multiplication and division

The preceding provides a method for computing $< a(x)q(x)/r(x) >$ where $\partial(q(x)) > \partial(r(x))$. When $\partial(q(x)) = n$ and $\partial(r(x)) = j < n$, we can write

5–5 $$< a(x)\frac{\beta_0x^n + \beta_1x^{n-1} + \cdots + \beta_n}{x^j + \alpha_1x^{j-1} + \cdots + \alpha_j} > \; = \; < x^{n-j}a(x)\frac{\beta_0x^n + \beta_1x^{n-1} + \cdots + \beta_n}{x^n + \alpha_1x^{n-1} + \cdots + \alpha_jx^{n-j}} >$$

Hence, the desired quotient can be obtained by taking $x^{n-j}a(x)$ (of maximal degree $k + n - j$) as the input polynomial to the QLSC with the transfer function

5–6 $$\mathfrak{T} = \frac{\beta_0 + \beta_1d + \cdots + \beta_nd^n}{1 + \alpha_1d + \cdots + \alpha_jd^j}$$

(see Fig. 6.8). The corresponding remainder, multiplied by x^{n-j}, is the internal polynomial of the QLSC at $t = k + n - j + 1$.

5–7 *Example:* The shift-register QLSC over $GF(3)$ shown in Fig. 6.9 has the transfer function ($n = 4$):

5–8 $$\mathfrak{T} = \frac{d + d^2 + 2d^3 + 2d^4}{1 + d + 2d^2 + d^4}$$

It can be used to compute $< a(x)q(x)/r(x) >$, where

5–9 $$\frac{q(x)}{r(x)} = \frac{2 + 2x + x^2 + x^3}{1 + 2x^2 + x^3 + x^4}$$

For example ($k = 2$):

5–10 $$a(x) = x + 2x^2$$

5–11 $$u(t)\colon 210.000 \ldots$$

5–12 $$U = 2 + d$$

5–13 $$Y = U\mathfrak{T} = \frac{(2 + d)(d + d^2 + 2d^3 + 2d^4)}{1 + d + 2d^2 + d^4} = 2d + d^2 + d^4 + \cdots$$

5–14 $$y(t)\colon 021 \ldots$$

5–15 $$b(x) = 1 + 2x = \; < (x + 2x^2)\frac{2 + 2x + x^2 + x^3}{1 + 2x^2 + x^3 + x^4} >$$

At $t = 3$: $\rho_1 = 2$, $\rho_2 = 0$, $\rho_3 = 1$, $\rho_4 = 0$. Hence, the remainder, as expected, is

5–16 $$w(x) = 2 + x^2$$

5–17 *Example:* The shift-register QLSC over $GF(3)$ shown in Fig. 6.10 has the transfer function ($n = 4$, $j = 3$, $n - j = 1$):

5–18 $$\mathfrak{T} = \frac{2 + d + 2d^2 + d^4}{1 + d + 2d^2 + 2d^3}$$

It can be used to compute $< a(x)q(x)/r(x) >$, where

5–19 $$\frac{q(x)}{r(x)} = \frac{1 + 2x^2 + x^3 + 2x^4}{2 + 2x + x^2 + x^3}$$

For example ($k = 2$, $k + n - j = 3$):

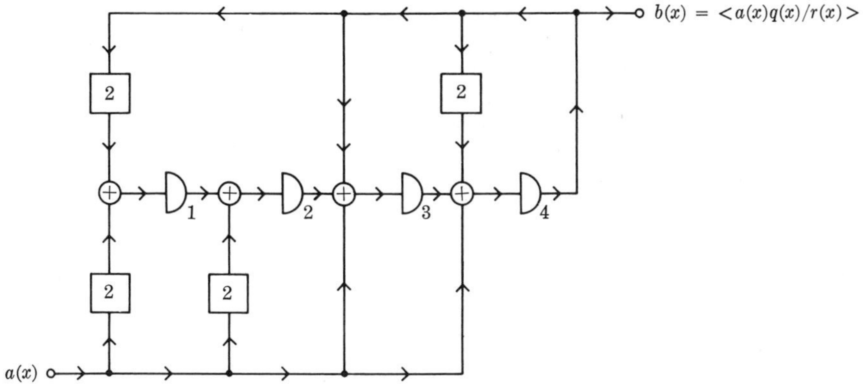

$$\frac{q(x)}{r(x)} = \frac{2 + 2x + x^2 + x^3}{1 + 2x^2 + x^3 + x^4}$$

FIG. 6.9—Computing circuit for $<a(x)(2 + 2x + x^2 + x^3)/(1 + 2x^2 + x^3 + x^4)>$

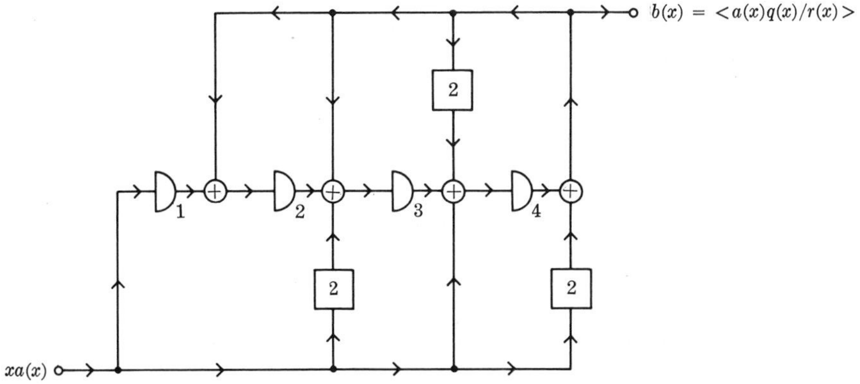

$$\frac{q(x)}{r(x)} = \frac{1 + 2x^2 + x^3 + 2x^4}{2 + 2x + x^2 + x^3}$$

FIG. 6.10—Computing circuit for $< a(x)(1 + 2x^2 + x^3 + 2x^4)/(2 + 2x + x^2 + x^3)>$

5–20 $$a(x) = 2 + x^2,\ xa(x) = 2x + x^3$$

5–21 $$u(t)\colon\ 1020.000$$

5–22 $$U = 1 + 2d^2$$

5–23 $$Y = U\mathfrak{T} = \frac{(1 + 2d^2)(2 + d + 2d^2 + d^4)}{1 + d + 2d^2 + 2d^3} = 2 + 2d + d^4 + \ldots$$

5–24 $$y(t)\colon\ 2200 \ldots$$

5–25 $$b(x) = 2x^3 + 2x^2 = \left< (2 + x^2)\frac{1 + 2x^2 + x^3 + 2x^4}{2 + 2x + x^2 + x^3} \right>$$

At $t = 4$: $\rho_1 = 0$, $\rho_2 = 2$, $\rho_3 = 0$, $\rho_4 = 1$. Hence, the remainder, as expected, is

5–26 $$w(x) = 2 + x^2$$

II. COMPUTATIONS IN GALOIS FIELDS

6. Galois Field Generators

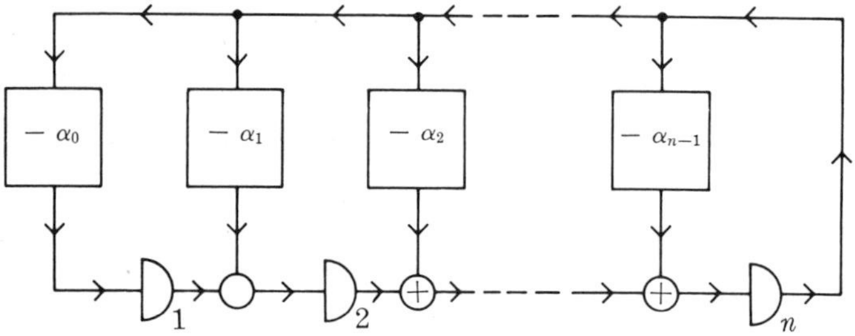

FIG. 6.11—Forward generator of $GF(p^n)$

Fig. 6.11 shows a multi-adder shift register $\mathcal{A}$, realizing $\mathbf{M}^{\mathrm{TR}}_{d(x)}$, where

6–1 $$d(x) = \alpha_0 + \alpha_1 x + \ldots + \alpha_{n-1}x^{n-1} + x^n \qquad (\alpha_0 \neq 0)$$

The internal polynomial of $\mathcal{A}$ will be represented by an element from $R_{d(\xi)}$ [the ring of polynomials over $GF(p)$ modulo $d(x)$]. Suppose at time $t = 0$ the internal polynomial is

6–2 $$s(\xi) = \sigma_0 + \sigma_1\xi + \ldots + \sigma_{n-1}\xi^{n-1}$$

[this polynomial can be imposed on $\mathcal{A}$ by applying the sequence $\sigma_{n-1}\sigma_{n-2} \ldots \sigma_0 000 \ldots$ to delayer 1 at $t = -n$, with $\mathbf{s}(-n) = \mathbf{0}$]. As shown in **5.10–4**, at $t = \nu$ the internal polynomial is $\xi^\nu s(\xi)$. Thus, starting at $t = 0$, the sequence of internal polynomials is

6–3 $$s(\xi),\ \xi s(\xi),\ \xi^2 s(\xi),\ \ldots$$

If $s(\xi) = 1$ (i.e., initial output of delayer 1 is 1, and initial outputs of all other delayers are 0), and if the exponent of $d(x)$ is T, **6–3** becomes

6–4 $$1,\ \xi,\ \xi^2,\ \ldots,\ \xi^{T-1},\ 1,\ \xi,\ \xi^2,\ \ldots,\ \xi^{T-1},\ \ldots$$

In particular, if $d(x)$ is a maximum-exponent polynomial ($T = p^n - 1$), the internal polynomials of $\mathcal{A}$ at the first $p^n - 1$ dits are the *distinct* polynomials

6–5 $$1, \xi, \xi^2, \ldots, \xi^{p^n-2}$$

In this case $R_{d(\xi)}$ is the Galois field $GF(p^n)$ whose modulus polynomial is $d(x)$, and **6–5** represents all nonzero elements of this field. $\mathcal{A}$ thus constructed will be called a *forward generator of* $GF(p^n)$.

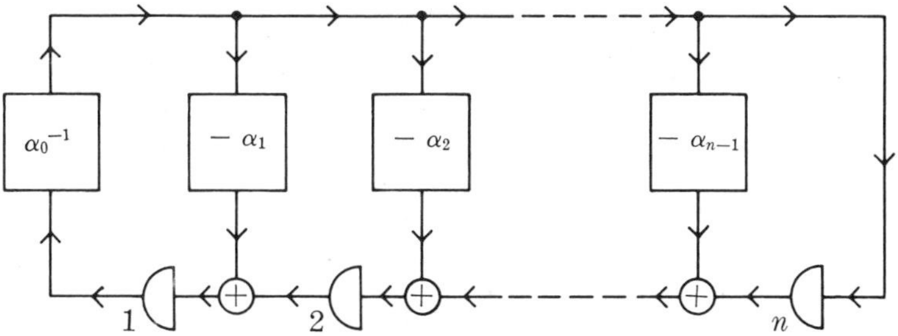

FIG. 6.12—Backward generator of $GF(p^n)$

Now, consider the multi-adder shift register $\mathcal{A}'$ of Fig. 6.12, where $d(x)$ is assumed to be a maximum-exponent polynomial. If at time t the internal polynomial of $\mathcal{A}'$ is $s(\xi)$ as given in **6–2**, then the internal polynomial $s'(\xi)$ at time $t + 1$ is given by

6–6
$$\begin{aligned} s'(\xi) &= \sigma_1 + \sigma_2\xi + \cdots + \sigma_{n-1}\xi^{n-2} \\ &\quad - \sigma_0\alpha_0^{-1}(\alpha_1 + \alpha_2\xi + \cdots + \alpha_{n-1}\xi^{n-2} + \xi^{n-1}) \\ &= \sigma_0\xi^{-1} + \sigma_1 + \alpha_2\xi + \cdots + \sigma_{n-1}\xi^{n-2} \\ &\quad - \sigma_0\alpha_0^{-1}(\alpha_0\xi^{-1} + \alpha_1 + \alpha_2\xi + \cdots + \alpha_{n-1}\xi^{n-2} + \xi^{n-1}) \\ &= \xi^{-1}s(\xi) - \sigma_0\alpha_0^{-1}\xi^{-1}d(\xi) = \xi^{-1}s(\xi) \end{aligned}$$

By induction, at time $t + \nu$ the internal polynomial of $\mathcal{A}'$ is $\xi^{-\nu}s(\xi)$. Thus, if at $t = 0$ we impose $s(\xi) = 1$, the internal polynomial of $\mathcal{A}'$ at the first $p^n - 1$ dits are

6–7 $$1, \xi^{-1}, \xi^{-2}, \ldots, \xi^{-(p^n-2)}$$

which, like **6–5**, represents all nonzero elements of $GF(p^n)$ whose modulus polynomial is $d(x)$. $\mathcal{A}'$ thus constructed will be called a *backward generator of* $GF(p^n)$.

Note that when $p = 2$, ($-\alpha_0 = \alpha_0^{-1} = 1$), $\mathcal{A}$ and $\mathcal{A}'$ are identical, except for the orientation of the delayers.

7. Multiplication and Division in Galois Fields

Let $\mathcal{A}_1$ and $\mathcal{A}_2$ be forward and backward generators, respectively, for $GF(p^n)$ [with some irreducible modulus polynomial $p(x)$]. Let their internal polynomials at $t = 0$ be $s_1(\xi)$ (nonzero) and $s_2(\xi)$, respectively. Suppose at $t = k$ the generator $\mathcal{A}_1$ assumes the internal polynomial 1, and $\mathcal{A}_2$ the internal polynomial $z(\xi)$. Then:

7–1 $$1 = \xi^k s_1(\xi)$$

7–2 $$z(\xi) = \xi^{-k}s_2(\xi) = s_1(\xi)\, s_2(\xi)$$

Thus, $\mathcal{A}_1$ and $\mathcal{A}_2$ can be used to multiply pairs of elements in $GF(p^n)$.

Let $\mathcal{A}_1$ and $\mathcal{A}_2$ be two forward generators for $GF(p^n)$, with initial internal polynomials $s_1(\xi)$ (nonzero) and $s_2(\xi)$, respectively. Again, let $t = k$ be the time at which $\mathcal{A}_1$ assumes the internal polynomial 1, and $\mathcal{A}_2$ the internal polynomial $z(\xi)$. Then:

7–3 $$1 = \xi^k s_1(\xi)$$

7–4 $$z(\xi) = \xi^k s_2(\xi) = \frac{s_2(\xi)}{s_1(\xi)}$$

Thus, $\mathcal{A}_1$ and $\mathcal{A}_2$ can be used to divide pairs of elements in $GF(p^n)$.

If $s_1(\xi) = \xi^{-i}$ $(0 \le i \le p^n - 2)$, we have $k = i$, and hence the multiplication or division process described above requires at most $p^n - 1$ dits.

8. Reduction of Polynominals in ζ

Let ζ be a nonzero element in $GF(p^n)$, with the minimum function (see **1.10–9**)

8–1 $$m_\zeta(x) = \alpha_0 + \alpha_1 x + \cdots + \alpha_{n-1}x^{n-1} + x^n$$

We shall consider polynomials in ζ over $GF(p)$, with maximal degree k:

8–2 $$a(\zeta) = \eta_k + \eta_{k-1}\zeta + \cdots + \eta_0\zeta^k$$

$\bar{a}(\zeta)$, the *reduced form* of $a(\zeta)$, will denote the (unique) polynomial in ζ, of degree at most $n - 1$, which equals $a(\zeta)$ [in $GF(p^n)$]:

8–3 $$\bar{a}(\zeta) = \rho_1 + \rho_2\zeta + \cdots + \rho_n\zeta^{n-1}$$

An LSC $\mathcal{A}$ capable of computing $\bar{a}(\zeta)$ is shown in Fig. 6.13. The input polynomial to $\mathcal{A}$ is $a(\zeta)$; $\bar{a}(\zeta)$ appears as the internal polynomial of $\mathcal{A}$ at $t = k + 1$.

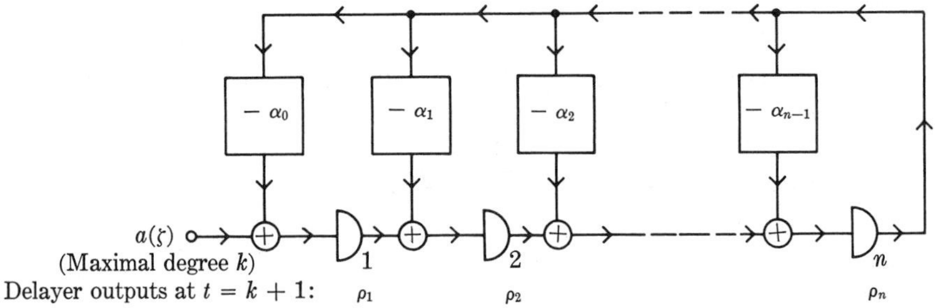

$$m_\zeta(x) = \alpha_0 + \alpha_1 x + \cdots + \alpha_{n-1}x^{n-1} + x^n$$
$$\bar{a}(\zeta) = \rho_1 + \rho_2\zeta + \cdots + \rho_n\zeta^{n-1}$$

FIG. 6.13—Reduction circuit for $a(\zeta)$

To verify this claim, define

8–4 $$s_1(\zeta) = \eta_0$$

8–5 $$s_\nu(\zeta) = \eta_{\nu-1} + \zeta s_{\nu-1}(\zeta) \qquad (\nu = 2, 3, \ldots, k+1)$$

Hence:

8–6 $$s_{k+1}(\zeta) = a(\zeta)$$

Suppose the reduced form of $s_\nu(\zeta)$ is given by

8–7 $$\bar{s}_\nu(\zeta) = \sigma_0 + \sigma_1\zeta + \cdots + \sigma_{n-1}\zeta^{n-1}$$

Hence, by **8–5**:

8–8
$$s_{\nu+1}(\zeta) = \eta_\nu + \zeta(\sigma_0 + \sigma_1\zeta + \ldots + \sigma_{n-1}\zeta^{n-1}) = \eta_\nu + \sigma_0\zeta + \sigma_1\zeta^2 + \ldots + \sigma_{n-1}\zeta^n$$

or, by **8–1**:

8–9
$$\bar{s}_{\nu+1}(\zeta) = \eta_\nu + \sigma_0\zeta + \sigma_1\zeta^2 + \ldots + \sigma_{n-2}\zeta^{n-1} - \sigma_{n-1}(\alpha_0 + \alpha_1\zeta + \ldots + \alpha_{n-1}\zeta^{n-1})$$

On the other hand, η_0 is the internal polynomial of $\mathfrak{A}$ at $t = 1$; moreover, if $\bar{s}_\nu(\zeta)$, as given in **8–7**, is the internal polynomial of $\mathfrak{A}$ at $t = \nu \leq k$, then $\bar{s}_{\nu+1}(\zeta)$ is precisely the internal polynomial of $\mathfrak{A}$ at $t = \nu + 1$ (see Fig. 6.13). Hence, by induction, $\bar{s}_{k+1}(\zeta) = \bar{a}(\zeta)$ is the internal polynomial of $\mathfrak{A}$ at $t = k + 1$.

As a special case, if $\zeta = \xi$, $m_\zeta(x)$ is the modulus polynomial of $GF(p^n)$, and $\mathfrak{A}$ can be used to compute the reduced form of any polynomial in ξ.

8–10 *Example:* Consider the field $GF(2^3)$ with the modulus polynomial $p(x) = 1 + x + x^3$ and the element $\zeta = 1 + \xi^2$. Following **1.10–14**, the minimum function of ζ can be found to be

8–11
$$m_\zeta(x) = 1 + x^2 + x^3$$

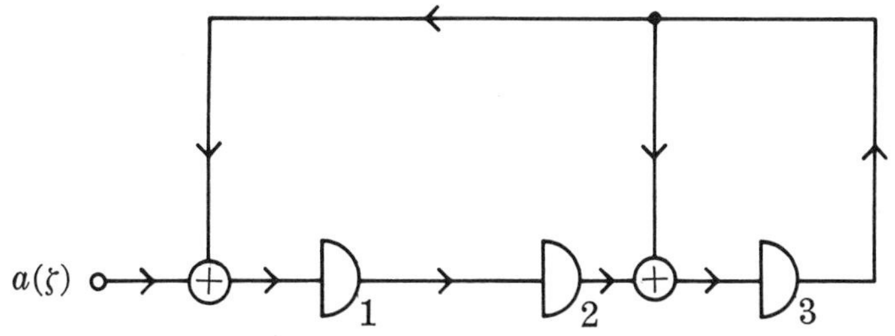

$$m_\zeta(x) = 1 + x^2 + x^3$$

FIG. 6.14—Reduction circuit for $a(\zeta)$ ($\zeta = 1 + \xi^2$)

Hence, the LSC over $GF(2)$ shown in Fig. 6.14 can be used to reduce polynomials in ζ. For example, to reduce

8–12
$$a(\zeta) = 1 + \zeta + \zeta^4$$

apply the input sequence

8–13
$$u(t)\text{: } 10011.000\ldots$$

The internal polynomial of the LSC at $t = 5$ is $\bar{a}(\zeta) = \zeta^2$. This is the correct form, since

8–14
$$1 + \zeta + \zeta^4 = \zeta^2 = 1 + \xi + \xi^2$$

9. Computation of Polynomials in ζ^h

Let ζ be a nonzero element in $GF(p^n)$. For any fixed non-negative integer h we can write

9–1
$$\begin{aligned}\zeta^h &= a_{11} + a_{21}\zeta + a_{31}\zeta^2 + \cdots + a_{n1}\zeta^{n-1}\\ \zeta^{h+1} &= a_{12} + a_{22}\zeta + a_{32}\zeta^2 + \cdots + a_{n2}\zeta^{n-1}\\ &\cdot\\ &\cdot\\ &\cdot\\ \zeta^{h+n-1} &= a_{1n} + a_{2n}\zeta + a_{3n}\zeta^2 + \cdots + a_{nn}\zeta^{n-1}\end{aligned}$$

or

9–2
$$(\zeta^h, \zeta^{h+1}, \ldots, \zeta^{h+n-1}) = (1, \zeta, \ldots, \zeta^{n-1})\mathbf{A}$$

where $\mathbf{A} = [a_{ij}]_{n\times n}$. Thus, if

9–3
$$s(\zeta) = \sigma_0 + \sigma_1\zeta + \cdots + \sigma_{n-1}\zeta^{n-1}$$

then

9–4
$$\begin{aligned}\zeta^h s(\zeta) &= \sigma_0' + \sigma_1'\zeta + \cdots + \sigma_{n-1}'\zeta^{n-1}\\ &= \zeta^h(\sigma_0 + \sigma_1\zeta + \cdots + \sigma_{n-1}\zeta^{n-1})\\ &= \sigma_0\zeta^h + \sigma_1\zeta^{h+1} + \cdots + \sigma_{n-1}\zeta^{h+n-1}\\ &= (\zeta^h, \zeta^{h+1}, \ldots, \zeta^{h+n-1})\begin{pmatrix}\sigma_0\\ \sigma_1\\ \cdot\\ \cdot\\ \cdot\\ \sigma_{n-1}\end{pmatrix}\\ &= (1, \zeta, \ldots, \zeta^{n-1})\mathbf{A}\begin{pmatrix}\sigma_0\\ \sigma_1\\ \cdot\\ \cdot\\ \cdot\\ \sigma_{n-1}\end{pmatrix}\end{aligned}$$

or

9–5
$$\begin{pmatrix}\sigma_0'\\ \sigma_1'\\ \cdot\\ \cdot\\ \cdot\\ \sigma_{n-1}'\end{pmatrix} = \mathbf{A}\begin{pmatrix}\sigma_0\\ \sigma_1\\ \cdot\\ \cdot\\ \cdot\\ \sigma_{n-1}\end{pmatrix}$$

Now, consider the LSC $\mathcal{A}$ whose characteristic matrix is **A** as defined above (see Fig. 6.15). From the preceding development it follows that, if at time t the internal polynomial of $\mathcal{A}$ is $s(\zeta)$ and the input to $\mathcal{A}$ is η, then at time $t + 1$ the internal polynomial is $\eta + \zeta^h s(\zeta)$. Thus, if the input to $\mathcal{A}$ is given by

9–6
$$u(t){:}\ \eta_0\eta_1 \ldots \eta_k 000 \ldots$$

the sequence of internal polynomials (all of degrees less than n) is

9–7
$$s_1(\zeta) = \eta_0$$

9–8
$$s_\nu(\zeta) = \eta_{\nu-1} + \zeta^h s_{\nu-1}(\zeta) \qquad (\nu = 2, 3, \ldots, k + 1)$$

By induction:

9–9
$$s_{k+1}(\zeta) = \eta_k + \eta_{k-1}\zeta^h + \eta_{k-2}\zeta^{2h} + \cdots + \eta_0\zeta^{kh}$$

Thus, if $a(x)$, of maximal degree k, is the input polynomial to $\mathcal{A}$, the internal polynomial of $\mathcal{A}$ at $t = k + 1$ is $a(\zeta^h)$, expressed as a reduced polynomial in ζ.

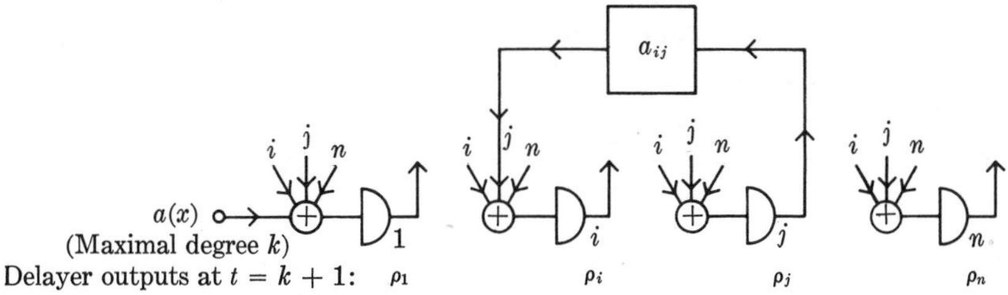

$$a(\zeta^h) = \rho_1 + \rho_2\zeta + \dots + \rho_n\zeta^{n-1}$$

FIG. 6.15—Computing circuit for $a(\zeta^h)$

9–10 *Example:* Consider the field $GF(2^3)$ with the modulus polynomial $p(x) = 1 + x + x^3$ and the element $\zeta = 1 + \xi^2$. Using **8–11**, the following identities can be developed ($h = 4$):

9–11
$$\begin{aligned} \zeta^4 &= 1 + \zeta + \zeta^2 \\ \zeta^5 &= 1 + \zeta \\ \zeta^6 &= \quad\;\; \zeta + \zeta^2 \end{aligned}$$

Hence,

9–12
$$\mathbf{A} = \begin{pmatrix} 1 & 1 & 0 \\ 1 & 1 & 1 \\ 1 & 0 & 1 \end{pmatrix}$$

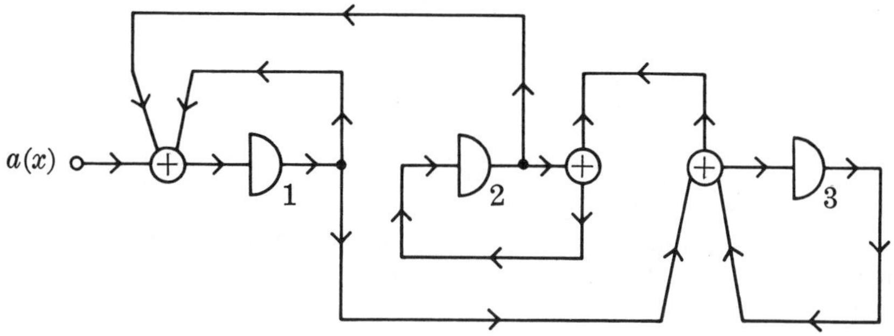

FIG. 6.16—Computing circuit for $a(\zeta^4)$ ($\zeta = 1 + \xi^2$)

Fig. 6.16 shows the corresponding LSC, which can be used to compute $a(\zeta^4)$ for any $a(x)$. For example, to compute $a(x) = 1 + x$ with $x = \zeta^4$, apply the input sequence

9–13
$$u(t)\text{: } 11.000 \dots$$

The internal polynomial of the LSC at $t = 2$ is $a(\zeta^4) = \zeta + \zeta^2$. This is the correct form, since

9–14
$$1 + \zeta^4 = \zeta + \zeta^2 = \xi$$

III. COUNTING

10. Modular Counters

A *counter modulo T* is an IC where the knowledge of the internal polynomial at any time $t \geq 0$ is sufficient to determine t modulo T (or, if $t < T$, to determine t uniquely).

Let $\mathcal{A}$ be a nonsingular IC whose internal polynomial at time t is $s_t(x)$. If the initial state $\mathbf{s}(0)$ of $\mathcal{A}$ has period T, then the sequence of states assumed by $\mathcal{A}$ is given by

10–1 $$s_0(x),\ s_1(x),\ \ldots,\ s_{T-1}(x),\ s_0(x),\ s_1(x),\ \ldots,\ s_{T-1}(x),\ \ldots$$

Hence, $\mathcal{A}$ with the initial state $\mathbf{s}(0)$ can be used as a counter modulo T.

More generally, if $\mathcal{A}$ has the cycle set

10–2 $$\Sigma = \{N_1[T_1] + N_2[T_2] + \ldots + N_r[T_r]\}$$

then $\mathcal{A}$ can be used as a counter modulo T_1, or modulo T_2, . . . , or modulo T_r [depending on $\mathbf{s}(0)$]. The design of $\mathcal{A}$ for a prescribed set of moduli is described in Sec. **5.25**. The selection of $\mathbf{s}(0)$ to initiate a desired count is described in Sec. **5.15**.

11. Linear Counters

A *linear counter up to k* is an IC whose internal polynomial at any time t, $0 \leq t \leq k - 1$, uniquely determines t.

11–1 *Assertion:* Let $\mathcal{A}$ be an IC of dimension $n > 1$ over $GF(p)$, used as a linear counter up to k. Then $k < p^n$.

Proof: Clearly, $k \leq p^n$. Suppose $k = p^n$. Then the p^n states

11–2 $$\mathbf{s}(0),\ \mathbf{s}(1),\ \ldots,\ \mathbf{s}(p^n - 1)$$

traversed by $\mathcal{A}$ at the first p^n dits are all distinct and must contain $\mathbf{0}$. Since $\mathbf{s}(t) = \mathbf{0}$ implies $\mathbf{s}(t+1) = \mathbf{0}$, we have $\mathbf{s}(p^n - 1) = \mathbf{0}$. The state diagram of $\mathcal{A}$, then, is as shown in Fig. 6.17. However, by **5.17–7**, such a state diagram is realizable only when $\mathcal{A}$ has exactly 2 states, which contradicts the assumption $n > 1$. Hence $k < p^n$.

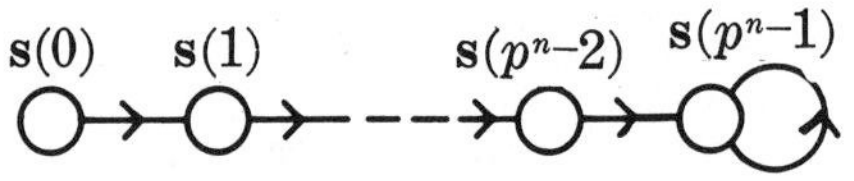

FIG. 6.17—For proof to **11–1**

A counter up to $p^n - 1$ can always be constructed from an n-dimensional shift register over $GF(p)$ realizing $\mathbf{M}_{d(x)}$, where $d(x)$ is a maximum-exponent polynomial. In this case any nonzero state is of period $p^n - 1$ and can be used to initiate the desired count. In view of **11–1**, such an IC is the least-dimensional linear counter up to $p^n - 1$.

11–3 *Example:* We wish to design a linear counter, over $GF(\mathbf{2})$, up to 1,000. The least integer n such that $2^n - 1 \geq 1{,}000$ is $n = 10$. A maximum-exponent polynomial over $GF(2)$ of degree 10 (see Table A5 in the Appendix) is $1 + x^3 + x^{10}$. Hence, an IC realizing $\mathbf{M}_{1+x^3+x^{10}}$ is a least-dimensional IC over $GF(2)$ which can be used as the desired counter.

IV. ERROR DETECTION AND CORRECTION

12. Linear Codes

In describing coding applications of LSCs we shall assume the communication system model shown in Fig. 6.18. In this model, the *message* consists of a sequence over $GF(p)$ of fixed length n (thus, p^n distinct messages can be transmitted through the system). The *encoder* transforms the message into a sequence over $GF(p)$, of length T, called a *code vector* (if the system is to have any error detecting or correcting capabilities, T must exceed n). The code vector is transmitted through a *channel,* whose output is called the *received vector*. The *noise* associated with the channel may be regarded as an independent sequence over $GF(p)$ which is added (component-wise) to the code vector to form the received vector. The *decoder* processes the received vector and generates a sequence which, with high probability, equals the original message (this process is called "error correction"). In a less ambitious scheme, the message is not recovered, but an indication is obtained as to whether or not the received vector is a code vector ("error detection").

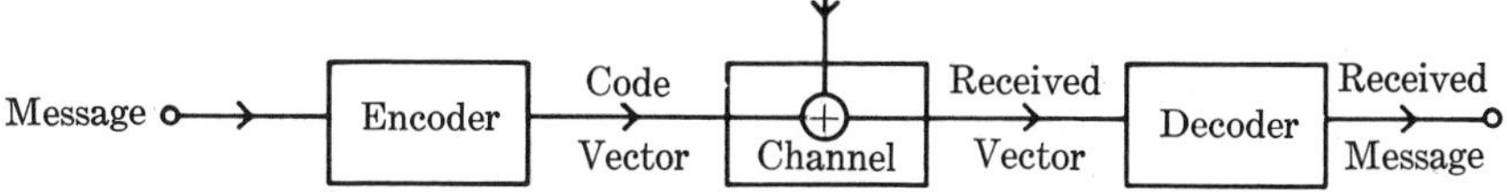

FIG. 6.18—Communication system

The set of p^n possible code vectors is called a *code.* If these vectors constitute an n-dimensional subspace of the T-dimensional vector space over $GF(p)$, the code is called a *(T,n) linear code over $GF(p)$*. Such a code can be uniquely specified by an $n \times T$ *code matrix* whose rows form a basis for the corresponding vector space. If the space is a cyclic space, the matrix may be any of the "basis matrices" described in Chap. 3 (see Secs. **3.6, 3.13, 3.14, 3.15**). In this case, the code is referred to as a *(T,n) cyclic code over $GF(p)$*.

The *weight* of a vector $\mathbf{v}$, denoted by $W(\mathbf{v})$, is the number of its nonzero components. The *distance* between two vectors $\mathbf{v}_1$ and $\mathbf{v}_2$, denoted by $D(\mathbf{v}_1, \mathbf{v}_2)$, is the number of coordinates in which they differ. The least nonzero weight and the least nonzero distance exhibited by a code, are called the *minimum weight* and *minimum distance*, respectively, of the code.

12–1 *Assertion:* In a linear code, the minimum distance equals the minimum weight.

Proof: Let δ denote the minimum distance, and w the minimum weight of the code. Then, for some distinct code vectors $\mathbf{v}_1$ and $\mathbf{v}_2$ (where $\mathbf{v}_1 - \mathbf{v}_2 = \mathbf{v}_3$ is a code vector),

12–2 $$\delta = D(\mathbf{v}_1, \mathbf{v}_2) = W(\mathbf{v}_1 - \mathbf{v}_2) = W(\mathbf{v}_3) \geq w$$

On the other hand, for some nonzero vector $\mathbf{v}_4$,

12–3 $$w = W(\mathbf{v}_4) = W(\mathbf{v}_4 - \mathbf{0}) = D(\mathbf{v}_4, \mathbf{0}) \geq \delta$$

Hence, $\delta = w$.

The difference between a received vector and a code vector is called an *error vector*. Thus, an error vector of weight w is capable of changing w components in any code vector. The effect of the noise on the channel is measured by the maximal weight that an error vector can assume.

12–4 *Assertion:* In a linear code, an error can be detected if and only if the error vector is not a code vector.

Proof: Let $\mathbf{e}$ be the error vector added to an arbitrary code vector $\mathbf{v}$ to result in the received vector $\mathbf{v}' = \mathbf{e} + \mathbf{v}$. If $\mathbf{e}$ is also a code vector, $\mathbf{e} + \mathbf{v}$ is in the code, and hence the presence of $\mathbf{e}$ cannot be detected. If $\mathbf{e}$ is not a code vector, $\mathbf{v}' - \mathbf{v}$ is not in the code, and hence $\mathbf{v}'$ is not in the code; thus, the presence of $\mathbf{e}$ can be detected.

If δ is the minimum distance of a code, then any error vector of weight $\delta - 1$ or less can be detected. Also, when δ is even, any error vector of weight $\frac{1}{2}(\delta - 2)$ or less can be corrected; when δ is odd, any error vector of weight $\frac{1}{2}(\delta - 1)$ or less can be corrected.

A *burst* of *length* b is a vector whose only nonzero components are among b (but not less than b) successive components. An error vector which is a burst, is called a *burst error*. It results from a common type of noise which tends to initiate a *succession* of errors rather than isolated ones.

Directly from **12–4** we have:

12–5 *Assertion:* In a linear code, every burst error of length b or less can be detected if and only if no code vector is a burst of length b or less.

13. Generation of Cyclic Codes

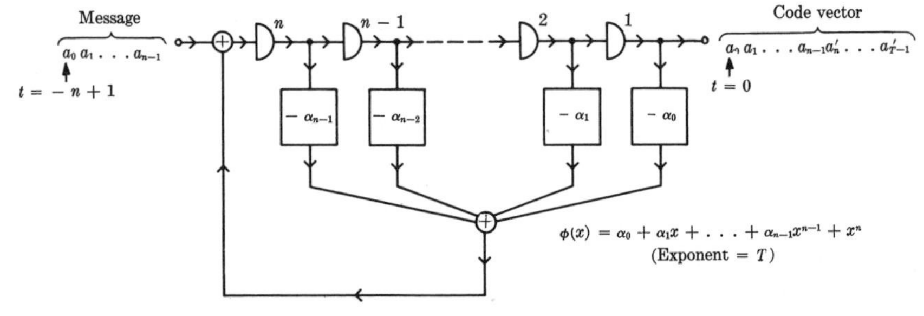

FIG. 6.19—Encoder for (T,n) cyclic code

By definition, the set of output sequences (restricted to one period) of a nonsingular simple ALSC $\mathcal{A}$ constitutes a cyclic code. If the feedback polynomial $\phi(x)$ of $\mathcal{A}$ is of degree n and exponent T over $GF(p)$, these sequences constitute a (T, n) cyclic code over $GF(p)$. The manner in which $\mathcal{A}$ can be used as an encoder is the following (see Fig. 6.19): The n message symbols are inserted into delayer n, say starting at $t = -n$; the code vector is the sequence of length T generated by $\mathcal{A}$ starting at $t = 0$. This encoding scheme has the advantage of retaining the original message in an unaltered form (as the first n elements of the code vector).

13–1 *Example:* Fig. 6.20 shows a 4-dimensional ALSC over $GF(2)$, with the feedback polynomial

13–2
$$\phi(x) = 1 + x + x^3 + x^4$$

whose exponent is 6. The ALSC can be used as an encoder for a (6, 4) cyclic code over $GF(2)$. For example, it transforms the message 1101 into the code vector 110110.

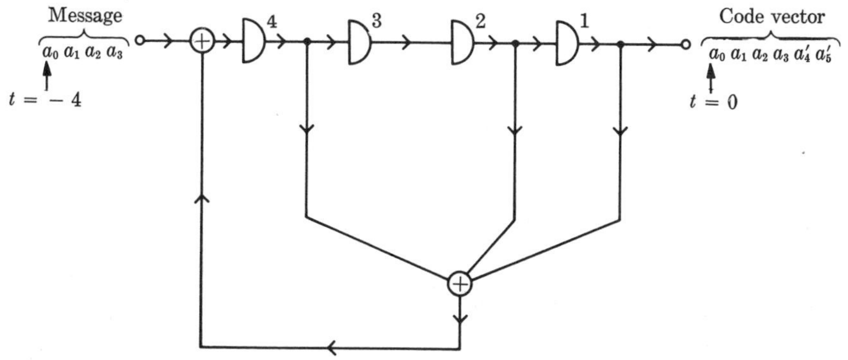

FIG. 6.20—Encoder for Example **13–1**

The cyclic code produced by $\mathcal{A}$ can be identified with the elements of the ideal $(g(\xi))_T$, where

13–3
$$g(x) = x^{T-n} + \gamma_1 x^{T-n-1} + \ldots + \gamma_{T-n-1}x + \gamma_{T-n}$$

in the following manner: $b_0b_1 \ldots b_{T-1}$ is a code vector if and only if $b(\xi) = b_0\xi^{T-1} + b_1\xi^{T-2} + \ldots + b_{T-1}$ is in $(g(\xi))_T$, i.e., if and only if $b(\xi)$ is a multiple of $g(\xi)$ in $R_{1-\xi^T}$. This suggests the following scheme for generating a cyclic code (see Fig. 6.21): Let $\mathcal{B}$ be a polynomial multiplying circuit of the

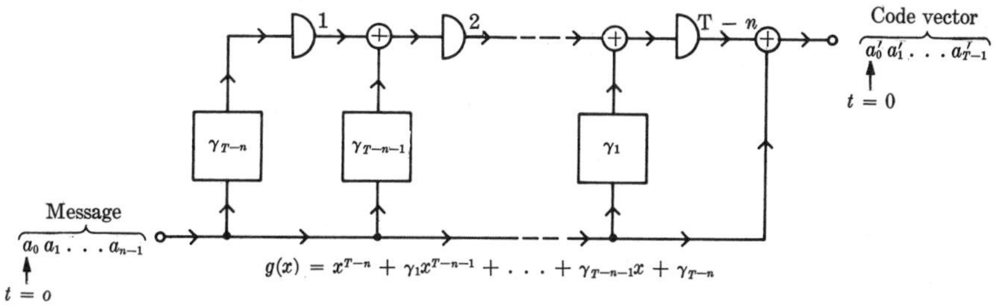

FIG. 6.21—Encoder for (T,n) cyclic code

type shown in Fig. 6.2, with $q(x) = g(x)$. If $a(x)$ (of maximal degree $n - 1$) is fed as an input polynomial into $\mathcal{B}$, the corresponding output polynomial is $b(x) = g(x)a(x)$. Since $b(x)$ is of degree at most $T - 1$, the set of all p^n possible polynomials $b(\xi)$ (corresponding to all possible input polynomials) is precisely $(g(\xi))_T$. This encoding scheme has the disadvantage of altering the message in forming the code vector. Its advantage over $\mathcal{A}$ is that, whenever $T - n < n$, it requires fewer delayers.

13–4 *Example:* When $\phi(x)$ is as in **13–2**,

13–5
$$g(x) = \frac{1 + x^6}{1 + x + x^3 + x^4} = 1 + x + x^2$$

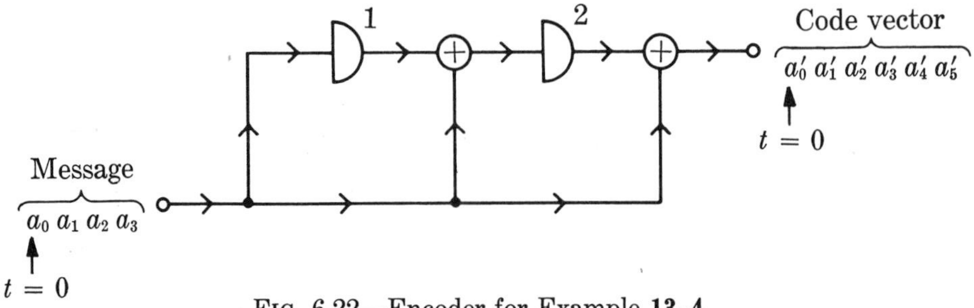

FIG. 6.22—Encoder for Example **13–4**

Fig. 6.22 shows the circuit which effects multiplication of input polynomials by $1 + x + x^2$, and hence which generates the (6, 4) code over $GF(2)$ represented by $(1 + \xi + \xi^2)_6$. For example, if the message is 1101, we have

13–6
$$a(x) = x^3 + x^2 + 1$$

13–7
$$b(x) = (1 + x + x^2)(1 + x^2 + x^3) = x^5 + x + 1$$

and hence the code vector is 100011.

A third coding scheme which enjoys the advantages of both the first and second schemes is shown in Fig. 6.23. The LSC $\mathcal{C}$ employed in this scheme is a polynomial multiplying and dividing circuit of the type shown in Fig. 6.7, where $q(x) = x^{T-n}$ and $r(x) = g(x)$. If $a(x)$ is the input polynomial (of maximal degree $n - 1$) applied to $\mathcal{C}$ at $t = 0$, the effect of $\mathcal{C}$ is to compute the principal part of $x^{T-n}a(x)/g(x)$ and leave the remainder $w(x)$ (of maximal degree $T - n - 1$) as the internal polynomial at $t = n$. Thus, we can write:

13–8
$$x^{T-n}a(x) = b(x)g(x) + w(x)$$

13–9
$$b'(x) = x^{T-n}a(x) - w(x) = b(x)g(x)$$

Since $b'(x)$ is of degree at most $T - 1$, the set of all p^n possible polynomials $b'(x)$ (corresponding to all possible input polynomials) is precisely $(g(\xi))_T$. Now, the T coefficients of $b'(x)$ (in order of descending powers of x) consist of the n coefficients of $a(x)$, followed by the $T - n$ coefficients of $-w(x)$. Hence, the code vector corresponding to $b'(x)$ can be transmitted by first transmitting the n message symbols (at times $0, 1, \ldots, n - 1$) and then the negated contents of delayers $T - n, T - n - 1, \ldots, 1$ (at times $n, n + 1, \ldots, T - 1$, respectively). Such a transmission is facilitated by the switching arrangement at the output of $\mathcal{C}$, as shown in Fig. 6.23. Clearly, $\mathcal{C}$ has the advantage of $\mathcal{A}$ in that it leaves the original message unaltered; like $\mathcal{B}$, it requires $T - n$ (rather than n) delayers. Note that, for a given message, the first n elements in the code vector obtained by $\mathcal{A}$ are the same as in the code vector obtained by $\mathcal{C}$. Since these code vectors are in the same n-dimensional subspace, their remaining $T - n$ elements must also be the same.

13–10 *Example:* Fig. 6.24 shows the encoding scheme $\mathcal{C}$ for the (6, 4) cyclic code over $GF(2)$, represented by $(1 + \xi + \xi^2)_6$.

FIG. 6.23—Encoder for (T,n) cyclic code

$$g(x) = x^{T-n} + \gamma_1 x^{T-n-1} + \cdots + \gamma_{T-n-1}x + \gamma_{T-n}$$

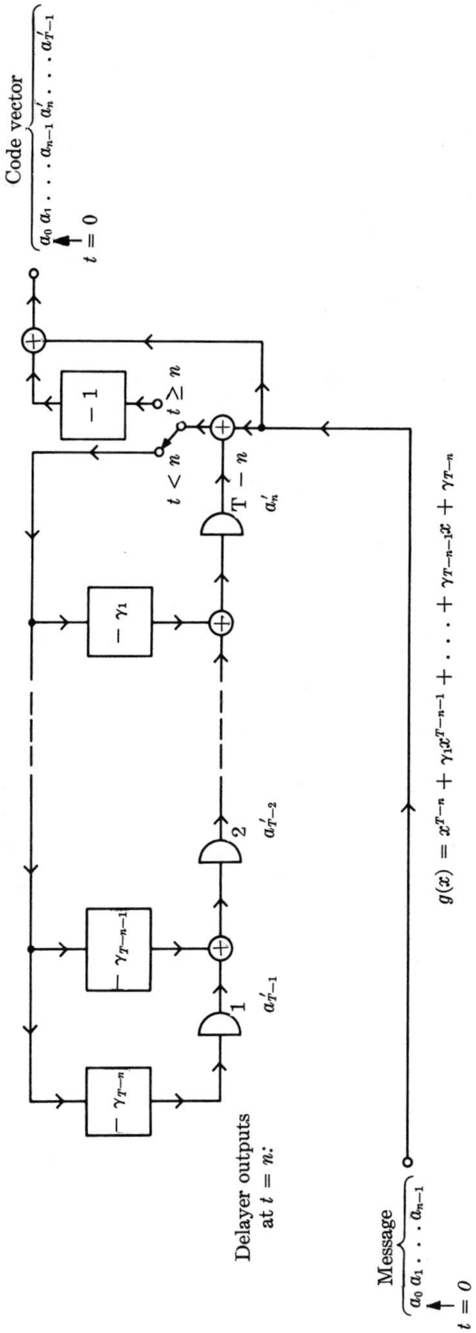

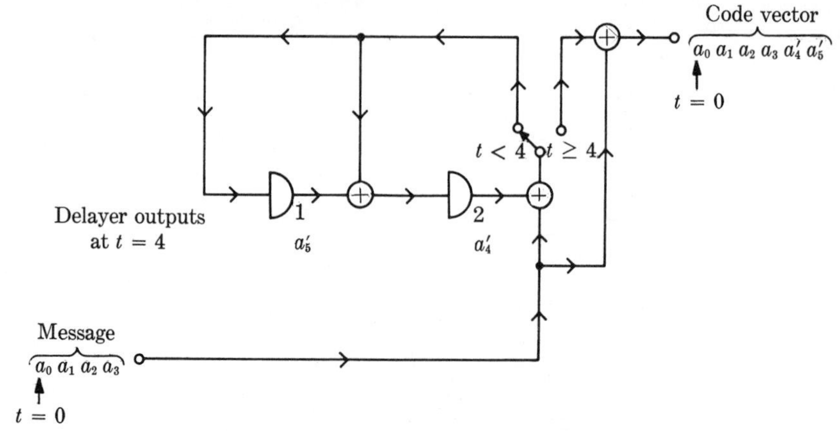

FIG. 6.24—Encoder for Example **13–10**

14. Error Detection for Cyclic Codes

To determine whether or not a polynomial $b(\xi) = b_0\xi^{T-1} + b_1\xi^{T-2} + \dots + b_{T-2}\xi + b_{T-1}$ belongs to $(g(\xi))_T$, it is sufficient to divide $b(x)$ by $g(x)$ and see whether or not the remainder is 0. Thus, to determine whether or not a received vector $b_0b_1 \dots b_{T-1}$ is a code vector, one can apply $b(x)$, at $t = 0$, as an input polynomial to a polynomial dividing circuit of the type shown in Fig. 6.5, where $r(x) = g(x)$ (see Fig. 6.25). If at $t = T$ the internal polynomial is 0, $b_0b_1 \dots b_{T-1}$ is a code vector; otherwise, $b_0b_1 \dots b_{T-1}$ is not a code vector, and one can state with assurance that the received vector contains an error. Note that when the code is the one produced by LSC $\mathcal{B}$ of Sec. **13**, the output polynomial of the circuit described here is—in the absence of error—precisely the polynomial $a(x)$ corresponding to the original message. In this case the circuit functions as an error detector and—when no error occurs—as a mechanism for recovering the message.

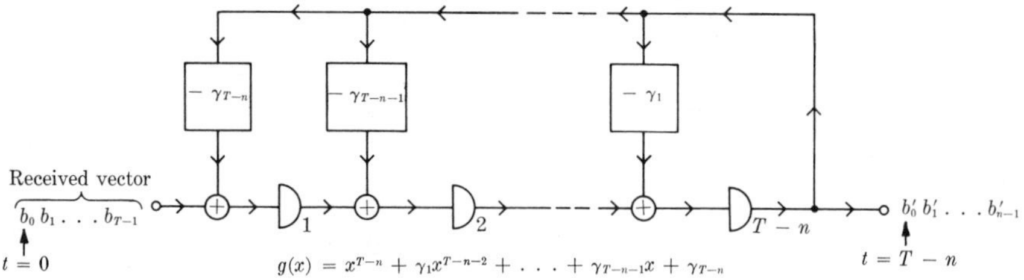

FIG. 6.25—Decoder for (T,n) cyclic code

14–1 *Assertion:* In a (T, n) cyclic code over $GF(p)$, any burst error of length $T - n$ or less can be detected.

Proof: Let the code be represented by $(g(\xi))_T$, and let

14–2 $$e(\xi) = e_j\xi^j + e_{j+1}\xi^{j+1} + \dots + e_{T-1}\xi^{T-1} \qquad (j \geq 0;\ e_j \neq 0)$$

ring-represent a burst of length $T - n$ or less. We can write $e(\xi) = \xi^j e'(\xi)$, where $e'(\xi)$ is of degree at most $T - n - 1$. Suppose $e(\xi)$ is in $(g(\xi))_T$. Then $g(x)$ divides $x^j e'(x)$ and hence divides $e'(x)$. But this is impossible, since $g(x)$ is of degree $T - n$. Hence $e(\xi)$ is not in $(g(\xi))_T$, and **14–1** follows from **12–5.**

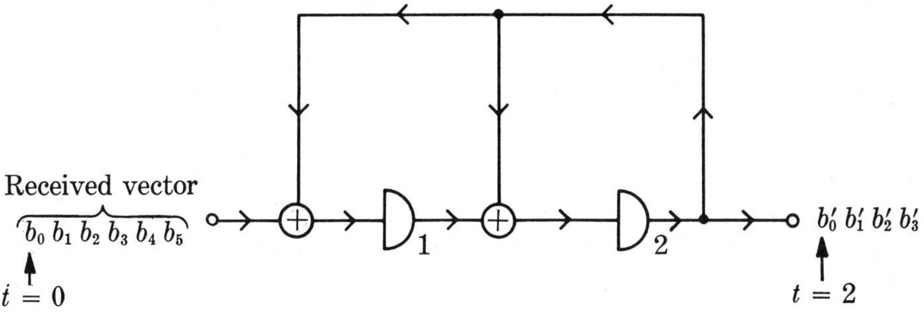

FIG. 6.26—Decoder for Example **14–3**

14–3 *Example:* Fig. 6.26 shows a polynomial dividing circuit, used as a decoder for the (6, 4) cyclic code over $GF(2)$ represented by $(1 + \xi + \xi^2)_6$. It is capable of detecting any burst error of length $6 - 4 = 2$ or less (i.e., all single errors and all pairs of adjacent errors).

15. Generalized Hamming Code

Consider a Galois field $GF(p^n)$ with the primitive element θ and the element

15–1 $$\rho = \theta^{p-1} = \rho_1 + \rho_2\xi + \dots + \rho_n\xi^{n-1}$$

Let $g(x)$ be the minimum function of ρ, and T the order of ρ in the field. By Sec. **3.16,** a polynomial $b(\xi) = b_0\xi^{T-1} + b_1\xi^{T-2} + \dots + b_{T-2}\xi + b_{T-1}$ is in $(g(\xi))_T$ if and only if

15–2 $$(b_0, b_1, \dots, b_{T-1})\mathbf{\Psi}^{\mathrm{TR}} = \mathbf{0}$$

where

15–3 $$\mathbf{\Psi} = \begin{pmatrix} \rho_1^{T-1} & \rho_1^{T-2} & \cdots & \rho_1 & 1 \\ \rho_2^{T-1} & \rho_2^{T-2} & & \rho_2 & 1 \\ \cdot & & & & \\ \cdot & & & & \\ \cdot & & & & \\ \rho_n^{T-1} & \rho_n^{T-2} & & \rho_n & 1 \end{pmatrix}$$

Since $p^n - 1$ is the least i such that $\theta^i = 1$, $(p^n - 1)/(p - 1)$ is the least i such that $\rho^i = 1$. Hence

15–4 $$T = \frac{p^n - 1}{p - 1}$$

Thus, the code consisting of all vectors $(b_0, b_1, \dots, b_{T-1})$ as defined by **15–2** and **15–3**, is a $((p^n - 1)/(p - 1), n)$ cyclic code over $GF(p)$. It is called a *generalized Hamming code.* When $p = 2$, it is referred to simply as a *Hamming code* (after its originator R. W. Hamming).

15-5 *Assertion:* A generalized Hamming code has minimum distance of at least 3 if and only if n and $p - 1$ are relatively prime.

Proof: A column of $\mathbf{\Psi}$ is a scalar multiple of another column if and only if there is a vector of weight 2, say

15-6 $$\mathbf{v} = (0, \ldots, 0, 1, 0, \ldots, 0, -\eta, 0, \ldots, 0) \qquad (\eta \neq 0)$$

such that $\mathbf{v}\mathbf{\Psi}^{\mathrm{TR}} = \mathbf{0}$, and hence if and only if the minimum distance of the code is at most 2 (see **12-1**). Now, supposing the minimum distance *is* at most 2, $\mathbf{v}$ of **15-6** is in the code and we can write, for some i and j $(0 \leq j < i \leq T - 1)$,

15-7 $$\rho^i - \eta\rho^j = 0 \qquad \text{or} \qquad \rho^{i-j} = \eta$$

By Fermat's theorem (see **1.5-8**), every nonzero element of $GF(p)$ must satisfy $x^{p-1} = 1$; hence, in view of **15-4**, the elements $1, \theta^T, \theta^{2T}, \ldots, \theta^{(p-2)T}$ of $GF(p^n)$ must constitute the nonzero elements of $GF(p)$. In particular, for some $k < p - 1$,

15-8 $$\eta = \rho^{i-j} = (\theta^{p-1})^{i-j} = \theta^{kT}$$

and hence

15-9 $$(p - 1)(i - j) = kT \qquad (k < p - 1)$$

Since $p - 1$ cannot divide k, **15-9** implies that T and $p - 1$ are not relatively prime. On the other hand, we can write

15-10 $$T = \frac{p^n - 1}{p - 1} = 1 + p + p^2 + \cdots + p^{n-1}$$
$$= (p - 1)(q_1 + q_2 + \cdots + q_{n-1}) + n$$

where $q_\nu = (p^\nu - 1)/(p - 1)$, which implies that T and $p - 1$ are relatively prime if and only if n and $p - 1$ are relatively prime. Thus, if the minimum distance is less than 3, n and $p - 1$ cannot be relatively prime. Now, suppose n and $p - 1$ *are* relatively prime. Then T and $p - 1$ are relatively prime; **15-8** is solvable only with $i = j$; the vector $\mathbf{v}$ of **15-6** cannot be in the code; hence, the minimum distance is greater than 2.

In conclusion, with a generalized Hamming code where n and $p - 1$ are relatively prime, any single error can be corrected and any pair of errors can be detected.

A generalized Hamming code represented by $(g(\xi))_T$ can be generated by LSCs $\mathcal{A}$ or $\mathcal{C}$ described in Sec. **13**, to result in code vectors where the first n elements constitute the original message. A corresponding error correction mechanism can be implemented by means of the LSC shown in Fig. 6.27, whose operation is described below.

Suppose the code vector is $b_0b_1 \ldots b_{T-1}$, and the corresponding received vector $b_0'b_1' \ldots b_{T-1}'$. Assume that

15-11 $$b_k' = \begin{cases} b_k & (k \neq i) \\ b_i + \alpha & (k = i) \end{cases}$$

where α may or may not be 0 [i.e., the received vector may have a single error in the $(i + 1)$st symbol]. As shown in the figure, the received vector is fed

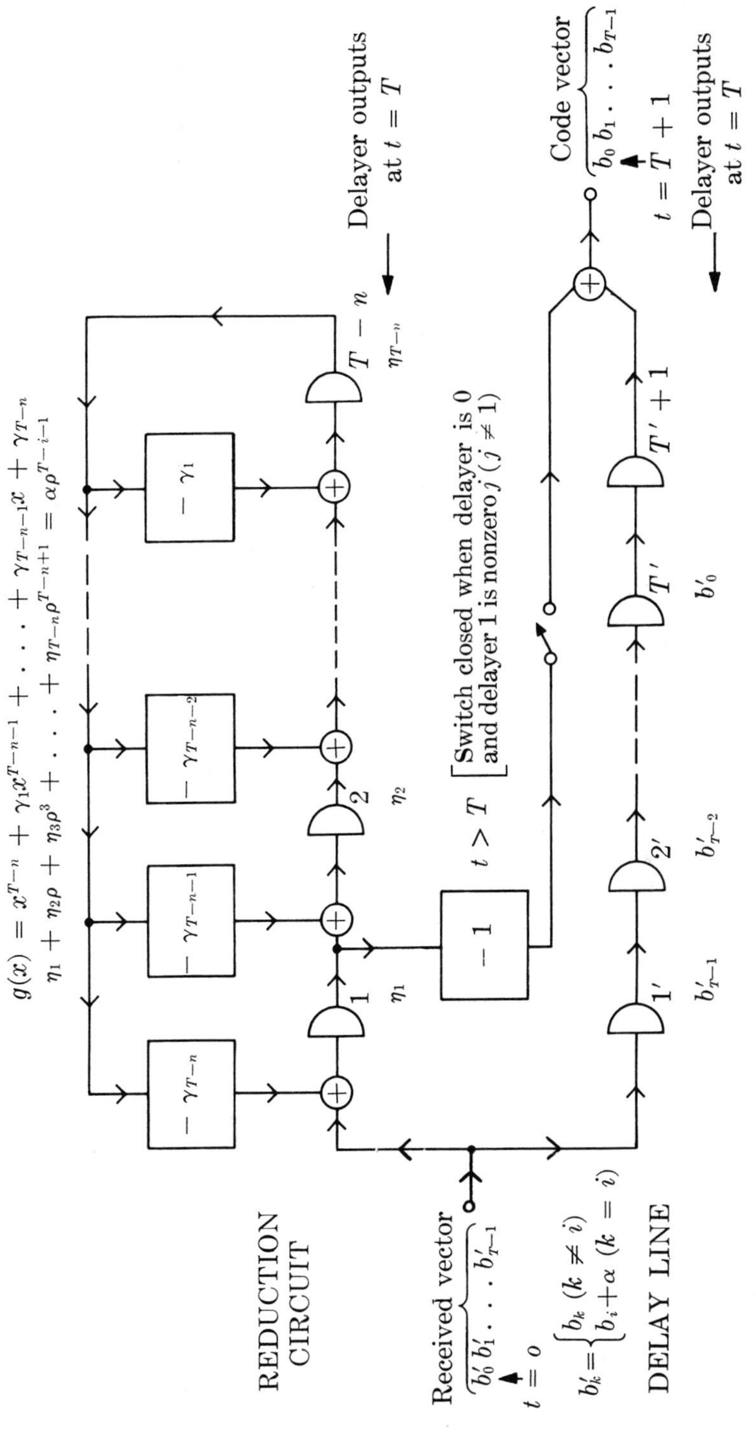

FIG. 6.27—Decoder for generalized Hamming code

simultaneously into a "reduction circuit" (of the type shown in Fig. 6.13) and into a "delay line," which consists simply of a string of $T + 1$ delayers (initially cleared). Now, by **15–2**, $b_0b_1 \ldots b_{T-1}$ is a code vector if and only if

15–12 $$b_0\rho^{T-1} + b_1\rho^{T-2} + \ldots + b_{T-2}\rho + b_{T-1} = 0$$

Hence, under the assumption **15–11**:

15–13 $$b'_0\rho^{T-1} + b'_1\rho^{T-2} + \ldots + b'_{T-2}\rho + b'_{T-1} = \alpha\rho^{T-i-1}$$

As shown in Sec. 8, the internal polynomial of the reduction circuit at $t = T$ is a polynomial in ρ (of degree at most $T - n - 1$) which equals $\alpha\rho^{T-i-1}$ in a reduced form. The reduction circuit is permitted to continue operation (with 0 input) from $t = T + 1$ through $t = 2T$. Since, at each dit in this interval, the internal polynomial of the circuit is multiplied by ρ (and reduced to a polynomial in ρ of degree at most $T - n - 1$), the internal polynomial obtained at $t = T + i + 1$ is (for the first time)

15–14 $$\alpha\rho^{T-i-1}\cdot\rho^{i+1} = \alpha\rho^T = \alpha$$

Also, at $t = T + i + 1$, the output of the delay line is b'_i. Hence, if $-\alpha$ is added to the output of the delay line at $t = T + i + 1$, the result is $b'_i - \alpha = b_i$, and hence the output of the delay line constitutes the original code vector. This correction operation is facilitated by adding the negated output of delayer 1 (which, at $t = T + i + 1$, generates α) to the output of the delay line via a switch (a "coincidence detector") functioning as follows: The switch closes if and only if, between $t = T + 1$ and $t = 2T$, the output of delayer 1 is nonzero and the outputs of delayers j are 0 for all $j \neq 1$. Note that, when $\alpha = 0$, the switch will never close and the output of the delay line will be the received vector, as expected. In all cases, the message can be recovered from the output sequence simply by picking up the first n elements (starting at $t = T + 1$).

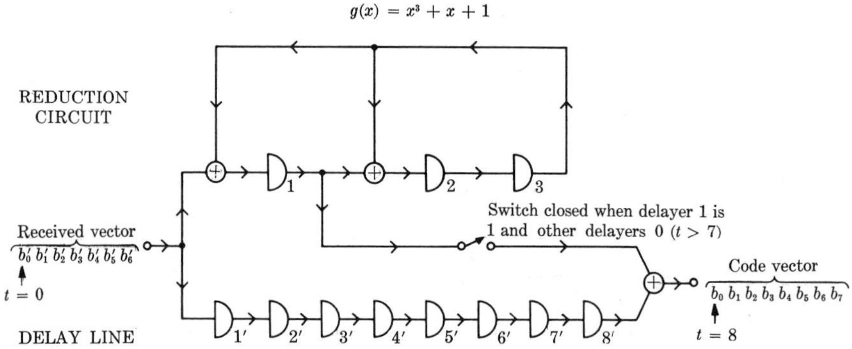

FIG. 6.28—Decoder for Example **15–15**

15–15 *Example:* A Hamming code ($p = 2$) which accommodates 8 messages can be constructed with $n = 3$ ($p^n = 8$) and $T = (2^3 - 1)/(2 - 1) = 7$. In this case one can select $\theta = \xi$, $\rho = \theta^{2-1} = \theta = \xi$, and $g(x)$ any maximum exponent polynomial of degree 3 over $GF(2)$, say $1 + x + x^3$. The error correction circuit for such a code (which corrects all single errors) is shown in Fig. 6.28. For example, suppose the message is 011. Using the encoding LSC $\mathcal{A}$ of Sec. **13**, the corresponding code vector is 0111010. If the error occurs at the third element ($\alpha = 1$, $i = 2$), the received vector is 0101010. If this received vector is fed into the reducing circuit at $t = 0$, the internal polynomial a $t = 7$ is $\xi^{7-2-1} = \xi^4 = \xi + \xi^2$. At $t = 7 + 3 = 10$, the internal polynomial is $\xi^{4+3} = \xi^7 = 1$. This 1 is added to the output of the delay line which, at $t = 10$, is the third element of the received vector. The overall output sequence, therefore, is 0111010, which is the correct code vector. The message consists of the first 3 output symbols, namely 011.

16. Maximum-Period Cyclic Codes

When $\phi(x)$ is a maximum-exponent polynomial of degree n over $GF(p)$, the ideal $(g(\xi))_T$, where $T = p^n - 1$ and $g(x) = (1 - x^T)/\phi(x)$, represents a $(p^n - 1, n)$ cyclic code over $GF(p)$. This code, which can be constructed for every n and prime p, is called a *maximum-period cyclic code.*

Immediately from **12–1** and **3.17–3**, we have:

16–1 *Assertion:* The minimum distance in a maximum-period code is $(p - 1)p^{n-1}$.

Thus, with a maximum-period code, the number of errors that can be corrected is

16–2 $$\tfrac{1}{2}[(p - 1)p^{n-1} - 2]$$

(or $2^{n-2} - 1$ when $p = 2$). The number of errors that can be detected is $(p - 1)p^{n-1} - 1$ (or $2^{n-1} - 1$ when $p = 2$).

V. MISCELLANEOUS APPLICATIONS

17. Generation of Pseudorandom Sequences

Maximum-period sequences (see Sec. **3.17**) are capable of passing a number of randomness tests which make them qualify as pseudorandom sequences. Such sequences are useful in the implementation of Monte Carlo techniques, and in a number of probabilistic experiments where it is advantageous to have a "standard" random sequence to be used repeatedly on different systems.

18. Range-Radar Applications

The autocorrelation properties of maximum-period sequences (see Sec. **3.18**) make them useful in range radar applications where extreme background noise is encountered. In these applications a maximum-period sequence is used to modulate the output pulse of a radar, enabling a long pulse to achieve the range resolution of a short one. A thorough treatment of this subject can be found in:

S. W. Golomb (ed.), "Digital Communication with Space Applications," Prentice-Hall, Inc., Englewood Cliffs, N.J., 1964.

19. Encipherment

One way of enciphering a series of digital messages (of uniform length) is the following: Before transmission, add a "key word" to each message; whoever possesses the key word can recover the messages simply by subtracting this word from each message. This method of encipherment and decipherment can be readily implemented with a QLSC, designed to provide the key word (or its negative) in a periodic fashion.

20. Addressing

Sequences generated by QLSCs can be used to convey a "mailing list," specifying a number of addresses associated with a certain activity. These addresses may refer to human recipients, or to locations in the memory of a digital computer.

In most cases it is advantageous to assign subsequences of equal length to all addresses, so that the required action (such as memory accessing) can be taken at equal intervals of time. In these cases one can use the "k-controllable" LSCs described in Sec. **2.20**.

21. Generation of Test Sequences

In the process of testing or repairing digital systems, it is often necessary to apply all possible sequences (over some set of symbols) of a specified length n. This can be readily implemented with an n-dimensional maximum-period QLSC. In this case, the time required for the test is the least possible.

A related application is that of recording a maximum-period sequence along a line (or around a circle, such as the track of a magnetic drum) in order to identify various positions along this line (or around the circle). With a maximum-period sequence, it is possible to identify the largest possible number of positions with a given number of digits.

Chapter 7
Some Related Systems

1. Introduction

In this chapter the *general sequential circuit* (of which the LSC is a special case) is defined, and an algorithm is given for characterizing such a circuit—whenever possible—as an LSC. It is also shown how linear sequential circuits defined over arbitrary fields [not necessarily over $GF(p)$] can be simulated by means of LSCs of the type treated in the preceding chapters.

The material in this chapter is based in part on the work of Cohn and Even,[25] and Stern and Friedland.[89]

2. General Sequential Circuits

A (general) *sequential circuit* $\mathcal{C}$ consists of a finite set U (the *input set*), a finite set Y (the *output set*) a finite set S (the *state set*), a *next-state function* δ and an *output function* λ defined as follows:

2–1 $$s(t+1) = \delta(s(t), u(t))$$

2–2 $$y(t) = \lambda(s(t), u(t))$$

where $u(t)$ (from U), $y(t)$ (from Y) and $s(t)$ (from S) are the *input, output,* and *state* of $\mathcal{C}$, respectively, at time t ($t = 0, 1, 2, \ldots$). $\mathcal{C}$ can be designated as $< U, Y, S, \delta, \lambda >$. δ and λ can be displayed in a tabular form, or in the form of a state-output diagram. The diagram contains a vertex for each state of $\mathcal{C}$, and a branch labeled u/y leads from vertex s to vertex s' if and only if $s' = \delta(s,u)$ and $y = \lambda(s,u)$.

In the remainder of this section we shall summarize some properties and results associated with general sequential circuits, to the extent that these are needed for the discussion in Sec. **3**. For more complete coverage, as well as for the missing proofs, the reader is referred to any of the following textbooks:

A. Gill, "Introduction to the Theory of Finite-State Machines,"McGraw-Hill Book Co., Inc., New York, 1962.

S. Ginsburg, "An Introduction to Mathematical Machine Theory," Addison-Wesley Publishing Co., Inc., Reading, Mass., 1962.

M. A. Harrison, "Inrtoduction to Switching and Automata Theory," McGraw-Hill Book Co., Inc., New York, 1965

State s_1 of circuit $\mathcal{C}_1$ and s_2 of $\mathcal{C}_2$ are said to be *equivalent* if $\mathcal{C}_1$ at state s_1 and $\mathcal{C}_2$ at state s_2, when simultaneously presented with the same input sequence, yield identical output sequences. ($\mathcal{C}_1$ and $\mathcal{C}_2$ may refer to the same circuit.) The *equivalence partition* of $\mathcal{C}_1$ and $\mathcal{C}_2$ divides the states of $\mathcal{C}_1$ and $\mathcal{C}_2$ into *equivalence classes* such that two states are in the same class if and only if they are equivalent.

Circuits $\mathcal{C}_1$ and $\mathcal{C}_2$ are said to be *equivalent* if to each state s_1 of $\mathcal{C}_1$ there corresponds at least one state of $\mathcal{C}_2$ which is equivalent to s_1, and to each state s_2 of $\mathcal{C}_2$ there corresponds at least one state in $\mathcal{C}_1$ which is equivalent to s_2.

$\mathcal{C}_1 = < U, Y, S, \delta_1, \lambda_1 >$ and $\mathcal{C}_2 = < U, Y, \overline{S}, \delta_2, \lambda_2 >$ are *isomorphic* if the orders of S and $\overline{S}$ are the same, and if a one-to-one correspondence can be established between elements of S and elements of $\overline{S}$ in the following manner: If $\bar{s}$ is the element from $\overline{S}$ which corresponds to s of S, then, for all u in U:

2–3 $$\delta_2(\bar{s}, u) = \overline{\delta_1(s, u)}$$

2–4 $$\lambda_2(\bar{s}, u) = \lambda_1(s, u)$$

Hence, if $\mathcal{C}_1$ and $\mathcal{C}_2$ are isomorphic, they are identical except, possibly, for state labeling. Clearly, if $\mathcal{C}_1$ and $\mathcal{C}_2$ are isomorphic, they are equivalent.

Consider the circuit $\mathcal{C} = < U, Y, S, \delta, \lambda >$. P_ν is a partition of S defined recursively as follows: $P_0 = \{S\}$; $P_{\nu+1}$ ($\nu = 0, 1, \ldots$) is a refinement of P_ν constructed in the following manner: s_1 and s_2 are in the same class of $P_{\nu+1}$ if and only if, for all u in U, $\lambda(s_1,u) = \lambda(s_2,u)$ and the states $\delta(s_1,u)$ and $\delta(s_2,u)$ are in the same class of P_ν. If k is the order of S, then P_{k-1} is the equivalence partition of $\mathcal{C}$.

Let $P_{k-1} = \{E_1, E_2, \ldots, E_w\}$. The *minimal form* $\breve{\mathcal{C}}$ of $\mathcal{C}$ is a circuit $< U, Y, \breve{S}, \breve{\delta}, \breve{\lambda} >$, defined as follows: $\breve{S} = \{\overline{E}_1, \overline{E}_2, \ldots, \overline{E}_w\}$; if s_i is any element belonging to equivalence class E_i and if $[s_j]$ denotes the class to which s_j belongs, then for all u in U:

2–5 $$\breve{\delta}(\overline{E}_i,u) = \overline{[\delta(s_i,u)]}$$

2–6 $$\breve{\lambda}(\overline{E}_i,u) = \lambda(s_i,u)$$

$\breve{\mathcal{C}}$ has the following properties: (a) $\breve{\mathcal{C}}$ is equivalent to $\mathcal{C}$. (b) No two states in $\breve{\mathcal{C}}$ are equivalent. (c) No circuit with fewer states than $\breve{\mathcal{C}}$ is equivalent to $\mathcal{C}$.

If the orders of $\breve{S}$ and S are the same, $\mathcal{C}$ is said to be *minimal*. Equivalent minimal circuits are isomorphic, and hence the minimal form of a circuit is unique except for state labeling.

An LSC is seen to be a special sequential circuit, where U, Y and S are vector spaces over $GF(p)$, and where δ and λ are linear transformations.

3. Linearization of Sequential Circuits

Let $\mathcal{C}$ be a minimal sequential circuit satisfying the following requirements: Its input set is an l-dimensional vector space over $GF(p)$; its output set is an m-dimensional vector space over $GF(p)$; its state set is of order p^n (for some n). The problem of interest is the following: Does there exist an LSC $\mathcal{A}$ equivalent to $\mathcal{C}$? When the answer is in the affirmative, $\mathcal{C}$ is said to be *linearly realizable*, and $\mathcal{A}$ a *linear realization* of $\mathcal{C}$.

Clearly, if $\mathcal{C}$ is linearly realizable, its linear realization can be assumed to have the minimal form described in Sec. **2.14.** In particular (see **2.15–7**), the linear realization $\mathcal{A}$, characterized by **A**, **B**, **C** and **D**, can be assumed to have the diagnostic matrix

3–1
$$\mathbf{K} = \begin{pmatrix} \mathbf{C} \\ \mathbf{CA} \\ \cdot \\ \cdot \\ \cdot \\ \mathbf{CA}^{n-1} \end{pmatrix}$$

where the first n linearly independent rows form the identity matrix $\mathbf{I}_n$.

3–2 *Assertion:* Let $S = \{s_1, s_2, \ldots, s_{p^n}\}$ and let $\mathbf{y}_0^j(t)$ denote the output of $\mathcal{C}$ at time t, with input **0** and initial state (at $t = 0$) s_j. Define:

3–3
$$\mathbf{L} = \begin{pmatrix} \mathbf{y}_0^1(0) & \mathbf{y}_0^2(0) & \cdots & \mathbf{y}_0^{p^n}(0) \\ \mathbf{y}_0^1(1) & \mathbf{y}_0^2(1) & \cdots & \mathbf{y}_0^{p^n}(1) \\ \cdot & & & \\ \cdot & & & \\ \cdot & & & \\ \mathbf{y}_0^1(n-1) & \mathbf{y}_0^2(n-1) & & \mathbf{y}_0^{p^n}(n-1) \end{pmatrix}$$

Let $\tilde{\mathbf{L}}$ consist of the first n linearly independent rows of **L**, and $\mathbf{s}_j$ denote the jth column vector of $\tilde{\mathbf{L}}$. Then, if $\mathcal{A}$ exists, state s_j of $\mathcal{C}$ is equivalent to state $\mathbf{s}_j$ of $\mathcal{A}$.

Proof: Assume that $\mathcal{A}$ exists and that $\boldsymbol{\sigma}_j$ is the state in $\mathcal{A}$ which is equivalent to s_j of $\mathcal{C}$. Then, for all $t \geq 0$,

3–4
$$\mathbf{y}_0^j(t) = \mathbf{CA}^t\boldsymbol{\sigma}_j$$

and hence

3–5
$$\begin{aligned} \mathbf{L} &= (\mathbf{K}\boldsymbol{\sigma}_1, \mathbf{K}\boldsymbol{\sigma}_2, \ldots, \mathbf{K}\boldsymbol{\sigma}_{p^n}) \\ &= \mathbf{K}(\boldsymbol{\sigma}_1, \boldsymbol{\sigma}_2, \ldots, \boldsymbol{\sigma}_{p^n}) \end{aligned}$$

Since $\tilde{\mathbf{L}}$ consists of the first n linearly independent rows of **L**, it is obtainable by multiplying the first n linearly independent rows of **K** (i.e., $\mathbf{I}_n$) by $(\boldsymbol{\sigma}_1, \boldsymbol{\sigma}_2, \ldots, \boldsymbol{\sigma}_{p^n})$. Hence,

3–6
$$\tilde{\mathbf{L}} = (\mathbf{s}_1, \mathbf{s}_2, \ldots, \mathbf{s}_{p^n}) = (\boldsymbol{\sigma}_1, \boldsymbol{\sigma}_2, \ldots, \boldsymbol{\sigma}_{p^n})$$

Let $\mathcal{C}'$ denote the circuit obtained from $\mathcal{C}$ when every state s_j is relabeled $\mathbf{s}_j$. δ and λ will refer to the next-state and output functions, respectively, of $\mathcal{C}'$. $\mathbf{s}^i$ and $\mathbf{u}^i$ will denote the unit state vector and unit input vector, respectively, where the ith component is 1 and all other components 0.

3–7 *Assertion:* Denote

3–8
$$\begin{aligned} \mathbf{s}_i' &= \delta(\mathbf{s}^i,\mathbf{0}) & \mathbf{s}_i'' &= \delta(\mathbf{0},\mathbf{u}^i) \\ \mathbf{y}_i' &= \lambda(\mathbf{s}^i,\mathbf{0}) & \mathbf{y}_i'' &= \lambda(\mathbf{0},\mathbf{u}^i) \end{aligned}$$

Then, if $\mathcal{A}$ exists,

3–9
$$\begin{aligned} \mathbf{A} &= (\mathbf{s}_1', \mathbf{s}_2', \ldots, \mathbf{s}_n') \\ \mathbf{B} &= (\mathbf{s}_1'', \mathbf{s}_2'', \ldots, \mathbf{s}_l'') \\ \mathbf{C} &= (\mathbf{y}_1', \mathbf{y}_2', \ldots, \mathbf{y}_n') \\ \mathbf{D} &= (\mathbf{y}_1'', \mathbf{y}_2'', \ldots, \mathbf{y}_l'') \end{aligned}$$

Proof: By definition, if $\mathcal{A}$ exists,

3–10
$$\begin{aligned}(\mathbf{s}_1', \mathbf{s}_2', \ldots, \mathbf{s}_n') &= \mathbf{A}(\mathbf{s}^1, \mathbf{s}^2, \ldots, \mathbf{s}^n) = \mathbf{AI} = \mathbf{A}\\ (\mathbf{s}_1'', \mathbf{s}_2'', \ldots, \mathbf{s}_l'') &= \mathbf{B}(\mathbf{u}^1, \mathbf{u}^2, \ldots, \mathbf{u}^l) = \mathbf{BI} = \mathbf{B}\\ (\mathbf{y}_1', \mathbf{y}_2', \ldots, \mathbf{y}_n') &= \mathbf{C}(\mathbf{s}^1, \mathbf{s}^2, \ldots, \mathbf{s}^n) = \mathbf{CI} = \mathbf{C}\\ (\mathbf{y}_1'', \mathbf{y}_2'', \ldots, \mathbf{y}_l'') &= \mathbf{D}(\mathbf{u}^1, \mathbf{u}^2, \ldots, \mathbf{u}^l) = \mathbf{DI} = \mathbf{D}\end{aligned}$$

After **A**, **B**, **C** and **D** are evaluated as shown in **3–7**, to ascertain that $\mathcal{A}$ indeed exists, it remains to verify that $\mathbf{s}' = \mathbf{As} + \mathbf{Bu}$ and $\mathbf{y} = \mathbf{Cs} + \mathbf{Du}$ are satisfied for all **s** and **u** (other than those represented by unit vectors). If this is not the case, then $\mathcal{C}$ is not linearly realizable (it may, however, be so realizable if relabeling is permitted of the input and/or output symbols of $\mathcal{C}$).

3–11 *Example:* Fig. 7.1 shows the state-output diagram of a minimal 8-state sequential circuit $\mathcal{C}$ for which a linear realization over $GF(2)$ is to be attempted. The input and output symbols a, b, c and d are identified with the vectors $\begin{pmatrix}0\\0\end{pmatrix}$, $\begin{pmatrix}0\\1\end{pmatrix}$, $\begin{pmatrix}1\\0\end{pmatrix}$ and $\begin{pmatrix}1\\1\end{pmatrix}$, respectively. Following **3–2** (with $n = 3$),

3–12
$$\mathbf{L} = \left(\begin{array}{cccccccc}1&1&0&0&1&1&0&0\\1&0&1&0&0&1&0&1\\ \hline 1&0&1&0&1&0&1&0\\0&0&0&0&0&0&0&0\\ \hline 1&1&0&0&0&0&1&1\\0&0&0&0&0&0&0&0\end{array}\right)$$

3–13
$$\tilde{\mathbf{L}} = \begin{pmatrix}1&1&0&0&1&1&0&0\\1&0&1&0&0&1&0&1\\1&0&1&0&1&0&1&0\end{pmatrix}$$

Hence:

3–14
$$\mathbf{s}_1 = \begin{pmatrix}1\\1\\1\end{pmatrix} \quad \mathbf{s}_2 = \begin{pmatrix}1\\0\\0\end{pmatrix} \quad \mathbf{s}_3 = \begin{pmatrix}0\\1\\1\end{pmatrix} \quad \mathbf{s}_4 = \begin{pmatrix}0\\0\\0\end{pmatrix}$$
$$\mathbf{s}_5 = \begin{pmatrix}1\\0\\1\end{pmatrix} \quad \mathbf{s}_6 = \begin{pmatrix}1\\1\\0\end{pmatrix} \quad \mathbf{s}_7 = \begin{pmatrix}0\\0\\1\end{pmatrix} \quad \mathbf{s}_8 = \begin{pmatrix}0\\1\\0\end{pmatrix}$$

Directly from the diagram, we have:

3–15
$$\mathbf{s}_1' = \begin{pmatrix}0\\0\\1\end{pmatrix} \quad \mathbf{s}_2' = \begin{pmatrix}0\\0\\1\end{pmatrix} \quad \mathbf{s}_3' = \begin{pmatrix}1\\0\\1\end{pmatrix}$$

3–16
$$\mathbf{s}_1'' = \begin{pmatrix}0\\1\\0\end{pmatrix} \quad \mathbf{s}_2'' = \begin{pmatrix}0\\1\\1\end{pmatrix}$$

3–17
$$\mathbf{y}_1' = \begin{pmatrix}1\\0\end{pmatrix} \quad \mathbf{y}_2' = \begin{pmatrix}0\\1\end{pmatrix} \quad \mathbf{y}_3' = \begin{pmatrix}0\\0\end{pmatrix}$$

3–18
$$\mathbf{y}_1'' = \begin{pmatrix}1\\1\end{pmatrix} \quad \mathbf{y}_2'' = \begin{pmatrix}0\\1\end{pmatrix}$$

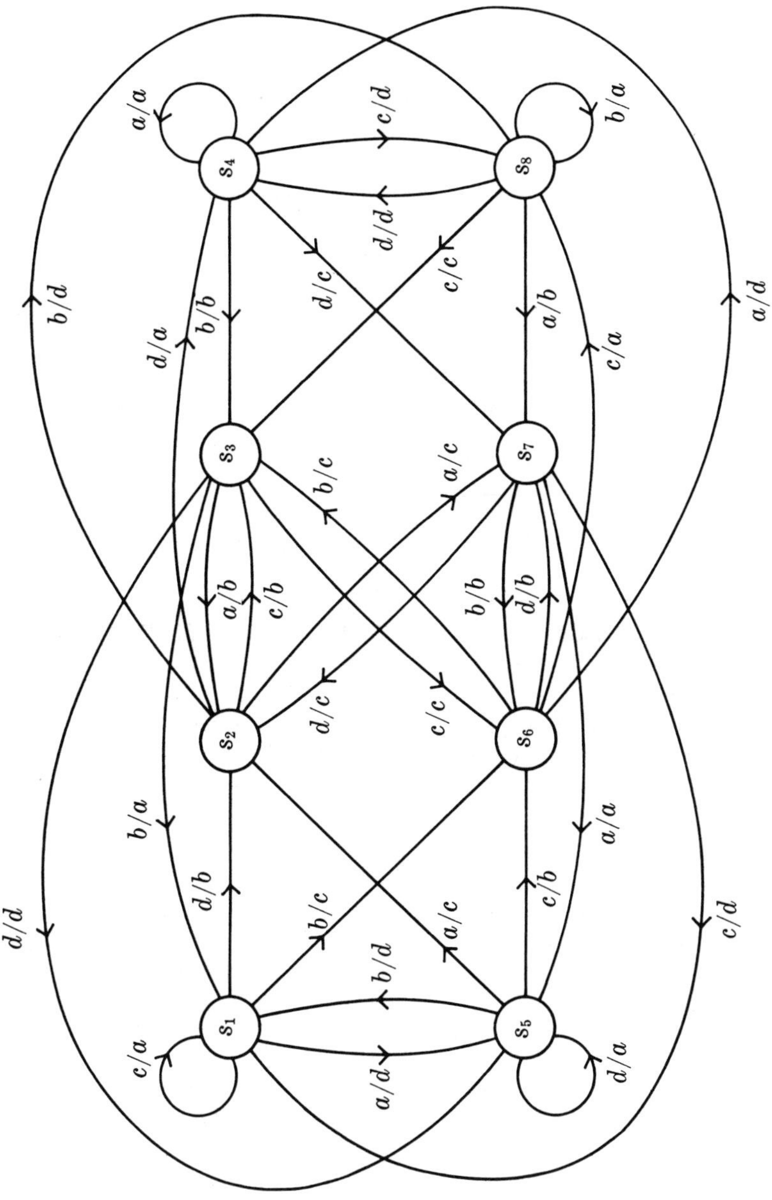

FIG. 7.1—State-output diagram of sequential circuit

Hence:

3–19
$$\mathbf{A} = \begin{pmatrix} 0 & 0 & 1 \\ 0 & 0 & 0 \\ 1 & 1 & 1 \end{pmatrix} \qquad \mathbf{B} = \begin{pmatrix} 0 & 0 \\ 1 & 1 \\ 0 & 1 \end{pmatrix}$$
$$\mathbf{C} = \begin{pmatrix} 1 & 0 & 0 \\ 0 & 1 & 0 \end{pmatrix} \qquad \mathbf{D} = \begin{pmatrix} 1 & 0 \\ 1 & 1 \end{pmatrix}$$

The realization of $\mathcal{C}$ as an LSC is shown in Fig. 7.2.

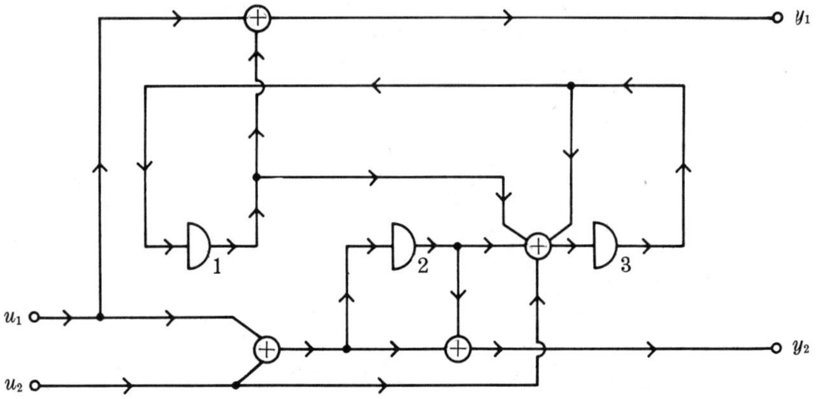

FIG. 7.2—LSC for Example **3–11**

4. LSCs over Arbitrary Finite Fields

An LSC over an arbitrary finite field F differs from an LSC over $GF(p)$ in that the input, output, and state vectors, as well as the characterizing matrices, are over F rather than $GF(p)$.

The purpose of this section is to show that every LSC $\mathcal{A}$ over F can be "simulated" by and LSC $\mathcal{A}'$ over $GF(p)$. The first step in the simulation is to represent F by some field $GF(p^k)$ (by **1.10–2**, if F is finite, it is isomorphic to every Galois field of identical order). Subject to this representation, $\mathcal{A}$ can be viewed as an LSC where the lines transmit polynomials in ξ over $GF(p)$ (of degree $k - 1$ or less), where the adders add such polynomials as per rules of $GF(p^k)$, where the scalers multiply such polynomials by fixed polynomials as per rules of $GF(p^k)$, and where the delayers delay such polynomials one dit.

The simulation $\mathcal{A}'$ of $\mathcal{A}$ is realized by replacing every line of $\mathcal{A}$ with a bundle of k lines, numbered 0, 1, . . ., $k - 1$. If a line in $\mathcal{A}$ carries the polynomial

4–1
$$a(\xi) = a_0 + a_1\xi + \cdots + a_{k-1}\xi^{k-1}$$

then the corresponding bundle in $\mathcal{A}'$ carries the elements $a_0, a_1, \ldots, a_{k-1}$ [from $GF(p)$], with line i of the bundle carrying a_i. Every adder of $\mathcal{A}$ is replaced with k adders over $GF(p)$, numbered 0, 1, . . ., $k - 1$, where adder i adds (modulo p) all the elements carried in lines i of the input bundle (see Fig. 7.3). Every delayer of $\mathcal{A}$ is replaced with k delayers over $GF(p)$, numbered 0, 1, . . ., $k - 1$, where delayer i delays the element carried in line i of the input bundle. Every scaler of $\mathcal{A}$ is replaced with a network of adders and scalers over $GF(p)$ in the manner described below.

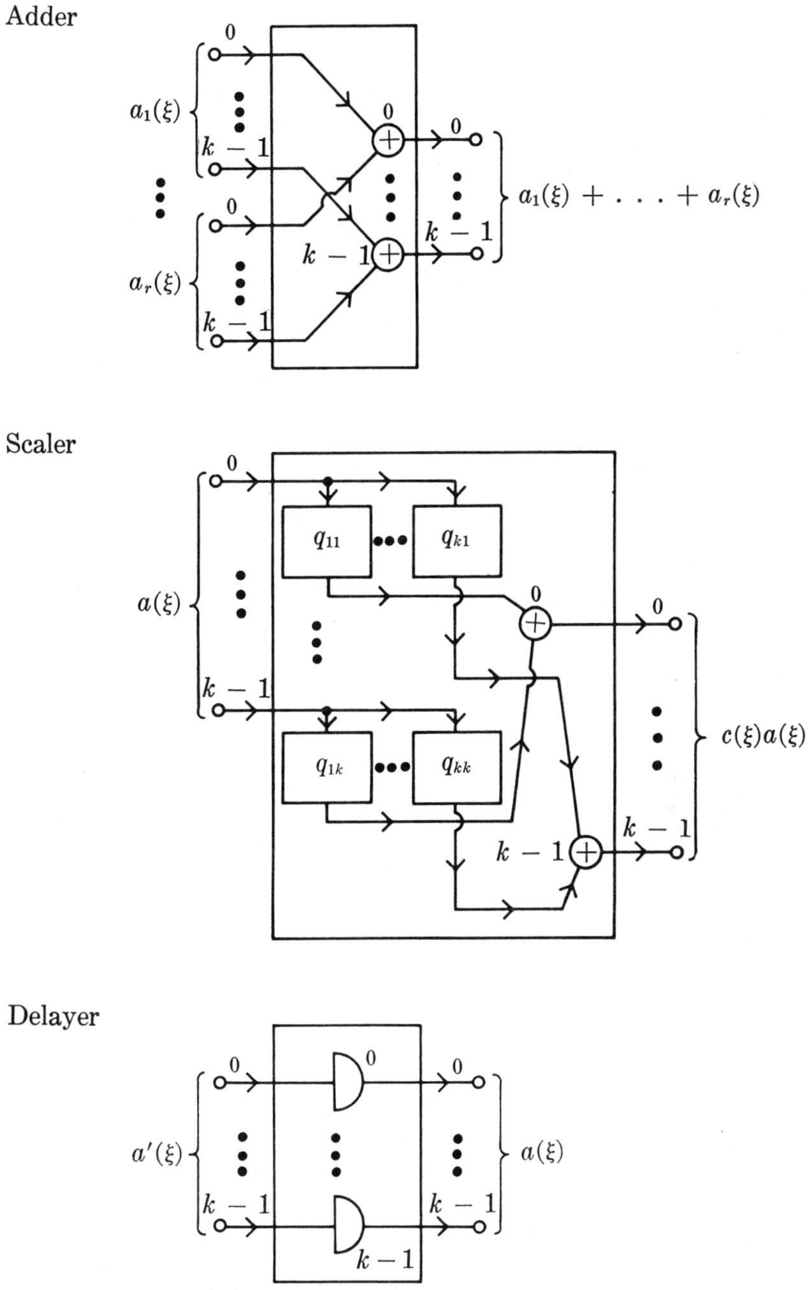

FIG. 7.3—$GF(p^k)$ operations with components over $GF(p)$

Let $a(\xi)$ be as given in **4–1**, and define

4–2
$$\mathbf{a} = \begin{pmatrix} a_0 \\ a_1 \\ \cdot \\ \cdot \\ \cdot \\ a_{k-1} \end{pmatrix}$$

Let

4–3
$$c(\xi) = c_0 + c_1\xi + \ldots + c_{k-1}\xi^{k-1}$$

be a constant associated with some scaler in $\mathcal{Q}$. If $p(x)$ is the modulus polynomial of $GF(p^k)$, define

4–4
$$\begin{aligned} \mathbf{Q} &= [q_{ij}]_{k\times k} = c(\mathbf{M}^{\mathrm{TR}}_{p(x)}) \\ &= c_0\mathbf{I} + c_1\mathbf{M}^{\mathrm{TR}}_{p(x)} + c_2(\mathbf{M}^{\mathrm{TR}}_{p(x)})^2 + \ldots + c_{k-1}(\mathbf{M}^{\mathrm{TR}}_{p(x)})^{k-1} \end{aligned}$$

Now, denote

4–5
$$(\mathbf{M}^{\mathrm{TR}}_{p(x)})^{\nu}\mathbf{a} = \mathbf{a}^{(\nu)} = \begin{pmatrix} a_0^{(\nu)} \\ a_1^{(\nu)} \\ \cdot \\ \cdot \\ \cdot \\ a_{k-1}^{(\nu)} \end{pmatrix}$$

Then, as shown in **5.10–4**,

4–6
$$a_0^{(\nu)} + a_1^{(\nu)}\xi + \ldots + a_{k-1}^{(\nu)}\xi^{k-1} = \xi^{\nu}a(\xi)$$

More generally, if

4–7
$$\mathbf{Qa} = c_0\mathbf{a}^{(0)} + c_1\mathbf{a}^{(1)} + \ldots + c_{k-1}\mathbf{a}^{(k-1)} = \begin{pmatrix} b_0 \\ b_1 \\ \cdot \\ \cdot \\ \cdot \\ b_{k-1} \end{pmatrix}$$

then

4–8
$$\begin{aligned} b_0 + b_1\xi + \ldots + b_{k-1}\xi^{k-1} &= c_0\xi^0a(\xi) + c_1\xi^1a(\xi) + \ldots + c_{k-1}\xi^{k-1}a(\xi) \\ &= c(\xi)a(\xi) \end{aligned}$$

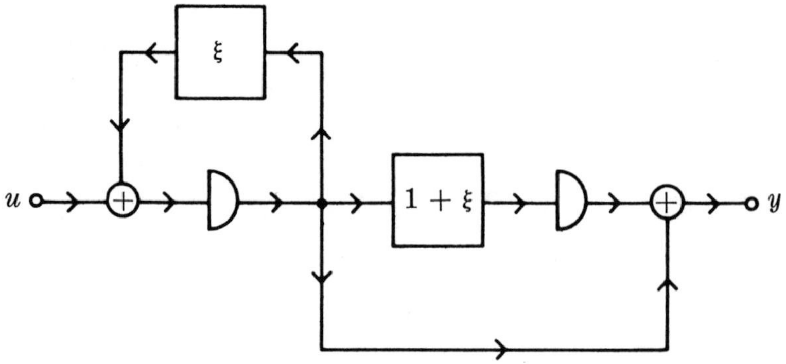

FIG. 7.4—LSC over $GF(2^2)$

Hence, the network to replace the scaler whose constant is $c(\xi)$ is simply that whose output bundle carries the elements of $\mathbf{Qa}$, whenever the input bundle carries the elements of $\mathbf{a}$ (see Fig. 7.3).

4–9 *Example:* Fig. 7.4 shows an LSC over $GF(2^2)$, where the modulus polynomial is $p(x) = 1 + x + x^2$. In this case the $\mathbf{Q}$ matrix for the scaler with the constant ξ is

4–10
$$\mathbf{M}_{p(x)}^{\mathrm{TR}} = \begin{pmatrix} 0 & 1 \\ 1 & 1 \end{pmatrix}$$

The $\mathbf{Q}$ matrix for the scaler with the constant $1 + \xi$ is

4–11
$$\mathbf{I} + \mathbf{M}_{p(x)}^{\mathrm{TR}} = \begin{pmatrix} 1 & 1 \\ 1 & 0 \end{pmatrix}$$

The LSC $\mathfrak{A}'$ over $GF(2)$ which simulates $\mathfrak{A}$ is shown in Fig. 7.5.

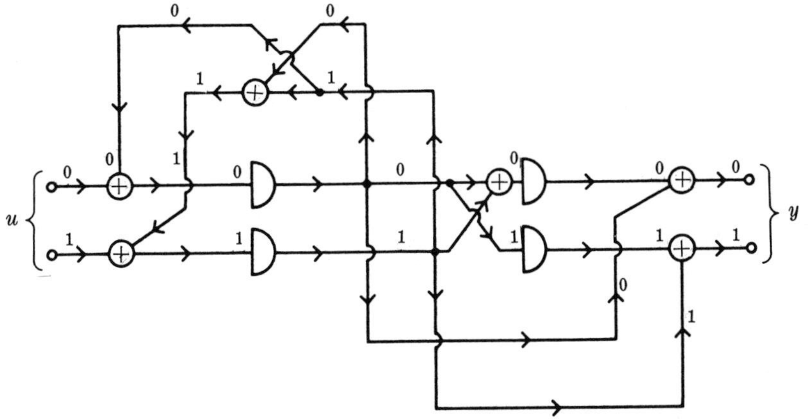

FIG. 7.5—Simulation of LSC of Fig. 7.4 by LSC over $GF(2)$

APPENDIX

1. Divisors of $p^n - 1$

Table A1, based on Peterson,[1] lists the prime factors of $2^n - 1$ for $2 \le n \le 34$.

Table A2 lists the least (nonzero) integer n such that T divides $p^n - 1$, for $p = 2, 3, 5, 7$ and $1 \le T \le 100$.

Table A1

n Prime factors of $2^n - 1$

n	Prime factors of $2^n - 1$
2	3
3	7
4	3, 5
5	31
6	3^2, 7
7	127
8	3, 5, 17
9	7, 73
10	3, 11, 31
11	23, 89
12	3^2, 5, 7, 13
13	8191
14	3, 43, 127
15	7, 31, 151
16	3, 5, 17,257
17	131071
18	3^3, 7, 19, 73
19	524287
20	3, 5^2, 11, 31, 41
21	7^2, 127, 337
22	3, 23, 89, 683
23	47, 178481
24	3^2, 5, 7, 13, 17, 241
25	31, 601, 1801
26	3, 2731, 8191
27	7, 73, 262657
28	3, 5, 29, 43, 113, 127
29	233, 1103, 2089
30	3^2, 7, 11, 31, 151, 331
31	2147483647
32	3, 5, 17, 257, 65537
33	7, 23, 89, 599479
34	3, 43691, 131071

Table A2

T	Least n such that T divides $p^n - 1$			
	$p = 2$	$p = 3$	$p = 5$	$p = 7$

T	Least n such that T divides $p^n - 1$			
	$p = 2$	$p = 3$	$p = 5$	$p = 7$

T	$p = 2$	$p = 3$	$p = 5$	$p = 7$
1	1	1	1	1
2	—	1	1	1
3	2	—	2	1
4	—	2	1	2
5	4	4	—	4
6	—	—	2	1
7	3	6	6	—
8	—	2	2	2
9	6	—	6	3
10	—	4	—	4
11	10	5	5	10
12	—	—	2	2
13	12	3	4	12
14	—	6	6	—
15	4	—	—	4
16	—	4	4	2
17	8	16	16	16
18	—	—	6	3
19	18	18	9	3
20	—	4	—	4
21	6	—	6	—
22	—	5	5	10
23	11	11	22	22
24	—	—	2	2
25	20	20	—	4
26	—	3	4	12
27	18	—	18	9
28	—	6	6	—
29	28	28	14	7
30	—	—	—	4
31	5	30	3	15
32	—	8	8	4
33	10	—	10	10
34	—	16	16	16
35	12	12	—	—
36	—	—	6	6
37	36	18	36	9
38	—	18	9	3
39	12	—	4	12
40	—	4	—	4
41	20	8	20	40
42	—	—	6	—

43	14	42	42	6
44	—	10	5	10
45	12	—	—	12
46	—	11	22	22
47	23	23	46	23
48	—	—	4	2
49	21	42	42	—
50	—	20	—	4
51	8	—	16	16
52	—	6	4	12
53	52	52	52	26
54	—	—	18	9
55	20	20	—	20
56	—	6	6	—
57	18	—	18	3
58	—	28	14	7
59	58	29	29	29
60	—	—	—	4
61	60	10	30	60
62	—	30	3	15
63	6	—	6	—
64	—	16	16	8
65	12	12	—	12
66	—	—	10	10
67	66	22	22	66
68	—	16	16	16
69	22	—	22	22
70	—	12	—	—
71	35	35	5	70
72	—	—	6	6
73	9	12	72	24
74	—	18	36	9
75	20	—	—	4
76	—	18	9	6
77	30	30	30	—
78	—	—	4	12
79	39	78	39	78
80	—	4	—	4
81	54	—	54	27
82	—	8	20	40
83	82	41	82	41
84	—	—	6	—
85	8	16	—	16
86	—	42	42	6
87	28	—	14	7
88	—	10	10	10
89	11	88	44	88
90	—	—	—	12
91	12	6	12	—
92	—	22	22	22
93	10	—	6	15
94	—	23	46	23
95	36	36	—	12
96	—	—	8	4
97	48	48	96	96
98	—	42	42	—
99	30	—	30	30
100	—	20	—	4

2. Irreducible and Maximum-Exponent Polynomials

The number $N(p,n)$ of irreducible monic polynomials of degree n over $GF(p)$ can be obtained by the recursive solution of

$$\sum_{k \mid n} kN(p,k) = p^n$$

where k extends over all integers which divide n. The number $M(p,n)$ of maximum-exponent (i.e., exponent $p^n - 1$) monic polynomials of degree n over $GF(p)$ is given by

$$M(p,n) = \frac{\phi(p^n - 1)}{n}$$

where $\phi(\nu)$ is the number of distinct positive integers which are relatively prime to and smaller than ν (including 1).

Table A3, based on Elspas,[1] lists $N(p,n)$ and $M(p,n)$ for $p = 2, 3, 5, 7$ and $n = 11, 7, 5, 4$ (respectively).

Table A4, based on Church,[1] lists all irreducible monic polynomials (other than x) of degree n over $GF(p)$ and their exponents e, for $p = 2, 3, 5, 7$ and $n = 11, 7, 5, 4$ (respectively). The polynomial $\alpha_0 x^n + \alpha_1 x^{n-1} + \ldots + \alpha_{n-1} + \alpha_n$ is listed as the sequence $\alpha_0\alpha_1 \ldots \alpha_n$ ($\alpha_0 = 1$).

Table A5, based on Golomb,[2] Peterson[1] and Watson,[1] lists maximum-exponent polynomials of degree n over $GF(2)$ for $1 \leq n \leq 100$, $n = 107$ and $n = 127$. The polynomials of degrees 1 through 36 are guaranteed to have the least number of nonzero coefficients.

Table A3

	$p = 2$		$p = 3$		$p = 5$		$p = 7$	
	$N(p,n)$	$M(p,n)$	$N(p,n)$	$M(p,n)$	$N(p,n)$	$M(p,n)$	$N(p,n)$	$M(p,n)$
1	2	1	3	1	5	2	7	2
2	1	1	3	2	10	4	21	8
3	2	2	8	4	40	20	112	48
4	3	2	18	8	150	48	588	160
5	6	6	48	22	624	304		
6	9	6	116	48				
7	18	18	312	156				
8	30	16						
9	56	48						
10	99	60						
11	186	176						

TABLE A4

2 IRREDUCIBLE POLYNOMIALS FOR THE MODULUS

$n = 1$	e
11	1

$n = 2$	e
111	3

$n = 3$	e
1011	7
1101	7

$n = 4$	e
10011	15
11001	15
11111	5

$n = 5$	e
100101	31
101001	31
101111	31
110111	31
111011	31
111101	31

$n = 6$	e
1000011	63
1001001	9
1010111	21
1011011	63
1100001	63
1100111	63
1101101	63
1110011	63
1110101	21

$n = 7$	e
10000011	127
10001001	127
10001111	127
10010001	127
10011101	127
10100111	127
10101011	127
10111001	127
10111111	127
11000001	127
11001011	127
11010011	127
11010101	127
11100101	127
11101111	127
11110001	127
11110111	127
11111101	127

$n = 8$	e
100011011	51
100011101	255
100101011	255
100101101	255
100111001	17
100111111	85
101001101	255
101011111	255
101100011	255
101100101	255
101101001	255
101110001	255
101110111	85
101111011	85
110000111	255
110001011	85
110001101	255
110011111	51
110100011	85
110101001	255
110110001	51
110111101	85
111000011	255
111001111	255
111010111	17
111011101	85
111100111	255
111110011	51
111110101	255
111111001	85

$n = 9$	e
1000000011	73
1000010001	511
1000010111	73
1000011011	511
1000100001	511
1000101101	511
1000110011	511
1001001011	73
1001011001	511
1001011111	511
1001100101	73
1001101001	511
1001101111	511
1001110111	511
1001111101	511
1010000111	511
1010010101	511
1010011001	73
1010100011	511
1010100101	511
1010101111	511
1010110111	511
1010111101	511
1011001111	511
1011010001	511
1011011011	511
1011110101	511
1011111001	511
1100000001	73
1100010011	511
1100010101	511
1100011111	511
1100100011	511
1100110001	511
1100111011	511
1101001001	73
1101001111	511
1101011011	511
1101100001	511
1101101011	511
1101101101	511
1101110011	511
1101111111	511
1110000101	511
1110001111	511
1110100001	73
1110110101	511
1110111001	511
1111000111	511
1111001011	511
1111001101	511
1111010101	511
1111011001	511
1111100011	511
1111101001	511
1111111011	511

$n = 10$	e
10000001001	1023
10000001111	341
10000011011	1023
10000011101	341

10000100111	1023
10000101101	1023
10000110101	93
10001000111	341
10001010011	341
10001100011	341
10001100101	1023
10001101111	1023
10010000001	1023
10010001011	1023
10010011001	341
10010101001	33
10010101111	341
10011000101	1023
10011001001	341
10011010111	1023
10011100111	1023
10011101101	341
10011110011	1023
10011111111	1023
10100001011	93
10100001101	1023
10100011001	1023
10100011111	341
10100100011	1023
10100110001	1023
10100111101	1023
10101000011	1023
10101010111	1023
10101100001	93
10101100111	341
10101101011	1023
10110000101	1023
10110001111	1023
10110010111	1023
10110011011	341
10110100001	1023
10110101011	341
10110111001	341
10111000001	341
10111000111	1023
10111100101	1023
10111110111	1023
10111111011	1023
11000010011	1023
11000010101	1023
11000100011	33
11000100101	1023
11000110001	341
11000110111	1023
11001000011	1023
11001001111	1023
11001010001	341
11001011011	1023
11001111001	1023
11001111111	1023
11010000101	93
11010001001	1023
11010100111	93
11010101101	341
11010110101	1023
11010111111	341
11011000001	1023
11011001101	341
11011010011	1023
11011011111	1023
11011110111	341
11011111101	1023
11100001111	341
11100010001	341
11100010111	1023
11100011101	1023
11100100001	1023
11100101011	93
11100110101	341
11100111001	1023
11101000111	1023
11101001101	1023
11101010101	1023
11101011001	1023
11101100011	1023
11101111011	341
11101111101	1023
11110000001	341
11110000111	341
11110001101	1023
11110010011	1023
11110101001	341
11110110001	1023
11111000101	341
11111011011	1023
11111101011	341
11111110011	1023
11111111001	1023
11111111111	11

$n = 11$	e
100000000101	2047
100000010111	2047
100000101011	2047
100000101101	2047
100001000111	2047
100001100011	2047
100001100101	2047
100001110001	2047
100001111011	2047
100010001101	2047
100010010101	2047
100010011111	2047
100010101001	2047
100010110001	2047
100011000011	89
100011001111	2047
100011010001	2047
100011100001	2047
100011100111	2047
100011101011	2047
100011110101	2047
100100001101	2047
100100010011	2047
100100100101	2047
100100101001	2047
100100110111	89
100100111011	2047
100100111101	2047
100101000101	2047
100101001001	2047
100101010001	2047
100101011011	2047
100101110011	2047
100101110101	2047
100101111111	2047
100110000011	2047
100110001111	2047
100110101011	2047
100110101101	2047
100110111001	2047
100111000111	2047
100111011001	2047
100111100101	2047
100111101111	89
100111110111	2047
101000000001	2047
101000000111	2047
101000010011	2047
101000010101	2047
101000101001	2047
101001001001	2047
101001100001	2047
101001101101	2047
101001111001	2047
101001111111	2047
101010000101	2047
101010010001	2047
101010011101	2047
101010100111	2047
101010101011	2047
101010110011	2047
101010110101	2047
101011010101	2047
101011011111	2047
101011100011	23
101011101001	2047
101011101111	2047
101011110001	2047
101011111011	2047
101100000011	2047
101100001001	2047
101100010001	2047
101100110011	2047

101100111111	2047
101101000001	2047
101101001011	2047
101101011001	2047
101101011111	2047
101101100101	2047
101101101111	2047
101101111101	2047
101110000111	2047
101110001011	2047
101110010011	2047
101110010101	2047
101110101111	2047
101110110111	2047
101110111101	2047
101111001001	2047
101111011011	2047
101111011101	2047
101111100111	2047
101111101101	2047
110000001011	2047
110000001101	2047
110000011001	2047
110000011111	2047
110000110001	89
110001010111	2047
110001100001	2047
110001101011	2047
110001110011	2047
110001110101	23
110010000101	2047
110010001001	2047
110010010111	2047
110010011011	2047
110010011101	2047
110010110011	2047
110010111111	2047
110011000111	2047
110011001101	2047
110011010011	2047
110011010101	2047
110011100011	2047
110011101001	2047
110011110111	2047
110100000011	2047
110100001111	2047
110100011101	2047
110100100111	2047
110100101101	2047
110101000001	2047
110101000111	2047
110101010101	2047
110101011001	2047
110101100011	2047
110101101111	2047
110101110001	2047
110110010011	2047
110110011111	2047
110110101001	2047
110110111011	2047
110110111101	2047
110111001001	2047
110111010111	2047
110111011011	2047
110111100001	2047
110111100111	2047
110111110101	2047
110111111111	89
111000000101	2047
111000011101	2047
111000100001	2047
111000100111	2047
111000101011	2047
111000110011	2047
111000111001	2047
111001000111	2047
111001001011	2047
111001010101	2047
111001011111	2047
111001110001	2047
111001111011	2047
111001111101	2047
111010000001	2047
111010010011	2047
111010011111	2047
111010100011	2047
111010111011	2047
111011001001	89
111011001111	2047
111011011101	2047
111011110011	2047
111011111001	2047
111100001011	2047
111100011001	2047
111100110001	2047
111100110111	2047
111101011101	2047
111101101011	2047
111101101101	2047
111101110101	2047
111101111001	89
111110000011	2047
111110010001	2047
111110010111	2047
111110011011	2047
111110100111	2047
111110101101	2047
111110110101	2047
111111001101	2047
111111010011	2047
111111100101	2047
111111101001	2047
111111111011	89

Irreducible Polynomials for the Modulus 3

$n = 1$	e
11	2
12	1

$n = 2$	e
101	4
112	8
122	8

$n = 3$	e
1021	26
1022	13
1102	13
1112	13
1121	26
1201	26
1211	26
1222	13

$n = 4$	e
10012	80
10022	80
10102	16
10111	40
10121	40
10202	16
11002	80
11021	20
11101	40
11111	5
11122	80
11222	80
12002	80
12011	20
12101	40
12112	80
12121	10
12212	80

$n = 5$	e
100021	242
100022	121
100112	121
100211	242
101011	242
101012	121
101102	121
101122	121
101201	242
101221	242
102101	242
102112	121
102122	11
102202	121
102211	242
102221	22
110002	121
110012	121
110021	242
110101	242
110111	242
110122	121
111011	242
111121	242
111211	242
111212	121
112001	242
112022	121
112102	11
112111	242
112201	242
112202	121
120001	242
120011	242
120022	121
120202	121
120212	121
120221	242
121012	121
121111	242
121112	121
121222	121
122002	121
122021	242
122101	242
122102	121
122201	22
122212	121

$n = 6$	e
1000012	728
1000022	728
1000111	364
1000121	364
1000201	52
1001012	728
1001021	364
1001101	91
1001122	104
1001221	182
1002011	364
1002022	728
1002101	182
1002112	104
1002211	91
1010201	52
1010212	728
1010222	728
1011001	91
1011011	364
1011022	728
1011122	728
1012001	182
1012012	728
1012021	364
1012112	728
1020001	52
1020101	52
1020112	728
1020122	728
1021021	364
1021102	56
1021112	728
1021121	91
1022011	364
1022102	56
1022111	182
1022122	728
1100002	728
1100012	56
1100111	364
1101002	728
1101011	28
1101101	364
1101112	728
1101212	728
1102001	364
1102111	91
1102121	91
1102201	364
1102202	728
1110001	364
1110011	364
1110122	728
1110202	728
1110221	182
1111012	728
1111021	182
1111111	7
1111112	728
1111222	728
1112011	91
1112201	182
1112222	728
1120102	728
1120121	91
1120222	728
1121012	728
1121102	728

1121122	104
1121212	728
1121221	364
1122001	91
1122002	104
1122122	104
1122202	728
1122221	364
1200002	728
1200022	56
1200121	364
1201001	364
1201111	182
1201121	182
1201201	364
1201202	728
1202002	728
1202021	28
1202101	364
1202122	728
1202222	728
1210001	364
1210021	364
1210112	728
1210202	728
1210211	91
1211021	182
1211201	91
1211212	728
1212011	91
1212022	728
1212121	14
1212122	728
1212212	728
1220102	728
1220111	182
1220212	728
1221001	182
1221002	104
1221112	104
1221202	728
1221211	364
1222022	728
1222102	728
1222112	104
1222211	364
1222222	728

$n = 7$	e
10000102	1093
10000121	2186
10000201	2186
10000222	1093
10001011	2186
10001012	1093
10001102	1093
10001111	2186
10001201	2186
10001212	1093
10002112	1093
10002122	1093
10002211	2186
10002221	2186
10010122	1093
10010222	1093
10011002	1093
10011101	2186
10011211	2186
10012001	2186
10012022	1093
10012111	2186
10012202	1093
10020121	2186
10020221	2186
10021001	2186
10021112	1093
10021202	1093
10022002	1093
10022021	2186
10022101	2186
10022212	1093
10100011	2186
10100012	1093
10100102	1093
10100122	1093
10100201	2186
10100221	2186
10101101	2186
10101112	1093
10101202	1093
10101211	2186
10102102	1093
10102201	2186
10110022	1093
10110101	2186
10110211	2186
10111001	2186
10111102	1093
10111121	2186
10111201	2186
10112002	1093
10112012	1093
10112021	2186
10112111	2186
10112122	1093
10120021	2186
10120112	1093
10120202	1093
10121002	1093
10121102	1093
10121201	2186
10121222	1093
10122001	2186
10122011	2186
10122022	1093
10122212	1093
10122221	2186
10200001	2186
10200002	1093
10200101	2186
10200112	1093
10200202	1093
10200211	2186
10201021	2186
10201022	1093
10201121	2186
10201222	1093
10202011	2186
10202012	1093
10210001	2186
10210121	2186
10210202	1093
10211101	2186
10211111	2186
10211122	1093
10211221	2186
10212011	2186
10212022	1093
10212101	2186
10212112	1093
10212212	1093
10220002	1093
10220101	2186
10220222	1093
10221122	1093
10221202	1093
10221212	1093
10221221	2186
10222012	1093
10222021	2186
10222111	2186
10222202	1093
10222211	2186
11000101	2186
11000222	1093
11001022	1093
11001112	1093
11001211	2186
11002012	1093
11002022	1093
11002121	2186
11002202	1093
11010001	2186
11010022	1093
11010121	2186
11010221	2186
11011111	2186
11011202	1093
11012002	1093
11012102	1093

11012212	1093
11020021	2186
11020022	1093
11020102	1093
11020112	1093
11020201	2186
11020222	1093
11021111	2186
11021122	1093
11021201	2186
11021212	1093
11022101	2186
11022122	1093
11022211	2186
11022221	2186
11100002	1093
11100022	1093
11100121	2186
11100212	1093
11101012	1093
11101022	1093
11101102	1093
11101111	2186
11101121	2186
11102002	1093
11102111	2186
11102222	1093
11110001	2186
11110012	1093
11110111	2186
11110112	1093
11110211	2186
11110222	1093
11111011	2186
11111021	2186
11111201	2186
11111222	1093
11112011	2186
11112221	2186
11120102	1093
11120111	2186
11120122	1093
11120212	1093
11120221	2186
11121001	2186
11121101	2186
11121202	1093
11122021	2186
11122112	1093
11122201	2186
11122222	1093
11200201	2186
11200202	1093
11201012	1093
11201021	2186
11201101	2186
11201111	2186
11201221	2186
11201222	1093
11202002	1093
11202121	2186
11202211	2186
11202212	1093
11210002	1093
11210011	2186
11210021	2186
11210101	2186
11211001	2186
11211022	1093
11211122	1093
11211212	1093
11211221	2186
11212012	1093
11212112	1093
11212202	1093
11220001	2186
11220112	1093
11220211	2186
11221022	1093
11221102	1093
11221112	1093
11221121	2186
11222011	2186
11222102	1093
11222122	1093
11222201	2186
11222221	2186
12000121	2186
12000202	1093
12001021	2186
12001112	1093
12001211	2186
12002011	2186
12002021	2186
12002101	2186
12002222	1093
12010021	2186
12010022	1093
12010102	1093
12010121	2186
12010201	2186
12010211	2186
12011102	1093
12011111	2186
12011212	1093
12011221	2186
12012112	1093
12012122	1039
12012202	1093
12012221	2186
12020002	1093
12020021	2186
12020122	1093
12020222	1093
12021101	2186
12021212	1093
12022001	2186
12022111	2186
12022201	2186
12100001	2186
12100021	2186
12100111	2186
12100222	1093
12101011	2186
12101021	2186
12101201	2186
12101212	1093
12101222	1093
12102001	2186
12102121	2186
12102212	1093
12110111	2186
12110122	1093
12110201	2186
12110212	1093
12110221	2186
12111002	1093
12111101	2186
12111202	1093
12112022	1093
12112102	1093
12112121	2186
12112211	2186
12120002	1093
12120011	2186
12120112	1093
12120121	2186
12120211	2186
12120212	1093
12121012	1093
12121022	1093
12121102	1093
12121121	2186
12122012	1093
12122122	1093
12200101	2186
12200102	1093
12201011	2186
12201022	1093
12201121	2186
12201122	1093
12201202	1093
12201212	1093
12202001	2186
12202111	2186
12202112	1093
12202222	1093
12210002	1093
12210112	1093
12210211	2186
12211021	2186

12211201	2186	12212221	2186	12221111	2186
12211211	2186	12220001	2186	12221122	1093
12211222	1093	12220012	1093	12221221	2186
12212012	1093	12220022	1093	12222011	2186
12212102	1093	12220202	1093	12222101	2186
12212122	1093	12221002	1093	12222211	2186
12212201	2186	12221021	2186		

IRREDUCIBLE POLYNOMIALS FOR THE MODULUS 5

$n = 1$	e
11	2
12	4
13	4
14	1

$n = 2$	e
102	8
103	8
111	3
112	24
123	24
124	12
133	24
134	12
141	6
142	24

$n = 3$	e
1011	62
1014	31
1021	62
1024	31
1032	124
1033	124
1042	124
1043	124
1101	62
1102	124
1113	124
1114	31
1131	62
1134	31
1141	62
1143	124
1201	62
1203	124
1213	124
1214	31
1222	124
1223	124
1242	124
1244	31
1302	124
1304	31
1311	62
1312	124
1322	124
1323	124
1341	62
1343	124
1403	124
1404	31
1411	62
1412	124
1431	62
1434	31
1442	124
1444	31

$n = 4$	e
10002	16
10003	16
10014	312
10024	312
10034	312
10044	312
10102	48
10111	78
10122	624
10123	624
10132	624
10133	624
10141	39
10203	48
10221	39
10223	208
10231	78
10233	208
10303	48
10311	156
10313	208
10341	156
10343	208
10402	48
10412	624
10413	624
10421	156
10431	156
10442	624
10443	624
11004	312
11013	624
11023	624
11024	104
11032	624
11041	52
11042	624
11101	78
11113	624
11114	312
11124	104
11133	208
11142	208
11202	624
11212	624
11213	208
11221	156
11222	208
11234	104
11244	312
11301	156
11303	624
11321	39
11342	624
11344	312
11402	208
11411	13
11414	312
11441	52
11443	624
12004	312
12013	624
12014	104
12021	26
12022	624
12033	624
12042	624
12102	208
12121	13
12123	624

12131	52
12134	312
12201	39
12203	624
12211	156
12222	624
12224	312
12302	624
12311	39
12312	208
12324	312
12332	624
12333	208
12344	104
12401	156
12414	104
12422	208
12433	624
12434	312
12443	208
13004	312
13012	624
13023	624
13031	13
13032	624
13043	624
13044	104
13102	208
13121	52
13124	312
13131	26
13133	624
13201	78
13203	624
13232	624
13234	312
13241	156
13302	624
13314	104
13322	624
13323	208
13334	312
13341	78
13342	208
13401	156
13413	208
13423	624
13424	312
13432	208
13444	104
14004	312
14011	52
14012	624
14022	624
14033	624
14034	104
14043	624
14101	39
14112	208
14123	208
14134	104
14143	624
14144	312
14202	624
14214	312
14224	104
14231	156
14232	208
14242	624
14243	208
14301	156
14303	624
14312	624
14314	312
14331	78
14402	208
14411	52
14413	624
14441	26
14444	312

$n = 5$	e
100041	1562
100042	3124
100043	3124
100044	781
100102	3124
100114	781
100124	71
100132	3124
100143	3124
100201	1562
100212	3124
100222	284
100231	1562
100244	781
100304	781
100313	3124
100323	284
100334	781
100341	1562
100403	3124
100411	1562
100421	142
100433	3124
100442	3124
101022	3124
101023	3124
101032	284
101033	284
101103	3124
101104	781
101141	1562
101142	3124
101203	3124
101204	781
101212	3124
101213	284
101301	1562
101302	3124
101312	284
101313	3124
101401	1562
101402	3124
101443	3124
101444	781
102001	1562
102004	781
102012	3124
102013	3124
102021	1562
102024	781
102112	3124
102114	781
102121	1562
102122	3124
102131	2156
102134	781
102202	3124
102203	3124
102211	1562
102213	3124
102242	284
102244	781
102302	3124
102303	3124
102312	3124
102314	781
102341	1562
102343	284
102411	1562
102413	3124
102423	3124
102424	781
102431	1562
102434	781
103002	3124
103003	3124
103011	1562
103014	781
103022	3124
103023	3124
103101	1562
103104	781
103111	1562
103112	3124
103143	3124
103144	71
103211	1562
103212	3124

120222	3124
120234	781
120242	3124
120243	3124
120244	781
120321	1562
120332	3124
120343	3124
120344	781
120401	1562
120402	3124
120424	781
120431	1562
120432	3124
120441	1562
121002	3124
121012	3124
121013	3124
121014	781
121023	3124
121031	1562
121043	3124
121102	3124
121103	284
121131	1562
121144	781
121201	1562
121202	3124
121223	3124
121232	44
121233	3124
121244	781
121304	781
121334	781
121342	3124
121413	3124
121422	3124
121424	781
121432	3124
121441	1562
122003	3124
122004	781
122033	3124
122043	3124
122112	3124
122123	284
122124	781
122132	3124
122141	142
122142	3124
122214	781
122224	781
122233	3124
122301	1562
122312	3124
122333	3124
122341	1562
122344	71
122403	3124
122414	781
122421	1562
122422	3124
122423	3124
122434	781
122444	781
123014	781
123021	1562
123033	3124
123034	781
123102	3124
123113	3124
123114	781
123133	3124
123141	1562
123142	3124
123224	781
123231	1562
123242	3124
123303	3124
123311	1562
123331	1562
123341	142
123344	781
123402	3124
123411	1562
123412	3124
123413	3124
123421	1562
123433	284
123444	781
124001	142
124011	1562
124022	3124
124023	3124
124024	781
124034	781
124043	3124
124114	11
124123	3124
124132	3124
124133	3124
124202	284
124203	3124
124221	1562
124231	1562
124232	3124
124244	781
124304	781
124313	3124
124321	1562
124402	3124
124412	3124
124414	781
124423	284
124433	3124
130002	3124
130012	3124
130043	3124
130103	3124
130104	781
130121	1562
130133	3124
130134	781
130144	781
130224	781
130233	3124
130241	1562
130242	3124
130304	781
130313	3124
130323	3124
130331	1562
130341	1562
130342	3124
130343	3124
130401	142
130414	781
130431	1562
130442	3124
130444	781
131003	3124
131011	1562
131012	3124
131013	3124
131022	3124
131034	781
131042	3124
131112	3124
131121	1562
131123	3124
131133	3124
131144	781
131201	1562
131231	1562
131243	3124
131303	3124
131304	781
131322	3124
131332	3124
131333	44
131341	1562
131402	284
131403	3124
131434	781
131441	1562
132001	1562
132002	3124
132032	3124
132042	3124
132102	3124
132111	1562

132122	3124
132123	3124
132124	781
132131	1562
132141	1562
132204	781
132213	3124
132232	3124
132241	142
132244	781
132311	1562
132321	1562
132332	3124
132413	3124
132421	1562
132422	284
132433	3124
132443	3124
132444	71
133011	1562
133024	781
133031	1562
133032	3124
133103	3124
133112	3124
133113	3124
133114	781
133124	781
133132	284
133141	1562
133202	3124
133214	781
133234	781
133241	1562
133244	71
133321	1562
133334	781
133343	3124
133403	3124
133411	1562
133412	3124
133432	3124
133443	3124
133444	781
134004	71
134014	781
134021	1562
134022	3124
134023	3124
134031	1562
134042	3124
134103	3124
134111	1562
134113	3124
134122	284
134132	3124
134201	1562
134212	3124
134224	781
134302	3124
134303	284
134324	781
134333	3124
134334	781
134341	1562
134411	22
134422	3124
134432	3124
134433	3124
140001	1562
140011	1562
140044	781
140102	3124
140114	781
140124	781
140133	3124
140141	1562
140143	3124
140144	781
140202	3124
140204	781
140223	3124
140232	3124
140234	781
140242	3124
140303	284
140312	3124
140333	3124
140341	1562
140342	3124
140422	3124
140434	781
140441	1562
140443	3124
141002	284
141012	3124
141021	1562
141023	3124
141024	781
141033	3124
141041	1562
141101	1562
141104	71
141122	3124
141132	3124
141134	781
141143	3124
141204	781
141213	3124
141214	781
141221	142
141231	1562
141313	44
141321	1562
141331	1562
141334	781
141403	3124
141411	1562
141422	3124
142013	3124
142022	3124
142031	1562
142033	3124
142123	3124
142132	3124
142144	781
142204	781
142211	1562
142212	3124
142214	781
142222	3124
142231	142
142243	3124
142304	781
142311	1562
142313	3124
142331	1562
142342	3124
142344	781
142401	1562
142412	3124
142432	3124
142442	284
142443	3124
143001	1562
143003	3124
143031	1562
143041	1562
143113	3124
143123	3124
143131	1562
143201	1562
143213	3124
143221	1562
143222	3124
143224	781
143233	3124
143243	3124
143314	781
143321	142
143323	3124
143334	781
143342	284
143344	781
143402	3124
143414	781
143431	1562
143442	3124
143443	284
144004	781
144011	1562

144013	3124	144131	1562	144301	142
144014	781	144134	11	144304	781
144021	1562	144143	3124	144332	3124
144032	3124	144211	1562	144343	3124
144041	1562	144223	3124	144403	3124
144102	3124	144224	781	144433	3124
144104	781	144234	781	144444	781
144121	1562	144242	3124		

IRREDUCIBLE POLYNOMIALS FOR THE MODULUS 7

$n = 1$	e
11	2
12	6
13	3
14	6
15	3
16	1

$n = 2$	e
101	4
102	12
104	12
113	48
114	24
116	16
122	24
123	48
125	48
131	8
135	48
136	16
141	8
145	48
146	16
152	24
153	48
155	48
163	48
164	24
166	16

$n = 3$	e				
1002	18	1035	171	1325	171
1003	9	1041	114	1333	171
1004	18	1046	57	1334	342
1005	9	1052	342	1335	171
1011	114	1055	171	1336	19
1016	57	1062	342	1341	38
1021	38	1065	171	1343	171
1026	19	1101	114	1352	342
1032	342	1103	171	1354	342
		1112	342	1362	342
		1115	171	1366	57
		1124	342	1401	114
		1126	57	1403	171
		1131	38	1413	171
		1135	171	1416	19
		1143	171	1422	342
		1146	57	1425	171
		1151	114	1431	38
		1152	342	1432	342
		1153	171	1433	171
		1154	342	1434	342
		1163	171	1444	342
		1165	171	1446	19
		1201	38	1453	171
		1203	171	1455	171
		1214	342	1461	114
		1216	57	1465	171
		1223	171	1504	342
		1226	57	1506	19
		1233	171	1511	114
		1235	171	1513	171
		1242	342	1521	114
		1245	171	1524	342
		1251	114	1532	342
		1255	171	1534	342
		1261	114	1542	342
		1262	342	1545	171
		1263	171	1552	342
		1264	342	1556	57
		1304	342	1563	171
		1306	57	1564	342
		1311	38	1565	171
		1314	342	1566	57
		1322	342	1604	342

1606	57
1612	342
1615	171
1621	114
1623	171
1632	342
1636	19
1641	114
1644	342
1653	171
1654	342
1655	171
1656	57
1662	342
1664	342

$n = 4$	e
10011	400
10012	1200
10014	1200
10023	480
10025	480
10026	160
10053	480
10055	480
10056	160
10061	400
10062	1200
10064	1200
10103	96
10106	32
10111	400
10112	600
10121	200
10135	2400
10145	2400
10151	200
10161	400
10162	600
10203	96
10205	96
10211	200
10214	1200
10224	600
10236	800
10246	800
10254	600
10261	200
10264	1200
10305	96
10306	32
10316	800
10322	1200
10326	800
10333	2400
10334	240
10335	2400
10343	2400
10344	240
10345	2400
10352	1200
10356	800
10366	800
10405	96
10406	32
10412	1200
10414	600
10422	600
10433	2400
10443	2400
10452	600
10462	1200
10464	600
10503	96
10505	96
10515	2400
10524	1200
10525	2400
10531	80
10533	2400
10536	800
10541	80
10543	2400
10546	800
10554	1200
10555	2400
10565	2400
10603	96
10606	32
10613	2400
10621	400
10623	2400
10632	240
10635	2400
10636	800
10642	240
10645	2400
10646	800
10651	400
10653	2400
10663	2400
11001	400
11003	480
11013	2400
11026	800
11031	400
11042	75
11054	300
11056	800
11062	1200
11063	2400
11101	400
11103	2400
11105	2400
11111	5
11112	1200
11124	75
11134	240
11136	800
11141	400
11152	1200
11153	2400
11161	100
11163	480
11166	800
11201	200
11204	600
11213	2400
11223	2400
11225	2400
11232	60
11233	2400
11236	800
11241	400
11244	1200
11245	2400
11252	240
11254	300
11266	160
11321	200
11323	2400
11324	150
11331	400
11332	300
11334	600
11351	200
11355	2400
11356	160
11362	120
11364	1200
11365	2400
11405	2400
11406	800
11412	1200
11415	480
11422	1200
11423	2400
11434	1200
11443	2400
11455	2400
11463	2400
11504	1200
11511	50
11523	2400
11533	2400
11542	75
11545	2400
11551	400
11556	800
11562	1200

11566	160
11602	240
11605	2400
11614	600
11625	2400
11626	800
11631	40
11643	2400
11646	160
11652	600
11653	2400
11654	300
11664	600
11665	2400
11666	800
12002	1200
12006	160
12016	800
12025	2400
12032	1200
12044	75
12051	100
12055	2400
12064	1200
12066	800
12101	200
12102	600
12116	800
12123	2400
12126	800
12134	60
12135	2400
12136	800
12141	400
12142	1200
12143	2400
12151	100
12154	240
12165	480
12203	2400
12205	2400
12213	480
12214	1200
12224	1200
12226	800
12231	400
12246	800
12253	2400
12266	800
12303	2400
12304	240
12311	200
12323	2400
12325	2400
12332	120
12345	480
12346	800
12351	100
12354	600
12356	800
12361	200
12363	2400
12365	2400
12402	1200
12403	2400
12406	800
12412	15
12414	1200
12421	25
12431	80
12435	2400
12442	1200
12454	1200
12456	800
12462	300
12465	2400
12466	160
12521	50
12522	600
12526	800
12531	200
12532	1200
12534	300
12552	600
12553	2400
12555	480
12561	400
12563	2400
12564	120
12601	400
12612	150
12626	800
12636	800
12643	2400
12644	75
12652	1200
12655	2400
12664	1200
12665	480
13004	1200
13005	480
13011	400
13015	2400
13022	300
13023	2400
13031	50
13044	1200
13053	2400
13065	2400
13103	2400
13106	800
13115	2400
13126	800
13135	2400
13142	1200
13151	400
13155	2400
13161	400
13166	160
13204	1200
13205	2400
13206	800
13213	2400
13214	300
13215	480
13221	400
13225	2400
13234	1200
13242	240
13243	2400
13252	150
13261	400
13264	30
13302	1200
13311	400
13313	480
13323	2400
13324	1200
13331	50
13336	800
13345	2400
13355	2400
13364	75
13402	600
13404	600
13413	480
13421	80
13422	300
13432	1200
13434	1200
13436	800
13441	20
13443	2400
13445	2400
13455	2400
13456	800
13465	2400
13501	80
13506	800
13512	600
13513	2400
13516	800
13521	200
13522	300
13525	2400
13533	480
13535	2400
13544	120
13553	2400
13556	800
13562	600

13611	40
13612	1200
13616	800
13623	480
13624	600
13626	800
13641	100
13642	600
13644	1200
13652	75
13654	600
13655	2400
14004	1200
14005	480
14015	2400
14023	2400
14034	1200
14041	25
14052	300
14053	2400
14061	400
14065	2400
14103	2400
14106	800
14111	400
14116	160
14121	400
14125	2400
14132	1200
14145	2400
14156	800
14165	2400
14204	1200
14205	2400
14206	800
14211	400
14214	15
14222	75
14232	240
14233	2400
14244	1200
14251	400
14255	2400
14263	2400
14264	300
14265	480
14302	1200
14314	150
14325	2400
14335	2400
14341	25
14346	800
14353	2400
14354	1200
14361	400
14363	480
14402	600
14404	600
14415	2400
14425	2400
14426	800
14431	20
14433	2400
14435	2400
14442	1200
14444	1200
14446	800
14451	80
14452	300
14463	480
14501	80
14506	800
14512	600
14523	2400
14526	800
14534	120
14543	480
14545	2400
14551	200
14552	300
14555	2400
14562	600
14563	2400
14566	800
14622	150
14624	600
14625	2400
14631	100
14632	600
14634	1200
14653	480
14654	600
14656	800
14661	40
14662	1200
14666	800
15002	1200
15006	160
15014	1200
15016	800
15021	100
15025	2400
15034	150
15042	1200
15055	2400
15066	800
15101	200
15102	600
15115	480
15121	100
15124	240
15131	400
15132	1200
15133	2400
15144	60
15145	2400
15146	800
15153	2400
15156	800
15166	800
15203	2400
15205	2400
15216	800
15223	2400
15236	800
15241	400
15254	1200
15256	800
15263	480
15264	1200
15303	2400
15304	240
15311	200
15313	2400
15315	2400
15321	100
15324	600
15326	800
15335	480
15336	800
15342	120
15353	2400
15355	2400
15361	200
15402	1200
15403	2400
15406	800
15412	300
15415	2400
15416	160
15424	1200
15426	800
15432	1200
15441	80
15445	2400
15451	50
15462	30
15464	1200
15511	400
15513	2400
15514	120
15522	600
15523	2400
15525	480
15541	200
15542	1200
15544	300
15551	25
15552	600
15556	800
15601	400

15614	1200	16161	10	16425	2400
15615	480	16162	1200	16433	2400
15622	1200	16201	200	16444	1200
15625	2400	16204	600	16452	1200
15633	2400	16216	160	16453	2400
15634	150	16222	240	16462	1200
15646	800	16224	300	16465	480
15656	800	16231	400	16504	1200
15662	75	16234	1200	16512	1200
16001	400	16235	2400	16516	160
16003	480	16242	60	16521	400
16012	1200	16243	2400	16526	800
16013	2400	16246	800	16532	150
16024	300	16253	2400	16535	2400
16026	800	16255	2400	16543	2400
16032	150	16263	2400	16553	2400
16041	400	16312	120	16561	25
16056	800	16314	1200	16602	240
16063	2400	16315	2400	16605	2400
16101	400	16321	200	16614	600
16103	2400	16325	2400	16615	2400
16105	2400	16326	160	16616	800
16111	100	16341	400	16622	600
16113	480	16342	300	16623	2400
16116	800	16344	600	16624	300
16122	1200	16351	200	16633	2400
16123	2400	16353	2400	16636	160
16131	400	16354	75	16641	40
16144	240	16405	2400	16655	2400
16146	800	16406	800	16656	800
16154	150	16413	2400	16664	600

Table A5

n	Maximum-exponent polynomial
1	$1 + x$
2	$1 + x + x^2$
3	$1 + x + x^3$
4	$1 + x + x^4$
5	$1 + x^2 + x^5$
6	$1 + x + x^6$
7	$1 + x + x^7$
8	$1 + x^2 + x^3 + x^4 + x^8$
9	$1 + x^4 + x^9$
10	$1 + x^3 + x^{10}$
11	$1 + x^2 + x^{11}$
12	$1 + x + x^4 + x^6 + x^{12}$
13	$1 + x + x^3 + x^4 + x^{13}$
14	$1 + x + x^3 + x^5 + x^{14}$
15	$1 + x + x^{15}$
16	$1 + x^2 + x^3 + x^5 + x^{16}$

n Maximum-exponent polynomial

17	$1 + x^3 + x^{17}$
18	$1 + x^7 + x^{18}$
19	$1 + x + x^2 + x^5 + x^{19}$
20	$1 + x^3 + x^{20}$
21	$1 + x^2 + x^{21}$
22	$1 + x + x^{22}$
23	$1 + x^5 + x^{23}$
24	$1 + x + x^2 + x^7 + x^{24}$
25	$1 + x^3 + x^{25}$
26	$1 + x + x^2 + x^6 + x^{26}$
27	$1 + x + x^2 + x^5 + x^{27}$
28	$1 + x^3 + x^{28}$
29	$1 + x^2 + x^{29}$
30	$1 + x + x^4 + x^6 + x^{30}$
31	$1 + x^3 + x^{31}$
32	$1 + x + x^2 + x^{22} + x^{32}$
33	$1 + x^{13} + x^{33}$
34	$1 + x + x^2 + x^{27} + x^{34}$
35	$1 + x^2 + x^{35}$
36	$1 + x^{11} + x^{36}$
37	$1 + x + x^2 + x^3 + x^4 + x^5 + x^{37}$
38	$1 + x + x^5 + x^6 + x^{38}$
39	$1 + x^4 + x^{39}$
40	$1 + x^3 + x^4 + x^5 + x^{40}$
41	$1 + x^3 + x^{41}$
42	$1 + x + x^2 + x^3 + x^4 + x^5 + x^{42}$
43	$1 + x^3 + x^4 + x^6 + x^{43}$
44	$1 + x^2 + x^5 + x^6 + x^{44}$
45	$1 + x + x^3 + x^4 + x^{45}$
46	$1 + x + x^2 + x^3 + x^5 + x^8 + x^{46}$
47	$1 + x^5 + x^{47}$
48	$1 + x + x^2 + x^4 + x^5 + x^7 + x^{48}$
49	$1 + x^4 + x^5 + x^6 + x^{49}$
50	$1 + x^2 + x^3 + x^4 + x^{50}$
51	$1 + x + x^3 + x^6 + x^{51}$
52	$1 + x^3 + x^{52}$
53	$1 + x + x^2 + x^6 + x^{53}$
54	$1 + x^2 + x^3 + x^4 + x^5 + x^6 + x^{54}$
55	$1 + x + x^2 + x^6 + x^{55}$
56	$1 + x^2 + x^4 + x^7 + x^{56}$
57	$1 + x^2 + x^3 + x^5 + x^{57}$
58	$1 + x + x^5 + x^6 + x^{58}$
59	$1 + x + x^3 + x^4 + x^5 + x^6 + x^{59}$
60	$1 + x + x^{60}$
61	$1 + x + x^2 + x^5 + x^{61}$
62	$1 + x^3 + x^5 + x^6 + x^{62}$
63	$1 + x + x^{63}$
64	$1 + x + x^3 + x^4 + x^{64}$
65	$1 + x + x^3 + x^4 + x^{65}$
66	$1 + x^2 + x^3 + x^5 + x^6 + x^8 + x^{66}$
67	$1 + x + x^2 + x^5 + x^{67}$
68	$1 + x + x^5 + x^7 + x^{68}$
69	$1 + x^2 + x^5 + x^6 + x^{69}$
70	$1 + x + x^3 + x^5 + x^{70}$
71	$1 + x + x^3 + x^5 + x^{71}$
72	$1 + x + x^2 + x^3 + x^4 + x^6 + x^{72}$
73	$1 + x^2 + x^3 + x^4 + x^{73}$

74	$1 + x^3 + x^4 + x^7 + x^{74}$
75	$1 + x + x^3 + x^6 + x^{75}$
76	$1 + x^2 + x^4 + x^5 + x^{76}$
77	$1 + x^2 + x^5 + x^6 + x^{77}$
78	$1 + x + x^2 + x^7 + x^{78}$
79	$1 + x^2 + x^3 + x^4 + x^{79}$
80	$1 + x + x^2 + x^3 + x^5 + x^7 + x^{80}$
81	$1 + x^4 + x^{81}$
82	$1 + x + x^4 + x^6 + x^7 + x^8 + x^{82}$
83	$1 + x^2 + x^4 + x^7 + x^{83}$
84	$1 + x + x^3 + x^5 + x^7 + x^8 + x^{84}$
85	$1 + x + x^2 + x^8 + x^{85}$
86	$1 + x^2 + x^5 + x^6 + x^{86}$
87	$1 + x + x^5 + x^7 + x^{87}$
88	$1 + x + x^3 + x^4 + x^5 + x^8 + x^{88}$
89	$1 + x^3 + x^5 + x^6 + x^{89}$
90	$1 + x^2 + x^3 + x^5 + x^{90}$
91	$1 + x^2 + x^3 + x^5 + x^6 + x^7 + x^{91}$
92	$1 + x^2 + x^5 + x^6 + x^{92}$
93	$1 + x^2 + x^{93}$
94	$1 + x + x^5 + x^6 + x^{94}$
95	$1 + x + x^2 + x^4 + x^5 + x^6 + x^{95}$
96	$1 + x^2 + x^3 + x^4 + x^6 + x^7 + x^{96}$
97	$1 + x^6 + x^{97}$
98	$1 + x + x^2 + x^3 + x^4 + x^7 + x^{98}$
99	$1 + x^4 + x^5 + x^7 + x^{99}$
100	$1 + x^2 + x^7 + x^8 + x^{100}$
107	$1 + x + x^2 + x^3 + x^5 + x^7 + x^{107}$
127	$1 + x + x^{127}$

3. Polynomials of Specified Exponents

Table A6, based on Elspas,[1] lists polynomials over $GF(2)$, of least degree n, having specified exponents e, for $1 \leq e \leq 28$.

Table A6

e	n	Polynomial
1	1	$1 + x$
2	2	$1 + x^2 = (1 + x)^2$
3	2	$1 + x + x^2$
4	3	$1 + x + x^2 + x^3 = (1 + x)^3$
5	4	$1 + x + x^2 + x^3 + x^4$
6	4	$1 + x^2 + x^4 = (1 + x + x^2)^2$
		$1 + x + x^3 + x^4 = (1 + x)^2 (1 + x + x^2)$
7	3	$1 + x + x^3$
		$1 + x^2 + x^3$
8	5	$1 + x + x^4 + x^5 = (1 + x)^5$
9	6	$1 + x^3 + x^6$
10	6	$1 + x + x^5 + x^6 = (1 + x)^2 (1 + x + \ldots + x^4)$
11	10	$1 + x + \ldots + x^{10}$
12	5	$1 + x^2 + x^3 + x^5 = (1 + x)^3 (1 + x + x^2)$
13	12	$1 + x + \ldots + x^{12}$
14	5	$1 + x + x^2 + x^5 = (1 + x)^2 (1 + x + x^3)$
		$1 + x^3 + x^4 + x^5 = (1 + x)^2 (1 + x^2 + x^3)$

15	4	$1 + x + x^4$
		$1 + x^3 + x^4$
16	9	$1 + x + x^8 + x^9 = (1 + x)^9$
17	8	$1 + x^3 + x^4 + x^5 + x^8$
		$1 + x + x^2 + x^4 + x^6 + x^7 + x^8$
18	8	$1 + x^2 + x^3 + x^5 + x^6 + x^8 = (1 + x)^2 (1 + x^3 + x^6)$
19	18	$1 + x + \ . \ . \ . \ + x^{18}$
20	7	$1 + x^2 + x^5 + x^7 = (1 + x)^3 (1 + x + \ . \ . \ . \ + x^4)$
21	5	$1 + x^4 + x^5 = (1 + x + x^2) (1 + x + x^3)$
		$1 + x + x^5 = (1 + x + x^2) (1 + x^2 + x^3)$
22	12	$1 + x + x^{11} + x^{12} = (1 + x)^2 (1 + x + \ . \ . \ . \ + x^{10})$
23	11	$1 + x^2 + x^4 + x^5 + x^6 + x^{10} + x^{11}$
		$1 + x + x^5 + x^6 + x^7 + x^9 + x^{11}$
24	7	$1 + x^3 + x^4 + x^7 = (1 + x)^5 (1 + x + x^2)$
		$1 + x + x^6 + x^7 = (1 + x)^3 (1 + x + x^2)^2$
25	20	$1 + x^5 + x^{10} + x^{15} + x^{20}$
26	14	$1 + x + x^{13} + x^{14} = (1 + x)^2 (1 + x + \ . \ . \ . \ + x^{12})$
27	18	$1 + x^9 + x^{18}$
28	6	$1 + x^3 + x^5 + x^6 = (1 + x)^3 (1 + x + x^3)$
		$1 + x + x^3 + x^6 = (1 + x)^3 (1 + x^2 + x^3)$

BIBLIOGRAPHY

1. Ash, R.: *Information Theory,* chap. 5, John Wiley & Sons, Inc., New York, 1965.
2. Bacon, G.: "Analysis of p-nary Time Series," series 60, issue 436, Electronics Research Laboratory, University of California, Berkeley, pp. 1-5, Feb. 15, 1962.
3. ———: "Linear Modular Circuits as Automata," Department of Electrical Engineering, University of California, Berkeley, 1962. (Mimeographed notes.)
4. Bailey, J. S.: "Generalized Single-ended Counter," *J. Assoc. Comp. Mach.,* vol. 13, pp. 412-418, 1966.
5. Bartee, T. C. and D. I. Schneider: "Computation with Finite Fields," *Information and Control,* vol. 6, pp. 79-98, 1963.
6. Birdsall, T. G. and M. P. Ristenbatt: "Introduction to Linear Shift-register Generated Sequences," Tech. Rep. No. 90, Cooley Electronics Laboratory, University of Michigan, Ann Arbor, Oct., 1958.
7. Bollman, D. A.: "On the Periodicity of States in Linear Sequential Machine Having a Composite Modulus," unpublished doctoral dissertation, University of Illinois, Urbana, 1963.
8. ———: "Some Periodicity Properties of Transformations on Vector Spaces over Residue Class Rings," *J. Soc. Ind. Appl. Math.,* vol. 13, pp. 902-912, 1965.
9. ———: "Some Periodicity Properties of Modules over the Ring of Polynominals with Coefficients in a Residue Class Ring," *J. SIAM Appl. Math.,* vol. 14, pp. 237-241, 1966.
10. Booth, T. L.: "Representation of Signal Flow through Linear and Nonlinear Sequential Networks," unpublished doctoral dissertation, University of Connecticut, Storrs, 1962.
11. ———: "Nonlinear Sequential Networks," *Trans. IEEE,* vol. CT-10, pp. 279-281, 1963.
12. ———: "An Analytic Representation of Signals in Sequential Networks," *Proc. Symp. on Math. Theory of Automata,* Polytechnic Institute of Brooklyn, vol. 12, pp. 301-340, 1963.
13. Brenner, J. L.: "Linear Recurrence Relations," *Amer. Math. Monthly,* vol. 61, pp. 171-173, 1954.
14. Bryant, P. R. and R. D. Killick: "Nonlinear Feedback Shift Registers," *Trans. IRE,* vol. EC-11, pp. 410-412, 1962.
15. ———, F. G. Heath, and R. D. Killick: "Counting with Feedback Shift Registers by Means of a Jump Technique," *Trans. IRE,* vol. EC-11, pp. 285-286, 1962.
16. Brzozowski, J. A.: "Regular Expressions for Linear Sequential Circuits," *Trans. IEEE,* vol. EC-14, pp. 148-156, 1965.
17. ——— and W. A. Davis: "On the Linearity of Autonomous Sequential Machines," *Trans. IEEE,* vol. EC-13, pp. 673-679, 1964.
18. Bussey, W. H.: "Galois Field Tables for $p^n \leq 169$," *Bull. Amer. Math. Soc.,* vol. 12, pp. 22-38, 1905.
19. ———: "Galois Field Tables of Order Less than 1000," *Bull. Amer. Math. Soc.,* vol. 16, pp. 188-206, 1909.
20. Campbell, L. L.: "Two Properties of Pseudo-random Sequences," *Trans. IRE,* vol. IT-5, p. 32, 1959.

21. Church, R.: "Tables of Irreducible Polynominals for the First Four Prime Moduli," *Ann. of Math.*, vol. 36, pp. 198-209, 1935.
22. Cohn, M.: "Controllability in Linear Sequential Networks," *Trans. IRE*, vol. CT-9, pp. 74-78, 1962.
23. ———: "A Theorem on Linear Automata," *Trans. IEEE*, vol. EC-13, pp. 52-53, 1964.
24. ———: "Properties of Linear Machines," *J. Assoc. Comp. Mach.*, vol. 11, pp. 296-301, 1964.
25. ——— and S. Even: "Identification and Minimization of Linear Machines," *Trans. IEEE*, vol. EC-14, pp. 367-376, 1965.
26. Crowell, R. H.: "Graphs of Linear Transformations over Finite Fields," *J. Soc. Indust. Appl. Math.*, vol. 10, pp. 103-112, 1962.
27. Davies, N. G.: "Some Properties of Linear Recursive Sequences," Tech. Rep. No. 1031, Defence Research Telecom. Establishment, Ottawa, Dec., 1959.
28. Davis, W. A.: "An Introduction to Linear Sequential Machines," Tech. Rep. No. 63-2, Electrical Engineering Department, University of Ottawa, Feb., 1963.
29. ———: "On the Linearity of Sequential Machines," unpublished master's thesis, Electrical Engineering Department, University of Ottawa, Sept., 1963.
30. ——— and J. A. Brzozowski: "On the Linearity of Sequential Machines," Proceedings of the Fifth Symposium on Switching Theory and Logical Design, Institute of Electrical and Electronics Engineers, pp. 197-208, Oct., 1964.
31. ——— and ———: "On the Linearity of Sequential Machines," *Trans. IEEE*, vol. EC-15, pp. 21-29, 1966.
32. Elspas, B.: "The Theory of Autonomous Linear Sequential Networks," *Trans. IRE*, vol. CT-6, pp. 45-60, 1959.
33. Even, S.: "An Extension of Linear Sequential Machines," Rep. No. BL-30, Sec. 7, Comp. Lab., Harvard University, Cambridge, Mass., pp. 1-9, 1962.
34. Fitzpatrick, G. B.: "Synthesis of Binary Ring Counters of Given Periods," *J. Assoc. Comp. Mach.*, vol. 7, pp. 287-297, 1960.
35. Friedland, B.: "Linear Modular Sequential Circuits," *Trans. IRE*, vol. CT-6, pp. 61-68, 1959.
36. ——— and T. E. Stern: "Linear Modular Sequential Circuits and Their Application to Multiple Level Coding," IRE National Convention Record, vol. 7, part 2, pp. 40-48, 1959.
37. ——— and ———: "On Periodicity of States in Linear Modular Sequential Circuits," *Trans. IRE*, vol. IT-5, pp. 136-137, 1959.
38. Fukunaga, K.: "A Theory of Nonlinear Autonomous Sequential Nets Using *z*-Transforms," *Trans. IEEE*, vol. EC-13, pp. 310-312, 1964.
39. Gill, A.: *Introduction to the Theory of Finite-state Machines*, chap. 6, McGraw-Hill Book Co., New York, 1962.
40. ———: "Analysis of Linear Sequential Circuits by Confluence Sets," *Trans. IEEE*, vol. EC-13, pp. 226-231, 1964.
41. ———: "Analysis and Synthesis of Stable Linear Sequential Circuits," *J. Assoc. Comp. Mach.*, vol. 12, pp. 141-149, 1965.
42. ———: "The Minimization of Linear Sequential Circuits," *Trans. IEEE*, vol. CT-12, pp. 292-294, 1965.
43. ———: "The Reduced Form of a Linear Automaton," in E. R. Caianiello (ed.), *Automata Theory*, pp. 164-175, Academic Press Inc., New York, 1966.
44. ———: "State Graphs of Autonomous Linear Automata," in E. R. Caianiello (ed.), *Automata Theory*, pp. 176-180, Academic Press Inc., New York, 1966.

45. ———: "On the Series-to-Parallel Transformation of Linear Sequential Circuits," *Trans. IEEE,* vol. EC-15, pp. 107-108, 1966.

46. ——— and J. P. Jacob: "On a Mapping Polynomial for Galois Fields," *Quarterly Appl. Math.,* vol. 24, pp. 57-62, 1966.

47. ——— and C. J. Tan: "The Factorization of Linear Cycle Sets," *Trans. IEEE,* vol. CT-12, pp. 630-632, 1965.

48. Golomb, S. W.: "Sequences with Randomness Properties," Terminal Progress Report, Glenn L. Martin Co., 1955.

49. ———: "Linear Recurring Sequences," Jet Propulsion Laboratory, Pasadena, Calif., Feb., 1961. (Dittoed notes.)

50. ——— (ed.): *Digital Communication with Space Applications,* Prentice-Hall, Inc., Englewood Cliffs, N.J., 1964.

51. ———, L. R. Welch, and R. M. Goldstein: "Cycles from Non-linear Shift Registers," Progress Rep. No. 20-389, Jet Propulsion Laboratory, Pasadena, Calif., Aug., 1959.

52. Gorenstein, D. and E. Weiss: "An Acquirable Code," *Information and Control,* vol. 7, pp. 315-319, 1964.

53. Hall, M.: "An Isomorphism between Linear Recurring Sequences and Algebraic Rings," *Trans. Amer. Math. Soc.,* vol. 44, pp. 196-218, 1938.

54. Hartmanis, J.: "Linear Multivalued Sequential Coding Networks," *Trans. IRE,* vol. CT-6, pp. 69-74, 1959.

55. ———: "Two Tests for the Linearity of Sequential Machines," *Trans. IEEE,* vol. EC-14, pp. 781-786, 1965.

56. Heath, F. G. and M. W. Gribble: "Chain Codes and Their Electronic Applications," *Proc. IEE,* vol. 108C, pp. 50-57, 1961.

57. Hotz, G.: "On the Mathematical Theory of Linear Sequential Networks," in H. Aiken and W. F. Main (ed.), *Switching Theory in Space Technology,* pp. 11-19, Stanford University Press, Stanford, Calif., 1963.

58. Hsiao, M. Y. and K. Y. Sih: "Series to Parallel Transformation of Linear-Feedback Shift-Register Circuit," *Trans. IEEE,* vol. EC-13, pp. 738-740, 1964.

59. Huffman, D. A.: "A Linear Circuit Viewpoint of Error-Correcting Codes," *Trans. IRE,* vol. IT-2, pp. 20-28, 1956.

60. ———: "The Synthesis of Linear Sequential Coding Networks," in C. Cherry (ed.), *Information Theory,* pp. 77-95, Academic Press Inc., New York, 1956.

61. ———: "An Algebra for Periodically Time-Varying Linear Binary Sequence Transducers," *Ann. Comp. Lab.,* Harvard University, Cambridge, Mass., vol. 29, pp. 189-203, 1959.

62. Jacob, J. P.: "The Design of Circuits for Performing Operations and Computing Functions over Finite Fields," Tech. Memo. M-106, Electronics Research Laboratory, University of California, Berkeley, Nov. 30, 1964.

63. Jury, E. I.: *Theory and Application of the z-Transform Method,* sec. 8.5, John Wiley & Sons, Inc., New York, 1964.

64. Kaneko, H.: "A Few Probabilistic Properties of Modular Circuits," series 60, issue 448, Electronics Research Laboratory, University of California, Berkeley, Apr. 30, 1962.

65. Kautz, W. H. (ed.): *Linear Sequential Switching Circuits—Selected Technical Papers,* Holden-Day Inc., San Francisco, 1965.

66. Kwakernaak, H.: "The Autocorrelation Function of a Complete Recurrent Sequence and the Cross Correlation Function of Two Complete Recurrent Sequences with Mutually Prime Periods," series 60, issue 436, Electronics

Research Laboratory, University of California, Berkeley, pp. 37-42, Feb. 15, 1962.

67. Lavallee, P.: "Some Further Group Properties of Singular Linear Sequential Circuits and Their Synthesis," Rep. No. 1250, Polytechnic Institute of Brooklyn, N.Y., Oct. 1964.

68. ———: "Nonstable Cycle and Level Sets for Linear Sequential Machines," *Trans. IEEE,* vol. EC-14, pp. 957-959, 1965.

69. ———: "Some New Group Theoretic Properties of Singular Linear Sequential Machines," *Trans. IEEE,* vol. EC-14, pp. 959-961, 1965.

70. Lechner, R. J.: "Affine Equivalence of Switching Functions," unpublished doctoral dissertation, Harvard University, Cambridge, Mass., Jan., 1963.

71. Lerner, R. M.: "Signals with Uniform Ambiguity Functions," IRE National Convention Record, vol. 6, part 4, p. 27, 1958.

72. Lunelli, L.: "Matrices in Theory of Autonomous Sequential Networks," *Trans. IRE,* vol. CT-6, pp. 392-393, 1959.

73. Magleby, K. B.: "The Synthesis of Nonlinear Feedback Shift Registers," Tech. Rep. No. 6207-1, Stanford Electronics Laboratories, Stanford University, Stanford, Calif., Oct., 1963.

74. Mandelbaum, D.: "A Comparison of Linear Sequential Circuits and Arithmetic Sequences," Communications Systems, Inc., Paramus, N.J., 1966.

75. Marcovitz, A. B.: "On Time-Varying Coding Networks," Proc. WESCON, Paper No. 34/1, 1961.

76. Marsh, R. W.: "Tables of Irreducible Polynomials over $GF(2)$ through Degree 19," National Security Agency, Washington, D.C., Oct. 24, 1957.

77. Massey, J. L. and R. W. Liu: "Equivalence of Nonlinear Shift Registers," *Trans. IEEE,* vol. IT-10, pp. 378-379, 1964.

78. Meggitt, J. E.: "The Mathematical Theory of Sequential Systems, with Particular Reference to Two-element Systems," IBM British Laboratory, Winchester, Hants., Oct., 1960.

79. Ormsby, J. F. A.: "A Note on Linear Recurring Sequences," series 60, issue 436, Electronics Research Laboratory, University of California, Berkeley, pp. 62-74, Feb. 15, 1962.

80. Peterson, W. W.: *Error-Correcting Codes,* The M.I.T. Press, Cambridge, Mass., 1961.

81. Preparata, F. P.: "On the Realizability of Special Classes of Autonomous Sequential Circuits," *Trans. IEEE,* vol. EC-14, pp. 791-797, 1965.

82. Pugsley, J. H.: "Sequential Functions and Linear Sequential Machines," *Trans. IEEE,* vol. EC-14, pp. 376-382, 1965.

83. Radchenko, A. N. and V. I. Filipov: "Shift Registers with Logical Feedback and Their Use as Counting and Coding Devices," *Automation and Remote Control,* vol. 20, pp. 1467-1473, 1959.

84. Richalet, J.: "Operational Calculus for Finite Rings," *Trans. IEEE,* vol. CT-12, pp. 558-570, 1965.

85. Robinson, I. J. W.: "A Study of the Generation of Linear Recursive Sequences," Tech. Rep. No. 1082, Defence Research Telecom. Establishment, Ottawa, Nov., 1961.

86. Roth, H. H.: "Linear Binary Shift Register Circuits Utilizing a Minimum Number of Mod-2 Adders," *Trans. IEEE,* vol. IT-11, pp. 215-220, 1965.

87. Solomon, G.: "Linear Recursive Sequences as Finite Difference Equations," Group Rep. No. 47.37, Lincoln Laboratory, Lexington, Mass., Mar., 1960.

88. Srinivasan, C. V.: "State Diagrams of Linear Sequential Machines," *J. Franklin Inst.*, vol. 273, pp. 383-418, 1962.
89. Stern, T. E. and B. Friedland: "The Linear Modular Sequential Circuit Generalized," *Trans. IRE,* vol. CT-8, pp. 79-80, 1961.
90. Tang, D. T.: "Transfer Function Synthesis of Linear Shift-Register Circuits," Proceedings of the Third Annual Allerton Conference on Circuit and System Theory, pp. 63-72, 1965.
91. Toda, I.: "A Theory of Linear Machines," ARPA Contract No. SD-185, University of California, Berkeley, 1965. (Dittoed notes.)
92. ———: "The Tree Set of a Linear Machine," *Trans. IEEE,* vol. EC-14, pp. 954-957, 1965.
93. van Heerden, P. J.: "Analysis of Binary Time Series in Periodic Functions," *Trans. IRE,* vol. EC-8, pp. 228-229, 1959.
94. ———: "Periodic Binary Time Series and Their Relation to Boolean Functions," *Trans. IRE,* vol. EC-9, p. 510, 1960.
95. Wang, K. C.: "On the Linearity of Sequential Machines," unpublished doctoral dissertation, Northwestern University, Evanston, Ill., Sept., 1965.
96. Ward, M.: "The Arithmetical Theory of Linear Recurring Series," *Trans. Amer. Math. Soc.*, vol. 35, pp. 600-628, 1933.
97. Watson, E. J.: "Primitive Polynomials (mod 2)," *Math. of Computation,* vol. 16, pp. 368-369, 1962.
98. Yau, S. S. and K. C. Wang: "Linearity of Sequential Machines," *Trans. IEEE,* vol. EC-15, pp. 337-354, 1966.
99. Young, F. H.: "Analysis of Shift Register Counters," *J. Assoc. Comp. Mach.*, vol. 5, pp. 385-388, 1958.
100. Zierler, N.: "Several Binary Sequence Generators," Tech. Rep. No. 95, Lincoln Laboratories, Lexington, Mass., Sept. 12, 1955.
101. ———: "Linear Recurring Sequences," *J. Soc. Indust. Appl. Math.*, vol. 7, pp. 31-48, 1959.

INDEX